After LM

NASA LUNAR LANDER **CONCEPTS**
BEYOND APOLLO

John F. Connolly, Editor

Acknowledgments

This catalog of human lunar lander concepts has been years in the making. Over that time, a number of individuals have contributed to the compilation of concepts included in this document, and we wish to acknowledge their contributions and thank them for their efforts. Special thanks to Alida Andrews and Kevin Watts for their painstaking research and hours of searching through decades of past studies. Thanks also to Susan Breeden and Cory Duke for the editing and formatting that gave this catalog of lunar lander concepts its final, polished form, and to Alberto Bertolin for the time-spanning cover art. And our thanks to all the contributors listed below (and apologies to those whose names have been unintentionally omitted or lost to history).

– JFC

Faisal Ali

Molly Anderson

Jason Budinoff

Tim Carnahan

Dave Cornelius

Brian Derkowski

Mark Dowman

Maria Garcia-Robles

Jim Geffre

Bob Gershman

Andy Gonzales

Kandyce Goodliff

David Helton

Steve Hoffman

Tupper Hyde

Gabe Karpati

Kriss Kennedy

Larry Kos

Kevin Larman

Ron Leung

Adam Matuszeski

Dan Mazanek

Tess McEnulty

Jeff Murch

Shuvo Mustafi

Dave North

Steven R. Oleson

Tara Polsgrove

Lloyd Purves

Brian F. Quigley

Pat Rawlings

Elisa Rivera

Josh Sams

Jeff Stewart

Andy Thomas

Dan Thomas

Brian Wilcox

and many others

Table of Contents

Introduction

Lander Concepts Since 1970

The iconic Apollo Lunar Module (LM). Borne of a Cold War race to the Moon, its form-follows-function silhouette is unmistakable. The LM consisted of a foil-wrapped descent stage containing fuel tanks and a descent engine, all supported on four spider-like legs, and an ascent stage built of soda-can-thickness metals sprouting a haphazard-looking array of fuel tanks, communications antennas, and reaction control thrusters. It looks otherworldly as it sits upon another world (as shown in the photo above), with the exception of some features that hint of its human origins – a ladder, a porch, a door, and some windows. Its task was both preternatural and human at the same time – to provide an Earth-like environment for two humans, to transport those crew members in and out

of the gravity well of the Moon, and to serve as their home on the lunar surface.

There is a reason why the Apollo LMs, and many of the subsequent lunar lander designs featured in this book, look the way they do – their shape and form is a response to the simple physics that governs the tasks they are asked to perform. For example, the physics of lunar landing demands the lander have the ability to execute large velocity changes – 2,000 m/s (4,473.9 mph) to decelerate to a soft landing from Low Lunar Orbit, and another 2,000 m/s (4,473.9 mph) to accelerate back into lunar orbit – and its design must include life support for the human crew members. Therefore, much of the lunar lander "design space" is determined by physics. Large tanks of propellant surrounded by structure, an attenuation system for landing, and a pressurized volume for crew habitation all directly address the physics of lander design. Those physics and engineering realities mean that the next lunar lander will bear little resemblance to the sleek vehicles of modern science fiction that fly through space like jet fighters with little regard to the mass of propellant or Tsiolkovsky's rocket equation. Instead, lunar landers will most likely look like the big brother of the Apollo LM because the physics of lunar landing is unchanged, and technology has only improved marginally since Apollo. Not only did Apollo's designers understand the physics of the problem perfectly, they were very smart, especially given that they were inventing much of the technology for the first time.

Since that time, engineers and designers have continued to dream of the next missions to the Moon, and look to apply the lessons learned from Apollo in combination with the incremental improvements to technology from the past 5 decades. This catalog documents the history of lunar lander concepts performed by and for NASA since Apollo, and tells the story of physics, technology, and the desire to return humans to the lunar surface. All of the 100+ lander concepts in this catalog are supported by underlying engineering. The propellant types, pressurized volumes, structural mass fractions, mass margins, crew size, and surface durations may vary; however,

in the end, each concept is a design that responds to the physics of lunar landing, and the ergonomics and human factors of crew spacecraft design.

The Apollo LM is a logical starting point for this collection; however, the endpoint is a less exact point in time. The reader will note that lunar lander design work is concentrated into periods of time where returning to the Moon was a given priority over other human space endeavors. Not much lunar lander work took place in the years immediately following Apollo, or during the formative years of the International Space Station. Likewise, lunar mission design was not a priority in the period following the close of NASA's Constellation Program and the Altair lunar lander project. That change of priority, however, formed a useful breakpoint. The end-point of the concepts contained in this human lunar lander concept catalog is the final design of Altair in 2010.

Human crews will eventually return to the Moon. When they do, it will likely be in a machine that borrows its resemblance and features from one or more of the human lunar lander concepts that are detailed in the pages that follow. The reasons for our return to the Moon will be different from the motives that originally propelled us there in 1969. However, the urge to return to, and further understand, our nearest neighbor is unmistakable. In the words of Krafft Ehricke, "If God wanted man to become a spacefaring species, he would have given man a moon."

Parametric vs. Bottoms-Up Design

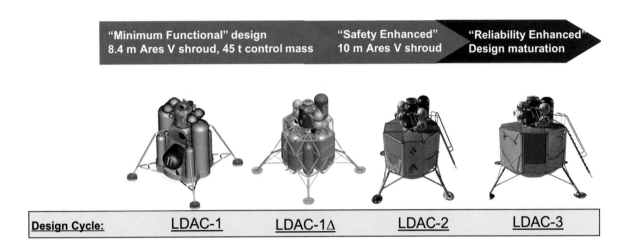

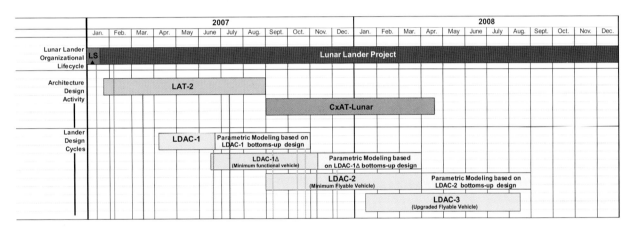

With the exception of the Apollo LMs, none of the lunar lander concepts described in this publication were ever built, nor were their designs even matured to the point where their construction and assembly was imminent. Since they were only conceptual in nature, most of these designs were developed using one of two conceptual engineering toolsets: preliminary "bottoms-up" engineering design or "parametric" design.

Conceptual vehicle design performed bottoms-up combines the preliminary design work of engineering experts in structures, propulsion, power, and the other spacecraft subsystem disciplines. A spacecraft systems engineer often coordinates these preliminary subsystem designs to produce an integrated estimate of vehicle performance, mass, power requirements, etc. Though the experts provide insightful details into the individual subsystems, preliminary bottoms-up design almost always suffers from omissions that

will only emerge as the design is matured.

An example of this phenomenon is secondary structure. A structural engineer can provide a quick and accurate estimate of primary structure for a new lander design; however, the scope of secondary structure and support brackets will become known only after the other subsystem designs have begun to mature. In lieu of detailed secondary structure design, mass estimating relationships are often utilized to estimate items that do not lend themselves to preliminary bottoms-up design. These mass estimating relationships are also an important ingredient of parametric mass estimation – i.e., vehicle design and performance estimation performed without the benefit of bottoms-up engineering design.

Parametric estimating utilizes historical mass-estimating relationships for spacecraft subsystems, and often combines these historical databases with analytical routines to perform simplified sizing of components, fuel calculations, etc. By the time they receive their undergraduate degrees, most aerospace engineers have already constructed one or more analytical spreadsheets to size spacecraft components, or calculated fuel requirements using Tsiolkovsky's rocket equation. Parametric lander design uses a similar technique, along with advanced parametric tools such as NASA's Envision, Examine, or Beyond LEO Architecture and Sizing Tool (BLAST), to iteratively link many specialized spreadsheets containing many thousands of lines of specialty code. These types of parametric tools produce vehicle design estimates through the careful selection of design parameters by a knowledgeable spacecraft systems engineer. More-advanced parametric designs are performed in consultation with subsystem design engineers. Hybrid designs that combine parts of bottoms-up design and parametric estimation are becoming more common. Generally, parametric designs are accompanied by concept drawings that illustrate the vehicle layout and configuration at a general level, whereas bottoms-up designs can produce drawings with some level of engineering detail.

Parametric tools attempt to account for design maturity that early bottoms-up designs lack, since the parametric tools are able to reference databases of completed (and often flown) designs. Conversely, bottoms-up designs will reflect vehicle performance using current technology and design solutions that may be absent in the databases that the parametric tools reference. Both methods of design are equally valid in the conceptual design phase of a lunar lander program. The designs in this concept catalog represent a wide cross section of parametric, bottoms-up, and hybrid designs.

This catalog includes designs from NASA and industry engineers, as proposed in various studies since Apollo. Although this is not a complete archive (landers were designed as early as 1939), it encompasses all U.S. designs since the 1980s and provides insight into the current state of technology advancement. The design concepts are listed chronologically and grouped by the organizational lifecycle, design activity, or lander design cycles in which they were developed (see Appendix B).

Lunar Lander Concept Taxonomy

Lunar lander concepts in this publication are identified by unique numeric-letter codes. The format is yymm-z, where yy is the 2-digit year, mm is the 2-digit month, and z is the sequence number or letter for that month when the concept was established. For example, the second lander concept investigated in August 2006 would be identified as 0608-B. If the concept is parametrically estimated, a "p" (for parametric) prefix is assigned to the alphanumeric identifier. For special studies (such as Lunar Lander Preparatory Study [LLPS] and Lunar Architecture Team [LAT]), additional fields may be added to identify those concepts with its particular study.

Example:

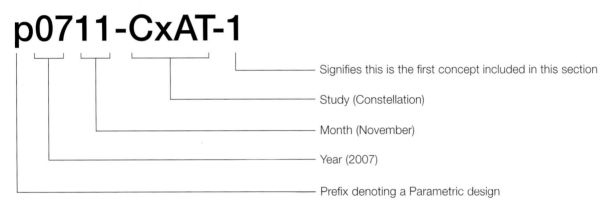

Signifies this is the first concept included in this section

Study (Constellation)

Month (November)

Year (2007)

Prefix denoting a Parametric design

Apollo Lunar Modules

The Apollo Lunar Module was the lander portion of the Apollo Program, and was built to achieve the transit from low lunar orbit to the surface and back. The module was also known by its acronym – LM – from the manufacturer designation (yet it was pronounced "LEM" – the acronym for its previous NASA-given name: Lunar Excursion Module). The 6.65 m³ (234.8 ft³) module was designed to carry a crew of two and support lunar missions up to 3 days in duration. The total module was 6.4 m (21 ft) high and 4.3 m (14.1 ft) across, and rested on four legs. It consisted of two stages: descent and ascent. The total mass of the module was 15,264 kg (33,651.4 lbm), with the majority of that (10,334 kg [22,782.6 lbm]) in the descent stage.

The Apollo LM is the starting point for this catalog. It represents the pinnacle of 1960's technology, and is the only human lunar lander yet to be flown. In studies that have followed over the ensuing decades, new generations of engineers have looked to the Apollo LM as a proof of concept for how a lightweight planetary lander could be designed, built, and operated. These same engineers have also marveled at how engineers in the mid-20th century could design such an efficient vehicle – one that had a 100% rate of success. To quote a NASA engineer 50 years following the Moon missions, "Those Apollo guys were really smart."

Apollo Lunar Module – G and H Series: 6809-LM-1 G/H

The G Series, on Apollo 11, was the first LM to touch down on the surface of the Moon. Apollo 12, 13, and 14 carried the H Series lander. Improvements in the H Series allowed for up to 2 days on the surface, compared with the 22 hours spent there by the Apollo 11 crew. The G and H Series missions could not carry the Lunar Roving Vehicle. Further upgrades, included in the J Series landers, allowed rovers to be carried on missions 15-17. The current location of each of the G and H Series landers is shown below:

Mission	Current Descent Stages Location
Apollo 11 "Eagle"	on Moon, Sea of Tranquility
Apollo 12 "Intrepid"	on Moon, Ocean of Storms
Apollo 13 "Aquarius"	Used as a lifeboat, burned up in Earth's atmosphere April 17, 1970
Apollo 14 "Antares"	on Moon, Fra Mauro

Descent Stage	
Power	Four silver-zinc batteries
Electrical Subassembly	Two electrical control assemblies integrated into the descent stage
Propulsion	80,068.4 N (18,000 lbf) N_2O_4/Aerozine 50
Protection	Multi-Layer Insulation (MLI)
Telecommunications	S-band was used for transmission of Pulse Code Modulation (PCM) telemetry, TV, voice, emergency key, and range data between LM and Earth; Very High Frequency (VHF) for linking LM and Command Module, and the LM and astronaut on the lunar surface; VHF telemetry capability from LM to Command Module on the far side of the Moon; Extravehicular Activity (EVA) astronaut link to Earth via VHF/S band relay
Thermal	Included a portion of the glycol loop (battery cold plates), water tank, an oxygen tank, and a pressure regulator
Structures	Composed primarily of machined parts and chemically milled panel/stiffener assemblies that were mechanically fastened
Environmental Control and Life Support System	Included the atmosphere revitalization section, oxygen supply and cabin pressure control section, water management, heat transport section, and outlets for oxygen and water servicing of the Portable Life Support System (PLSS). The descent stage oxygen supply provided descent flight phase and lunar stay oxygen needs, and the descent water management system consisted of a 166.5 kg (367 lbm) capacity, nitrogen-pressurized bladder-type tank. Cabin pressure = 33.1 kPa (4.8 psi)

Ascent Stage	
Power	Two silver-zinc batteries
Electrical Subassembly	Two electrical control assemblies, a relay junction box, a dead face relay, two circuit breaker panels, two inverters, and one lighting control assembly
Propulsion	23,130.9 N (5,200 lbf) of N_2O_4/Aerozine 50
Protection	MLI
Thermal	Included a portion of the glycol loop (battery cold plates), water tank, an oxygen tank, and a pressure regulator
Structures	Contained four subassemblies: the front face, the cabin skin, a midsection, and an aft equipment bay
Environmental Control and Life Support System	Included the atmosphere revitalization section, oxygen supply and cabin pressure control section, water management, heat transport section, and outlets for oxygen and water servicing of the PLSS. The ascent stage oxygen supply provided oxygen for the ascent and rendezvous stages, and the ascent water management system consisted of two nitrogen-pressurized bladder-type tanks, each with 47.5-pound capacity. Cabin pressure = 33.1 kPa (4.8 psi)

Mass Breakdown				
Subsystem	**Descent Stage**		**Ascent Stage**	
	lbm	kg	lbm	kg
Apollo 11				
Dry Mass	4,484	2,034	5,390	2,445
Propellant	18,184	8,248	5,238	2,376
Apollo 11 Gross Mass	**22,668**	**10,282**	**10,628**	**4,821**
Apollo 12				
Dry Mass	4,484	2,034	4,806	2,180
Propellant	18,104	8,212	5,818	2,639
Apollo 12 Gross Mass	**22,588**	**10,246**	**10,624**	**4,819**
Apollo 13				
Dry Mass	4,650	2,109	4,668	2,117
Propellant	18,339	8,318	5,229	2,372
Apollo 13 Gross Mass	**22,989**	**10,427**	**9,897**	**4,489**
Apollo 14				
Dry Mass	4,705	2,134	4,740	2,150
Propellant	18,078	8,200	5,622	2,550
Apollo 14 Gross Mass	**22,783**	**10,334**	**10,362**	**4,700**

Apollo Lunar Module — J Series: 6809-LM-1J

The Extended Lunar Modules used on the final three J-class missions – Apollo 15, 16, and 17 – were significantly upgraded to allow for greater landed payload weights and longer lunar surface stay times. The descent engine power was improved by the addition of a 254-mm (10-in.) extension to the engine bell, and the descent fuel tanks were increased in size. A waste storage tank was added to the descent stage, with plumbing from the ascent stage. These upgrades allowed stay times of up to 75 hours on the Moon for the two-man crew.

The Extended Lunar Module also carried the Lunar Roving Vehicle, stowed on Quadrant 1 of the module's descent stage and deployed by astronauts after landing. This allowed them to explore much larger areas and return a greater variety of lunar samples. The current locations of the J series descent stages are:

The Extended Lunar Modules (ELMs) used on the final three "J-class missions."

Mission	Current Descent Stage Location
Apollo 15 "Falcon"	on Moon, Hadley-Apennine
Apollo 16 "Orion"	on Moon, Descartes
Apollo 17 "Challenger"	on Moon, Taurus-Littrow

Descent Stage	
Power	Five silver-zinc batteries
Electrical Subassembly	Two electrical control assemblies were integrated into the descent stage
Propulsion	N_2O_4/Aerozine 50
Protection	MLI
Telecommunications	S-band was used for transmission of PCM telemetry, TV, voice, emergency key, and range data between LM and Earth; VHF for linking LM and Command Module, and the LM and astronaut on the lunar surface; VHF telemetry capability from LM to Command Module on the far side of the Moon; EVA astronaut link to Earth via VHF/S band relay
Thermal	This subsystem was made up of five integrated sections: atmosphere revitalization, oxygen supply and cabin pressure control, heat transport, water management, and a cold plate
Structures	Composed primarily of machined parts and chemically milled panel/stiffener assemblies that were mechanically fastened
Guidance, Navigation & Control	The Massachusetts Institute of Technology's Instrumentation Laboratory developed the Primary GN&C System for the LM, and Raytheon manufactured the Guidance Computer. A similar system was used in the Command Module. TRW, Inc. developed the Abort Guidance System, which was the backup navigation tool.
Environmental Control and Life Support System	A portion of the glycol loop (battery cold plates), water tank, an oxygen tank, and a pressure regulator were in the descent stage. Cabin Design Pressure: 34.5 kPa (5 psi)

Ascent Stage	
Power	Two silver-zinc ascent batteries
Electrical Subassembly	Two ascent electrical control assemblies, a relay junction box, a dead face relay, two circuit breaker panels, two inverters, and one lighting control assembly
Propulsion	N_2O_4/Aerozine 50
Protection	MLI
Thermal	A portion of the glycol loop and two gaseous oxygen tanks were in the ascent stage aft equipment bay
Structures	Consisted of the following subassemblies: front face, cabin skin, midsection, and aft equipment bay
Environmental Control and Life Support System	Consisted of five integrated sections: atmosphere revitalization, oxygen supply and cabin pressure control, heat transport, water management, and cold plate. The major portion of the Environmental Control System was the pressurized equipment compartment in the ascent stage. Two Environmental Control System water tanks were in the tankage section of the ascent stage.

Mass Breakdown				
Subsystem	**Descent Stage**		**Ascent Stage**	
	lbm	**kg**	**lbm**	**kg**
1.0 Structure	1,014	460	1,025	465
2.0 Protection	463	210	364	165
3.0 Propulsion	1,091	495	712	323
4.0 Power	807	366	734	333
5.0 Control	0	0	0	0
6.0 Avionics	64	29	399	181
7.0 Environment	428	194	681	309
8.0 Other	602	273	650	295
9.0 Growth	0	0	0	0
Dry Mass w/ Growth	**4,469**	**2,027**	**4,565**	**2,071**
10.0 Non-cargo	763	346	0	0
11.0 Cargo	1,100	499	375	170
Inert Mass	**6,332**	**2,872**	**4,940**	**2,241**
12.0 Non-propellant	558	253	137	62
13.0 Propellant	18,799	8,527	5,494	2,492
Gross Mass	**25,689**	**11,652**	**10,571**	**4,795**

Post-Apollo

Following the success of the Apollo lunar landing missions, NASA's attention turned back toward Low Earth Orbit (LEO), with a number of missions utilizing heritage Apollo hardware. The end of the 1970s and beginning of the 1980s saw the space agency shift its focus toward the Space Shuttle, and on continuing LEO missions. A return to the Moon would periodically appear as a strategic initiative; however, for the decade and a half following the Apollo missions, other achievements in space took center stage.

In the late 1980s, Eagle Engineering's Lunar Base Systems Study (LBSS) was initiated at the NASA Johnson Space Center to develop plans for a lunar base. This was to be accomplished around the year 2000. The study included development of a set of construction and assembly tasks required on the lunar surface, determination of different concepts for equipment applicable to the tasks, and identification of leading candidate systems for future conceptual design. The landers for this study were designed to carry equipment to be used in cargo handling, construction, and assembly operations for the base/habitat, as well as the crew and logistics required for an extended stay on the lunar surface.

Rendering of a lunar base concept.

Eagle Engineering Lunar Base Systems Study LO$_2$/LH$_2$ and N$_2$O$_4$/MMH: 8801-EE-1

This study looked at the problem of building a lunar lander to support a small lunar surface base using one lander that could either land 25 mt (28 t), one way, or take a 6-mt (7-t) crew capsule up and down. The initial idea was to build a reusable lander, suitable for minimizing the transportation cost to a permanent base, and use it from the first crewed mission on, taking some penalty and perhaps expending expensive vehicles early in the program to avoid building multiple types of landers while focusing the effort on a space-maintainable, single-stage, reusable vehicle. A four-engine design for a multi-purpose vehicle, with total thrust in the range 155,688 to 177,929 N (35 to 40,000 lbf) – 53,379 to 57,827 N (12 to 13,000 lbf) per engine – and a throttling ratio in the 13:1 to 20:1 range was proposed. Initial work indicated a regeneratively cooled, pump-fed engine would be required due to difficulties with regenerative cooling over wide throttling ranges with pressure-fed systems. Three cases of interest were studied. The first scenario assumed the lunar lander was used only to place a payload on the surface and was called the "Cargo Down" case. In this case, the lander did not have propellant to ascend to orbit after delivering its payload; it, therefore, stayed on the lunar surface until refueled. The second case also placed a

payload on the surface, but it carried enough propellant to return its inert mass to orbit, and was called the "Inert Returned" case. The third scenario described a case in which the lunar lander carried a crew module down to the surface and then back to orbit. This case was called the "Crew Module Round Trip."

All three scenarios focused on a single-stage, reusable lander using nitrogen tetroxide/monomethyl hydrazine (N$_2$O$_4$/MMH) propellants. While the N$_2$O$_4$/MMH lander is considerably heavier than an LO$_2$/LH$_2$ lander in the previous section, it is much smaller, due to higher propellant density. However, features in both landers are essentially the same. The propellant capacity of either version of the lander was 35 mt (38.6 t) divided into four tanks of 16 m^3 (565 ft^3) each. The tank diameter was 2.5 m (8.2 ft) for all tanks.

Important features included the following:

- An airlock/servicing tunnel down the center of the lander to allow easy access on the surface and pressurized volume for Line Replaceable Units. Many engine connections could be made and broken inside the pressurized volume.

- A removable crew module. The lander was flyable without the crew module.

- The lander fit in a 9-m (30-ft) heavy-lift vehicle shroud with landing gear stowed.
- The landing gear had electromechanical shock absorbers.
- Emergency ascent with one or two crew members was possible without the crew module. In that case, the crew would ride in suits in the airlock/servicing tunnel.

The figure shows this lander being serviced on the lunar surface and illustrates how the airlock/servicing tunnel allowed pressurized access to a surface vehicle. An engine is being removed in the figure.

Mass breakdowns are included below for the multi-purpose versions of all three cases, using both LO_2/LH_2 and N_2O_4/MMH propellants.

Mass Breakdown – Multi-Purpose Lander Using LO_2/LH_2 Propellant						
	Cargo Down		Crew Module Round Trip		Inert Returned	
Delta-v, Ascent (km/s)	0		2.28*		2.28*	
Delta-v, Descent (km/s)	2.10		2.10		2.10	
	lbm	kg	lbm	kg	lbm	kg
Structure	3,706	1,681	3,706	1,681	3,706	1,681
Engines	1,812	822	1,812	822	1,812	822
RCS Dry	906	411	906	411	906	411
Landing Systems	1,728	784	1,728	784	1,728	784
Thermal Protection	4,447	2,017	4,447	2,017	4,447	2,017
Tanks	6,669	3,025	6,669	3,025	6,669	3,025
Data Management System/GN&C	331	150	331	150	331	150
Electrical Power**	1,054	478	1,054	478	1,054	478
Airlock/Tunnel	1,003	455	1,003	455	1,003	455
Inert Mass	**21,656**	**9,823**	**21,656**	**9,823**	**21,656**	**9,823**
Ascent Prop.	0	0	24,987	11,334	15,961	7,240
Descent Prop.	49,818	22,597	39,985	18,137	45,164	20,486
Unusable Prop. (3%)	1,495	678	1,949	884	1,834	832
FPR Prop. (4%)	1,993	904	2,599	1,179	2,445	1,109
Usable RCS	1,891	858	1,519	689	1,715	778
Unusable RCS	95	43	75	34	86	39
FPR (20%)	379	172	304	138	344	156
Total Propellant Mass	**55,671**	**25,252**	**71,418**	**32,395**	**67,549**	**30,640**
Deorbit or Gross Mass (less Payload)	**77,327**	**35,075**	**93,074**	**42,218**	**89,205**	**40,463**
Payload, Descent	55,116	25,000	13,228	6,000	30,865	14,000
Payload, Ascent	0	0	13,228	6,000	0	0
Deorbit or Gross Mass (with Payload)	**132,443**	**60,075**	**106,302**	**48,218**	**120,070**	**54,463**

Mass Breakdown – Multi-Purpose Lander Using N_2O_4/MMH Propellant						
	Cargo Down		Crew Module Round Trip		Inert Returned	
Delta-v, Ascent (km/s)	0		2.28*		2.28*	
Delta-v, Descent (km/s)	2.10		2.10		2.10	
	lbm	kg	lbm	kg	lbm	kg
Structure	4,310	1,955	4,310	1,955	4,310	1,955
Engines	2,107	956	2,107	956	2,107	956
RCS Dry	1,054	478	1,054	478	1,054	478
Landing Systems	2,010	912	2,010	912	2,010	912
Thermal Protection	2,218	1,006	2,218	1,006	2,218	1,006
Tanks	3,327	1,509	3,327	1,509	3,327	1,509
Data Management System/GN&C	331	150	331	150	331	150
Electrical Power**	1,054	478	1,054	478	1,054	478
Airlock/Tunnel	1,003	455	1,003	455	1,003	455
Total Inert Mass	**17,414**	**7,899**	**17,414**	**7,899**	**17,414**	**7,899**
Descent	72,446	32,861	67,605	30,665	70,387	31,927
Ascent	0	0	34,617	15,702	20,737	9,406
Unusable (3%)	2,174	986	3,067	1,391	2,734	1,240
FPR Prop. (4%)	2,897	1,314	4,090	1,855	3,644	1,653
Usable RCS	2,183	990	2,035	923	2,119	961
Unusable RCS	110	50	101	46	106	48
FPR (20%)	437	198	408	185	423	192
Total Propellant Mass	**80,247**	**36,399**	**111,923**	**50,767**	**100,150**	**45,427**
Deorbit or Gross Mass (less Payload)	**97,661**	**44,298**	**129,337**	**58,666**	**117,564**	**53,326**
Payload, Descent	55,116	25,000	13,228	6,000	30,865	14,000
Payload, Ascent	0	0	13,228*	6,000*	0 (Inert Mass returned to LLO)	0 (Inert Mass returned to LLO)
Total Mass at Deorbit	**152,777**	**69,298**	**142,565**	**64,666**	**148,429**	**67,326**

* Delta-v = 1.85 + 0.43 km/s (1.15 + 0.27 mi/s) for a 15-deg plane change in a 93 km (58 mi) circular orbit.

** Electrical power provided for 3 days only, (2 kW). 100% redundant fuel cells/tank sets.

Space Exploration Initiative

On July 20, 1989 – the 20th anniversary of the Apollo 11 lunar landing mission – President George H. W. Bush announced plans for the Space Exploration Initiative (SEI), which called for a long-range continuing commitment based on construction of the Space Station Freedom, sending humans back to the Moon, and ultimately sending astronauts to Mars.

Following this announcement, NASA Administrator Richard Truly initiated a study of the options to achieve the president's goals, headed by Johnson Space Center Director Aaron Cohen. The "90-Day Study" team, assembled from program offices and field centers, developed a reference base from which strategic options could be derived while still meeting the basic objectives of the Human Exploration Initiative. The final package consisted of an end-to-end strategy that began with robotic missions, exploited the unique capabilities of Space Station Freedom, and moved forward to the development of planetary surface systems that could support human life, without losing sight of programmatic matters such as resources, management systems, international participation, and national benefits. On November 29, 1989, Truly briefed the National Space Council's Blue Ribbon Panel on the resulting 90-Day Study report.

This time period is bookended by a comprehensive series of lunar base studies performed by Eagle Engineering for NASA in 1988-89 and a focused return-to-the-Moon study, First Lunar Outpost, in 1992-3. This period ended when the next administration, mindful of its promise to balance the budget, canceled the SEI.

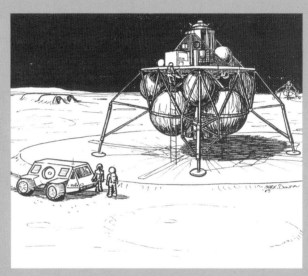

Rendering of a planetary surface system concept.

Lunar Excursion Vehicle: 8901-90 Day Study-1

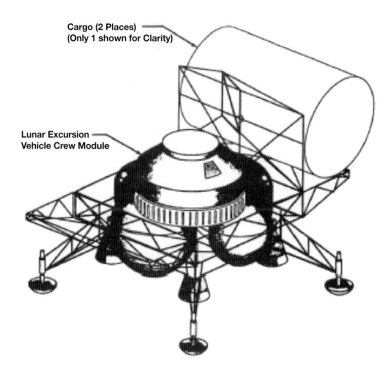

Cargo (2 Places)
(Only 1 shown for Clarity)

Lunar Excursion
Vehicle Crew Module

The Lunar Excursion Vehicle (LEV) was designed to be delivered by the lunar transfer vehicle first to Space Station Freedom, and from there to lunar orbit. It then provided transportation for cargo and crew from lunar orbit to the lunar surface. Sized to deliver approximately 33 mt (33.8 t) to the lunar surface in expendable cargo-only mode or approximately 13 mt (14.3t) to 15 mt (16.5 t) of cargo plus a crew module in a piloted mode, it could be based on the surface, covered by a thermal tent and ready for launch and rendezvous with the lunar transfer vehicle or stored in Low Lunar Orbit (LLO) awaiting return of the transfer vehicle.

The LEV elements included a propulsion system, landing legs and pads with height control for landing on unimproved areas, a crew cab, and other subsystems. It shared a common design with the lunar transfer vehicle for some systems, including the main engines, cryogenic reaction control system thrusters, avionics and selected software, and communications. Four advanced fuel cells were to provide electrical power. Solar arrays were also required for LLO storage.

While reusable cargo missions used automated rendezvous and docking in LLO for cargo missions, piloted missions provided crew monitoring and control. The propellant system was designed for 30 days on the lunar surface, and provided a capability to utilize lunar-generated oxygen (hydrogen was to be provided by fluid transfer from the lunar transfer vehicle in LLO).

The primary purpose of the crew module was to transfer four crewmembers from lunar orbit to the lunar outpost. It shared a common system design with the transfer crew module, and although it accommodated both lunar-gravity and microgravity operations, it had no radiation shielding. During landing operations, two crewmembers were provided with console positions and windows from which to visually monitor all critical landing activities, including forward landing and touchdown. Systems were planned to be quiescent except for 2 days during crew descent and initial surface operations, and 2 days for preparation and return to LLO. During quiescent periods on the Moon, power, thermal control, and propellant conditioning were to be provided by surface support systems.

Transfer between modules was envisioned to be performed initially by Extravehicular Activity (EVA), and later by pressurized transfer using surface-based systems. The lunar excursion crew module had no airlock; therefore, EVA was to be supported by depressurizing the module. Repressurization gas was planned to be provided for two contingency EVAs. Additionally, a docking adapter was provided for LLO docking and crew transfer for incoming and outgoing crews.

Mass Breakdown – Piloted Mode		
	lbm	kg
Inert Mass	12,787	5,800
Propellant Load	49,384	22,400
Cargo	33,069	15,000
Crew Module (including crew)	9,700	4,400
Gross Mass	**104,940**	**47,600**

First Lunar Outpost Lander: 9205-FLO-1

The key element of the First Lunar Outpost (FLO) plan was that it employed crew landers (left) and cargo landers (right) that both used a common descent stage consisting of four RL-10 engines modified for 4:1 throttling, LOX/LH propellant tankage, and four landing legs. The one-way cargo lander was to arrive prior to the crew, and included a habitat and enough consumables for a 45-day lunar stay. Once the crew arrived, each astronaut was to make three 8-hour Extravehicular Activities – i.e., spacewalks – per week, which made new, comfortable space suits a requirement.

During their stay, the astronauts were to perform nine traverses within a 25 km (15.5-mi) radius of the landing site. As with Apollo, the crew members planned to use a lunar rover to extend the distance they could travel around the landing site. The FLO rover could carry a crew of four on traverses out to walk-back distance from the lander. Alternatively, the rover could be outfitted with a 100 kg (220.5 lbm)

telerobotic control module that allowed for uncrewed transport of science payloads up to 100 km (62.1 mi) from base.

Mission plans called for the astronauts to deploy 2.72 mt (6,000 lbm) of scientific equipment, including a geophysical monitoring package, a solar system physics package, a geophysical package, a lunar geologic tool set, a lunar transit telescope, a small solar telescope, a robotic package for the rover, and a life science package. Crew surface activities were to include a demonstration of oxygen extraction techniques from the lunar soil, the making of bricks from in-situ materials, and testing of pneumatic size sorting methods for regolith material.

This vehicle concept also performed lunar orbit insertion, adding another 1,000 m/s (2,237 mph) delta-v capability. The ascent stage also featured direct-to-Earth return capability, adding another 1,000 m/s (2,237 mph) to systems capability.

Mass Breakdown								
Subsystem	Crew Module		Return Stage		Crewed Lander Stage		Cargo Lander Stage	
	lbm	kg	lbm	kg	lbm	kg	lbm	kg
1.0 Structure	4,321	1,960	1,294	587	3,902	1,770	3,902	1,770
2.0 Protection	798	362	370	168	926	420	926	420
3.0 Propulsion	317	144	3,038	1,378	10,955	4,969	10,955	4,969
4.0 Power	1,193	541	2,690	1,220	340	154	849	385
5.0 Control	0	0	0	0	0	0	0	0
6.0 Avionics	1,058	480	293	133	256	116	677	307
7.0 Environment	2,412	1,094	503	228	0	0	0	0
8.0 Other	1,603	727	22	10	3,239	1,469	3,239	1,469
9.0 Growth	2,341	1,062	1,642	745	3,924	1,780	4,140	1,878
Dry Mass w/Growth	14,043	6,370	9,852	4,469	23,542	10,678	24,688	11,198
10.0 Non-cargo	1,343	609	1,197	543	3,823	1,734	3,823	1,734
11.0 Cargo	0	0	0	0	11,023	5,000	79,133	35,894
Inert Mass	15,386	6,979	11,049	5,012	38,388	17,412	107,644	48,826
12.0 Non-propellant	181	82	2,282	1,035	132	60	132	60
13.0 Propellant	439	199	39,853	18,077	97,405	44,182	97,336	44,151
Gross Mass	16,006	7,260	53,184	24,124	135,925	61,654	205,112	93,037

Faster, Better, Cheaper

In 1992, NASA administrator Daniel Goldin began using a new approach to project management of its Space and Earth Science Missions. This methodology, which became known as the "Faster, Better, Cheaper" (FBC) initiative, was intended to shorten development times, reduce cost, and increase the scientific return by flying more missions in less time, employing both smaller spacecraft and cheaper technology to undertake less complex and more specific tasks. In all, 16 missions were launched under the FBC banner, including the successful Mars Pathfinder mission, which touched down on Mars on July 4, 1997, and was a resounding success. Others, such as Mars Polar Lander and Mars Climate Orbiter, did not accomplish their intended missions. In all, six of the 16 FBC missions failed, resulting in an unacceptably low success rate and cancellation of the FBC initiative in 1999.

Human exploration missions took a backseat to other exploration endeavors during this time period; however, a few notable studies began exploring creative mission concepts. Two such studies were LUNOX, which was NASA's first attempt to study the full utilization of in-situ resources for spacecraft propellant production, and Human Lunar Return, a study to assess a hyper-economical return to the Moon using the Space Shuttle and minimalist transit and landing spacecraft.

August 1996 marked a turning point in human exploration as an announcement of possible past life on Mars became public. Those declarations changed the focus of NASA's exploration studies from the Moon to Mars, and defining "Martian reference missions" would become NASA's priority into the early 2000s.

Phoenix/LUNOX Lander: 9306-LUNOX-1

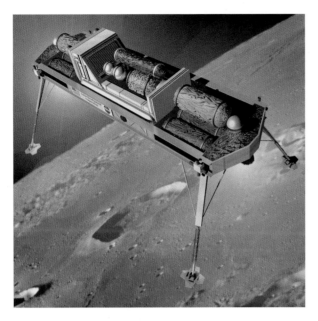

In 1993, a Johnson Space Center proposal known as LUNOX was introduced. This proposal tried to reduce the cost of a First Lunar Outpost by producing LOX propellant from lunar soil. This was to be used in the crew lander for ascent from the surface and the return trip to Earth. The lighter LH_2 fuel would still be brought from Earth since hydrogen was not believed to be readily available on the Moon.

The LUNOX Uncrewed Lander was planned to carry the LUNOX lunar oxygen production plant, storage facility, and nuclear power reactor to the Moon's surface (left in figure above). Use of oxygen produced in-situ from lunar regolith was expected to reduce the

cost of subsequent crewed lunar missions and outpost activities by up to 50%. The mass of the LUNOX cargo package was 12,454 kg (27,456 lbm). The total mass to Low Earth Orbit (LEO) for the lander, LUNOX cargo package, and propellants was 83,809 kg (184,767 lbm).

Subsequent uncrewed lander cargo missions were to deliver components for the incremental buildup of a lunar outpost, including tankers, regolith loaders and haulers, pressurized rovers, mobile power units, science payloads, and various other support elements. Eventually, the Phoenix Crewed Lander was to deliver a crew of four to the lunar outpost in an Apollo-type crew module (right in figure above).

Mass Breakdown		
Uncrewed Lander		
	(lbm)	**(kg)**
Phoenix Uncrewed Lander (dry)	10,399	4,717
Cargo Package	27,456	12,454
Propellants	36,548	16,578
Trans-Lunar Injection Stage (dry)	13,515	6,130
Propellants	96,849	43,930
Total Mass in Low Earth Orbit	**184,767**	**83,809**
Crewed Lander		
Apollo-type Crew Module	13,084	5,935
Crew and Support	1,343	609
"Phoenix" Crewed Lander *(4 x 31 150 KN thrust engines)*	12,137	5,505
Cargo	4,409	2,000
Trans-Lunar Injection Stage *(3 x RL-10-A4 engines)*	13,514	6,130
Elements	**44,487**	**20,179**
Crew Module Propellant	439	199
Lander Propellant	37,355	16,944
Liquid Hydrogen Fuel for Return Trip	5,494	2,492
Trans-Lunar Injection Stage Propellant	96,849	43,930
Propellant	**140,137**	**63,565**
Total Mass in Low Earth Orbit	**184,624**	**83,744**
Lunar Oxygen Required	22,410	10,165
Total Mass, including Lunar Oxygen	**207,034**	**93,909**

Human Lunar Return Lander: 9508-HLR-1

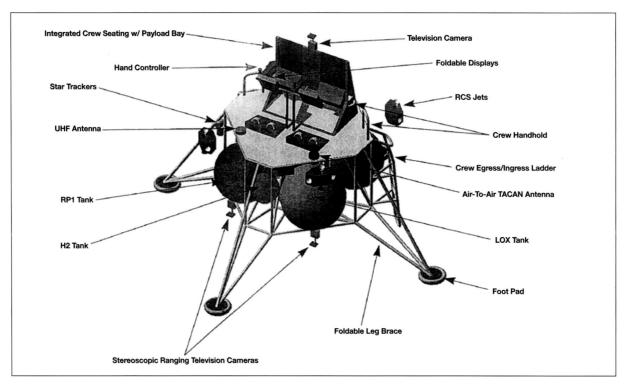

Integrated Crew Seating w/ Payload Bay
Hand Controller
Star Trackers
UHF Antenna
RP1 Tank
H2 Tank
Stereoscopic Ranging Television Cameras
Foldable Leg Brace
Television Camera
Foldable Displays
RCS Jets
Crew Handhold
Crew Egress/Ingress Ladder
Air-To-Air TACAN Antenna
LOX Tank
Foot Pad

NASA Administrator Dan Goldin initiated the "Human Lunar Return" (HLR) study in September 1995 to investigate innovative, fast-track approaches for crewed spaceflight. The HLR team worked through two initial concepts in an effort to produce the ultimate cut-rate faster-better-cheaper human lunar mission. The 1996 baseline design was a bare-minimum lightweight concept in which anything not absolutely necessary (e.g., the LEO cryo fuel depot or lunar orbit station) was deleted. It consisted of a Lunar Orbit Stage (LOS), the Lunar Landing Vehicle (LLV), and the Habitat.

The LOS was protected by a 9.144-m (30-ft) diameter aeroshell since it would be aerobraking back into LEO when returning from the Moon. The shell was to be launched in seven segments to save space, assembled on orbit, and moored to the International Space Station (ISS) pending integration with the Lunar Orbit Stage. A Space Shuttle flight would deliver the crew and propellant for the lunar vehicles to the ISS, and the LOS and LLV, together with the crew, would depart for the Moon. On the return trip, the LOS would again dock with the ISS after which the crew was to return to Earth via the Space Shuttle.

The 15.6-mt (17.2-t) LOS vehicle carried only enough propellant for lunar orbit insertion and trans-Earth injection; two expendable 20-mt (22-t) propulsion modules (derived from the Russian "Breeze" upper stage and launched on two Proton rockets) performed the Trans-Lunar Injection (TLI) burn. The LOS carried a small, unpressurized LLV and a 2.5-m (8.2-ft) long Command Module capable of supporting two astronauts for up to 19 days during the Earth-Moon transfer.

The open-cockpit LLV weighed just 4,565.3 kg (10,064.9 lbm), including fuel, and was 3.9 m (12.8 ft) tall by 5.6 m (18.4 ft) wide. The space-suited crew of two received oxygen and other life support consumables via umbilicals from the LLV. After landing, they were to live in the inflatable Surface Habitat that had been delivered prior to their arrival. Following departure from the lunar surface, the crew reboarded the LOS and the LLV was jettisoned prior to trans-Earth injection.

Baseline for the Expendable Crewed Lander

Vehicle	• Open cockpit sized for two crew in Extravehicular Mobility Unit (EMU)/Portable Life Support System (PLSS) • LOX servicing at pad pre-launch; vent and servicing interfaces integrated into upgraded non-toxic Orbiter
Structures	• Truss frame structure, composites where feasible • Single-stage, four-leg landing gear with load attenuation • Cockpit frame/payload box provides structural interface to PLSS
Propulsion	• Single-stage pressure-fed LOX/RP1 • 14,679 N (3,300 lbf) 4:1 throttling main engine w/no gimbal • 200 N (45 lbf) 6 DOF Reaction Control System (RCS)
Guidance Navigation & Control	• Auto-rendezvous and Auto-Land w/Redesignation • Daytime hazard detection (shadow based) • Star Tracker, Deep Space Network, Inertial Navigation System, Laser altimeter, Beacon, LIght Detection And Ranging (LIDAR)
Power	• Two low-mass Proton Exchange Membrane (PEM) fuel cells (load sharing/redundant)
Avionics/Communication	• Non-Commercial Off-the-Shelf reduced mass • Computer, S-Band, Ultra-high Frequency, video (descent and ascent)
Life Support	• New EMU with amine swing bed CO_2 removal • EVA resources via umbilical during ascent/descent
Thermal	• Multi-Layer Insulation, Passive with heaters/radiators
Mission	• dV's: Descent = 1,910 m/s (6,266 ft/s), Ascent = 1,822 m/s (5,978 ft/s); RCS = 40 m/s (131 ft/s) • Land and surface operations during lunar day only

Mass Breakdown

	(lbm)	(kg)
Primary Structure	892.4	404.8
Payload Box/Seat	63.5	28.8
Landing Gear	218.9	99.3
Propulsion	556.7	252.5
TPS/Protection	250.2	113.5
Power	277.1	125.7
Avionics	264.8	120.1
Life Support	123.5	56.0
Stage Inert	**2,647.1**	**1,200.7**
Residual Propellant (3%)	216.1	98.0
LOX Boil-off	94.4	42.8
Final Stage Inert	**2,957.6**	**1,341.5**
Usable Propellants	7,107.3	3,223.8
Gross Stage Mass	**10,064.9**	**4,565.3**
2 Crew + EMU/PLSS	933.2	423.3
Payload	110.2	50.0
Total Lunar Landing Vehicle Mass to Low Earth Orbit	**11,108.3**	**5,038.6**

Decadal Planning Team

The L1 Lunar Mission Architecture was a conceptual study performed in 2000 that looked at a possible means of returning humans to the Moon within the next 10 years while providing development of the core capabilities needed to enable human missions to Mars. This study was conducted as part of the Decadal Planning Team study activities in the late 1990s early 2000s. The capabilities of these concepts included advanced systems and technologies that could be tested in a near-Earth operational environment, such as those needed for autonomous deep space operations, and planetary surface operations such as Mars analog operations at a base at the lunar south pole.

Several important assumptions were made at the outset to enable the development of the mission architecture. These included deferring the development of high-capacity launch systems by assuming utilization of existing launch vehicle systems, and making use of lunar libration point number one (L1) and the International Space Station (ISS) as transfer nodes between the two planetary surfaces. In addition, it was assumed that no long-term commitment regarding extensive lunar surface infrastructure was to be made while initial transportation capabilities were established, allowing for the future expansion of science and commercialization activities. Finally, it was expected that a crew of four could be transported to the Moon for expeditionary missions or for extended stay missions and returned to Earth. Any cargo to the lunar surface was to be transported separately from the crew and was pre-deployed on the lunar surface before the crew arrived.

The L1 Lunar Mission Architecture was composed of a suite of elements for sending humans to the Moon. These elements included:
• a lunar depot called the L1 Gateway, to be located at L1;
• a Lunar Transfer Vehicle (LTV) to ferry the crew from the ISS to the L1 Gateway;
• a high-energy injection stage to provide an initial boost for the LTV;
• the L1 Lunar Hab Lander to support the crew for 30-days at the lunar south pole;
• the L1 Lunar Lander, which performed 3-day expeditionary missions to any point on the lunar surface or 30-day extended missions at the lunar south pole; and
• high-efficiency Solar Electric Propulsion transfer vehicles that were used to spiral the L1 Gateway and landers to the L1 staging area.

Other supporting elements of the architecture included the Space Shuttle to launch both crew to the ISS and the L1 Gateway to Low Earth Orbit (LEO); the ISS, which stored the LTV and served as the nominal terminal for returning lunar astronauts; the Delta-IV expendable launch vehicle, used to bring the LTV and landers to LEO; the Global Positioning System for navigation; and a lunar positioning system to aid in lunar navigation and communication with Earth.

L1 Mission Architecture Lander: 0011-DPT-1

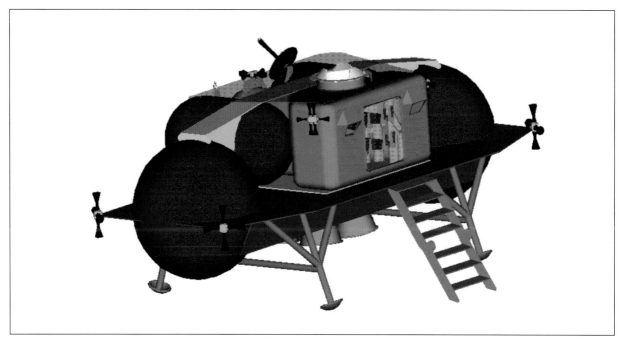

The primary design objective of the L1 Lunar Lander was crew transportation to and from the L1 Gateway at L1 to any point on the lunar surface. It was intended to fulfill two types of missions: an expeditionary-type mission in which the lander acted as a habitation base camp, sustaining a crew of four for short durations, and a transport-type mission, where it could ferry the crew to and from the L1 Lunar Hab Lander, which was to be located at the lunar south pole.

The final lander design was comprised of two stages – an ascent and a descent stage. The descent stage consisted of landing gear, main propulsion system descent tanks, the descent Reaction Control System (RCS), and support structure. To minimize the payload mass going back to the L1 Gateway, the descent stage was left behind on the lunar surface. The ascent stage hosted the crew module, avionics, Environmental Control and Life Support System (ECLSS), ascent propulsion tanks, ascent RCS, and the main propulsion system. In addition to the crew, the ascent stage was capable of delivering 50 kg (110.23 lbm) of lunar samples to the L1 Gateway for transfer back to Earth for scientific analysis.

Along with the systems listed above, the descent stage contained a 240 kg (529.1 lbm) unpressurized rover, used both as a mobility aid for crew surface traverses during extravehicular activities (EVAs) and to transfer the crew to and from the L1 Lunar Hab Lander. A storage pallet was also included with the descent stage, to be used for up to 430 kg (947.99 lbm) of science equipment for expeditionary surface missions or logistics for resupply of the L1 Lunar Hab Lander.

The L1 Lunar Lander, as designed, met the primary objectives as well as the following design requirements:

- total delta-v of 5,562 m/s (18,248 ft/s) for transit to/from L1 Gateway, descent, and ascent;
- a capability of precision landing and hazard avoidance with manual override;
- use of a Solar Electric Propulsion stage for delivery to the L1 Gateway;
- up to four cabin repressurizations after depressurization for surface EVAs;
- 2:1 throttleable LOX/Methane main propulsion system;
- LOX/Methane RCS;
- the ability to abort-to-surface (engine out) or abort-to-orbit (L1 Gateway);
- automated rendezvous and docking with L1 Gateway with manual override;
- 70.3 kPa (10.2 psi) cabin atmosphere; and
- sized to be packaged within a launch payload shroud with a 6 m (19.7 ft) diameter by 18 m (59.1 ft) height.

Mass Breakdown						
Subsystem	Total Mass		Wet Mass		Dry Mass	
	lbm	kg	lbm	kg	lbm	kg
Electrical Power	551.15	250.00	59.52	27.00	491.63	223.00
Field Equipment	1,028.19	466.38	0.00	0.00	1,028.19	466.38
LL1 Space Suit	882.09	400.11	0.00	0.00	882.09	400.11
2.5 kW Thermal Control System	503.20	228.25	10.16	4.61	493.04	223.64
Lunar Roving Vehicle	530.45	240.61	0.00	0.00	530.45	240.61
ECLSS + Crew Accommodations + Health Care	2,099.82	952.46	404.55	183.50	1,695.27	768.96
Propulsion	56,880.70	25,800.65	50,278.78	22,806.07	6,601.92	2,994.58
Structure	2,651.06	1,202.50	0.00	0.00	2,651.06	1,202.50
Avionics	251.99	114.30	0.00	0.00	251.99	114.30
Total Gross Mass	65,378.65	29,655.26	50,753.01	23,021.18	14,625.64	6,634.08

Return to Exploration

On January 14, 2004, President George W. Bush announced a "new course" for the nation's space program. Soon to be known as the Vision for Space Exploration, this new course shifted NASA's long-term focus from the Space Shuttle and the International Space Station to the creation of a new human spacecraft, planned to fly with a crew in 10 years and to return humans to the Moon within 16 years. The NASA Administrator, Sean O'Keefe, embraced the policy as laid out by President Bush and proposed a strategic plan to implement the proposed goals and objectives. Congress also endorsed the vision, passing the NASA Authorization Act of 2005 to support this plan.

NASA's Office of Exploration Systems was formed to implement the Vision for Space Exploration, and quickly began studies to define the systems needed to achieve the vision. One component of this process was to involve industry in the process. "Concept Exploration and Refinement" studies were solicited from a wide breadth of the aerospace industry. As Michael Griffin took the helm as NASA administrator, he initiated an Exploration Systems Architecture Study to define the systems for the upcoming Constellation Program. As Constellation was standing up, a number of other lunar lander studies were undertaken to explore a wide breadth of human lander concepts. In-house NASA studies – the Lunar Lander Preparatory Study and Lunar Surface Access Module pre-project studies – captured NASA's internal concepts, while an industry Request for Information captured industry's early concepts for lunar landers.

Concept Exploration and Refinement Landers

On September 1, 2004, in support of the objective to land humans on the Moon and Mars as defined in the Vision for Space Exploration, NASA contracted with 11 companies* to conduct preliminary concept studies for human lunar exploration and the development of a crew exploration vehicle. These Concept Exploration and Refinement (CE&R) studies proposed a "Mars-Back" philosophy, which first considered the requirements for Mars missions, then worked backward to design a lunar mission in a manner that developed necessary technology and demonstrated relevant operational approaches. Most details of a Mars mission were undefined; however, two features were common to nearly all Mars mission proposals: very long surface stays and In Situ Resource Utilization (ISRU). Therefore, lunar landers proposed for this study were designed to perform an initial series of exploratory sortie missions quickly and effectively, and then focus on lunar base operations that prepared NASA for future Mars exploration. They also required compatibility with eventual transition to lunar-produced propellants to demonstrate ISRU operations for a Mars mission, and to reduce the cost of ongoing lunar missions. The CE&R studies were meant to solicit comprehensive plans for human lunar and Mars exploration, with the definition of multiple spacecraft elements to complete an overall architecture. With this broad scope, the technical depth of any particular spacecraft element, such as the human lunar landers, varied widely by study. Concluded in early 2005, the CE&R studies permitted each of the contractors to present unique ideas about the space transportation systems needed for future journeys, and, as stated by retired Navy Rear Admiral Craig E. Steidle, associate administrator of NASA's Exploration Systems Mission Directorate at the time, ". . . reflect NASA's new commitment to find the best outside expertise that will work in partnerships to benefit the nation's goals for space exploration."

* No data was available for CE&R-9 for this publication.

Andrews Space Common Planetary Lander: 0503-CE&R-1

The Common Planetary Lander was designed around an inline arrangement of two LOX tanks (for balance) on either side of a cylindrical LH_2 tank, all designed to fit within a 5m (16.4 ft) fairing for initial launch. Two (redundant) RL-10 class engines were mounted at one end of the tank set; the opposite end featured a common mechanical attachment ring for mounting to the lander vehicle or the Earth-Moon Lagrange Point 1 (L1) station. Payload attachment and landing gear were located to one "side" of the tank set. The payload was attached to the lander just before departure from the L1 station and arrived at the Moon "underslung" from the structural backbone formed by the tankage. Landing and takeoff were performed using four redundant deeply throttleable thrusters, splayed away from the payload module to minimize reflective debris impact. Soft landing was affected on four widely spaced legs with mechanical energy attenuation. Twelve redundant Attitude Control System (ACS) thrusters were distributed around the vehicle.

A reusable Common Planetary Lander was to deliver 15 mt (16.5 t) of cargo from L1 to the lunar surface on a one-way mission, or a 5.4 mt (6 t) crewed module from L1 to the lunar surface and back to L1. It would accommodate underslung 5 x 10 m (16.4 x 32.8 ft) Payload Modules, and be powered by two RL-10 LOX/LH_2 main engines. Reaction control would be via a GOX/GH2 thruster system. Propellant for the lander was to initially be electrolyzed from water delivered from Earth to the L1 Transfer Hub (LTH) depot. Later it would come from water generated from a lunar ISRU plant. Critical technology that needed to be developed included the GOX/GH2 ACS thrusters, long-duration/low boil-off cryogenic tanks, and automatic lunar landing guidance and control technology. Mass breakdown of the Common Planetary Lander is shown on the following page.

Descent Stage	
Power	Solar arrays/batteries
Main Propulsion	Two LOX tanks: Volume = 24.8 m³ (875 ft³) each; Wetted Area = 7.5 m² (265 ft²) each; Total Mass = 24.7 mt (27.2 t) on either side of a cylindrical LH₂ tank (for balance) Cylindrical LH₂ tank: Volume = 69.4 m³ (2,450 ft³); Wetted Area = 83.6 m² (900 ft²); Mass = 4,990 kg (11,001.1 lbm) All designed to fit within a 5 m (16.4 ft) fairing for initial launch. Two (redundant) RL 10 class engines were mounted at one end of the tank set, with a Thrust Force of 106.7 kN (24 klbf) each; Gimbal = ±4°
Structures	Mechanical shock absorption landing leg structure
Landing Propulsion	Four redundant deeply-throttleable landing GOX/GH2 thrusters: Location was off main tanks; Throttle = 30% - 100%; Thrust Force = 13.3 kN (3 klbf) each; and 12 GOX/GH2 ACS thrusters: Thrust Force = 0.45 kN (100 lbf)

Mass Breakdown		
Subsystem	lbm	kg
Structure/Thermal	10,516	4,770
Propulsion	3,726	1,690
Equipment	2,138	970
Margin	2,458	1,115
Dry Mass	**18,838**	**8,545**
Propellant/Fluids	73,414	33,300
Payload	33,069	15,000
Launch Mass	**125,321**	**56,845**

Boeing Lunar Surface Access Module: 0503-CE&R-2

Boeing employed a common, single-stage, LOX/LH$_2$, reusable Lunar Surface Access Module (LSAM) for both crew and cargo missions. The initial concept used the Earth-Moon L1 Lagrange Point as the lunar rendezvous location between the Crew Exploration Vehicle (CEV) and the LSAM. The two-way crew mission from the L1 Lagrange Point down to the lunar surface and the return trip back to the L1 Lagrange Point sized the LSAM. Cargo missions used the same LSAM design and the cargo capability was a direct function of crew mission requirements. The LSAMs were not initially to be reused for cargo missions and, therefore, all propellant was expended for descent and landing. Using the LSAM one-way for the cargo missions dramatically increased the payload capability over the two-way crew mission, and consequently reduced the number of required cargo landings.

Descent Stage	
Power	The driving requirement for surface power systems was the need to store energy for the relatively long polar nights (6 months at the poles compared to just 14 days at the equator). Nuclear power based on either a U-235 reactor or advanced PU-238 radioisotope was the only viable, mass efficient power and energy storage method. If a nuclear reactor was used, it was assumed that the reactor would be a surface derivative of the Jupiter Icy Moons Orbiter (JIMO) spacecraft reactor, but at a lower power level. The mass allocation for the nuclear reactor was 4.5 mt (5 t), which corresponds to about 50 kW of continuous power based on JIMO technology. Any significant ISRU production facilities would have required additional surface power sources.
Propulsion	LOX/LH$_2$ propulsion with a vacuum Isp of 455 sec
Telecommunications	The Deep Space Network system has demonstrated fast Internet and improved video capability on several Mars and lunar missions since 2005, particularly with the step up to Ka-Band in 2010. An optical network that enabled high-definition television transmissions would begin operations in 2015. The successful use of Consultative Committee for Space Data Systems (CCSDS) by Jet Propulsion Laboratory on the Mars Exploration Rover missions enabled the replacement of X-band systems on the Mars Science Lab (MSL) mission with Ultra-High Frequency (UHF) systems. This marriage of enhanced standards and protocols with lower rate data transmission resulted in a higher data throughput system that was a paradigm shift implemented in the architecture. To exploit the commonality of systems developed for autonomous military vehicles, communication protocols such as Tactical Common Data Link with an uplink rate of 200 kbps could have been employed. For most communications, low rate data on UHF frequencies was sufficient.
Structures	<6 m (19.7 ft) diameter

Draper Surface Access Module Concept: 0503-CE&R-3

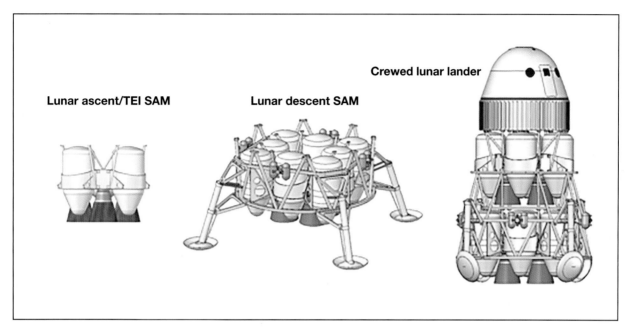

Lunar ascent/TEI SAM **Lunar descent SAM** **Crewed lunar lander**

The Surface Access Module (SAM) was defined as the vehicle that transported the crew (in the associated crew compartment) to the lunar surface and back to lunar orbit or to Earth, depending on the architecture chosen. According to this definition, the SAM included propulsion stage(s), engines, and the landing gear. In the direct return architecture chosen by the Draper/Massachusetts Institute of Technology (MIT) team, the SAM consisted of the ascent/Trans-Earth Injection (TEI) stage, the lunar descent stage, and the lunar landing gear and exoskeleton. Because the Draper/MIT CE&R team decided to adopt the Mars-Back approach for their Moon and Mars exploration architecture designs, the lunar mission was not the only one that placed requirements on the SAM. The Mars-Back approach included high-level commonality within and between the Moon and Mars architecture elements, including propulsion stages. For the SAM, this meant that all the propulsion stages used for maneuvers in the vicinity of the Moon and Mars were based on the same design. The associated maneuvers were:

- Lunar ascent and TEI (human lunar missions)
- Lunar descent (human lunar missions and lunar surface habitat)
- Mars ascent (Mars Ascent Vehicle [MAV])
- Mars descent (MAV and Transfer and Surface Habitat)
- Mars TEI (Earth Return Vehicle)

The lunar ascent/TEI stage was planned to transport a crew of up to five and 100 kg (220.5 lbm) of lunar samples in the lunar CEV from the surface of the Moon to lunar orbit. After appropriate phasing, this restartable stage was burned again for TEI, putting the spacecraft on a return trajectory to Earth. It was also to be used for mid-course correction and retargeting of the Earth landing site. The lunar ascent/TEI stage carried the smallest propellant quantity of all the propulsion stages utilized in the Moon and Mars architectures, and it represented the core stage design.

A regenerative fuel cell system provided power to the core stage. The system was not recharged for lunar landing applications because lunar landing occurs after only a few days of transit. For lunar ascent and all of the Mars maneuvers, the fuel cells had to be recharged (i.e., the product water needed to be broken down into hydrogen and oxygen) by another energy source (surface power system or Earth Return Vehicle power system) before the stage could be used for propulsive maneuvers.

Although the core stage had a reduced number of Reaction Control System (RCS) jets compared to other SAM applications, the interfaces for additional RCS engines and also for add-on tanks and structure were accounted for in the core stage design. Since the additional SAM modules were mounted during the regular production process on Earth (as opposed to in-space), the actual interface mass was small compared to the overall element mass. This would also have allowed for just one production line with a single set of fixtures and equipment to be used for all SAM versions.

The lunar descent stage could be used for landing cargo, the crew (specifically, the CEV with the ascent/TEI stage), or the habitat on the lunar surface from Low Lunar Orbit (LLO). The lunar descent stage thus included the lunar landing gear, the exoskeleton, and two throttleable descent engines.

Compared to the lunar ascent stage, the lunar descent stage had an upgraded RCS system, and carried the XL add-on tanks and the lunar landing gear and exoskeleton. In addition, two descent engines were used instead of the ascent engines. Other than that, the core stage design was identical to that of the lunar ascent stage.

Descent Stage	
Power	Regenerative Fuel Cells
Propulsion	Propellant Combination: LCH_4/LOX Minimum Isp: 362 sec Number of Engines (Throttleable): 2 (Oxidizer-to-Fuel (O/F) Ratio: 3.5 to 1

Ascent Stage	
Power	Regenerative Fuel Cells (recharged by another energy source prior to ascent)
Propulsion	Propellant Combination: LCH_4/LOX Minimum Isp: 362 sec Number of Engines: 2 O/F Ratio: 3.5 to 1

Mass Breakdown				
Subsystem	**Descent Stage**		**Ascent Stage**	
	lbm	kg	lbm	kg
1.0 Structure	8,283	3,757	2,017	915
2.0 Protection	0	0	0	0
3.0 Propulsion	2,687	1,219	1,263	573
4.0 Power	882	400	882	400
5.0 Control	1,510	685	1,870	848
6.0 Avionics	441	200	441	200
7.0 Environment	0	0	0	0
8.0 Other	950	431	366	166
9.0 Growth	0	0	0	0
Dry Mass w/Growth	**14,753**	**6,692**	**6,839**	**3,102**
10.0 Non-cargo	0	0	0	0
11.0 Cargo	0	0	0	0
Inert Mass	**14,753**	**6,692**	**6,839**	**3,102**
12.0 Non-propellant	0	0	0	0
13.0 Propellant	65,213	29,580	33,561	15,223
Gross Mass	**79,966**	**36,272**	**40,400**	**18,325**

Lockheed Martin Lunar Surface Access Module: 0503-CE&R-4

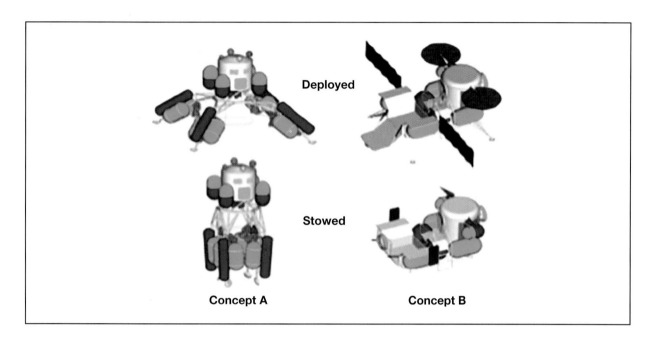

Deployed

Stowed

Concept A　　　　　　　　　**Concept B**

The Lockheed Martin LSAM was the functional equivalent of the Apollo Lunar Excursion Module (LEM) . . . and then some. Its primary function was to transport four crew and 0 to ~8 mt (~8.8 t) of nonhazardous surface systems, equipment, or logistics supplies from the transfer stack in LLO to a pre-deployed habitat on the surface of the Moon, and then to transport the crew and 250 kg (551.2 lbm) of lunar

return cargo and samples from the surface of the Moon back to the CEV. Given that it was designed for an exploration-driven architecture, the plan used a two-stage LSAM with separate ascent and descent stages to maximize mass delivered to the lunar surface, thus satisfying lunar exploration objectives (i.e., useful payload mass).

Descent Stage	
Power	The power system was modular, designed to meet ever-expanding power requirements that could evolve from initial tens of kWs to hundreds, but an initial capacity of 25 kW during the day and 12.5 kW at night were determined to be the minimal power requirements for supporting a human presence and initial test bed activities.
Propulsion	A throttleable RL10 engine was determined to be approximately the right size for a single-engine descent stage, but a new quarter-scale engine could be developed for a multistage application (throttling to ~15% of full thrust, which was required for touchdown).
Telecommunications	Initial communication featured the following: Direct link between Earth and the nearside equatorial-based outpost (required full use of Deep Space Network on Earth). Additional direct links between the Earth and surface rovers (crewed or uncrewed). Selected small on-orbit communications payloads deployed as secondary payloads on a mission-by-mission basis (i.e., no dedicated orbiting large-scale infrastructure). A Local Area Network in the immediate vicinity of the outpost, using either wire or wireless UHF line-of-sight links (there is no atmosphere available, and high-frequency communication signals are not possible beyond line of sight without the reflective action of an atmosphere). This distributed system was to operate as a single end-to-end network within the NASA Deep Space Network.

Descent Stage (continued)	
Thermal	Long-term storage of LOX/LH$_2$ on the lunar surface was considered to be a solvable problem. Thermal analysis indicated that an average heat leak of 3.5-15 W into the LH$_2$ tank and 0-7 W into the LOX tank could be expected, depending on the aggressiveness of Multi-Layer Insulation (MLI) assumptions. Resulting boil-off rates were 0.05% to 0.5% per 24 hours during daylight. Low boil-off rates associated with passive storage were determined to be acceptable for mission durations up to 60-180 days, depending on the insulation level achieved. Active cryo coolers were an option for longer missions, but would have required several kW of power, were considered unreliable at LH$_2$ temperatures, and were at a low Technology Readiness Level for this application. Storage of MMH/N$_2$O$_4$ during lunar night was considered feasible with insulation and a few W of heat input to prevent freezing.
Structures	Concept A from the Lockheed Martin LSAM Descent Stage was an Apollo-like vertical stack configuration in which cargo was suspended from beneath the crew ascent stage, from the structural frame, and easily lowered to the lunar surface or onto a transportation vehicle. Concept B featured a horizontal descent stage where cargo was transported in the open framework of the cargo bed.

Ascent Stage	
Propulsion	Optimum liftoff thrust to weight ratio ~0.35 Four ascent engines, 8 to 12 kN each (1,800 to 2,700 lbf) or 1 engine, 25 to 35 kN (5,600 to 7,900 lbf) Propellant load: 2.3 to 3.6 mt (2.5 to 4 t) Lunar surface mission duration 4 to 500 days Traded ascent main propulsion only; did not address RCS

Mass Breakdown				
Stage	**Descent Stage**		**Ascent Stage**	
	lbm	**kg**	**lbm**	**kg**
Cargo Mass	22,046	10,000	551	250
Dry Mass	4,630	2,100	10,141	4,600
Propellant Mass	20,723	9,400	7,055	3,200
Gross Mass	**47,399**	**21,500**	**17,747**	**8,050**

Northrop Grumman Lunar Surface Access Module: 0503-CE&R-5

The Northrop Grumman LSAM was a single-stage vehicle designed to provide transportation from LLO to any point on the lunar surface. The LSAM design fits in a 5 m (16.4 ft) fairing and was to be launched on a 22.7 mt (25 t) Evolved Expendable Launch Vehicle. All configurations could accommodate a 4.5 m (14.8 ft) diameter by 10 m (32.8 ft) cargo module and could be adapted to serve as the LSAM. The four throttling main engines were clustered together to package within a 5 m (16.4 ft) fairing. It was desirable to use existing 5 m (16.4 ft) fairings over new, wider fairings where possible, since the 5 m (16.4 ft) fairings provided higher Launch Vehicle capability while reducing costs. Mounting engines alongside a 4.5 m (14.8 ft) cargo would have required a much wider fairing or have the engines stowed inboard and then deployed outward after fairing separation. The engine cluster also provided improved center-of-gravity control, in case of an engine-out occurrence.

Descent Stage	
Power	Pump-fed LH_2/LO_2 engines similar to the RL10-A5 engines demonstrated on DC-X vehicle.
Propulsion	Three different propellant combinations (i.e., LH_2/LO_2, LCH_4/LO_2, and NTO/MMH) were examined for use in the Cargo Lander Module, and both pump and pressure-fed engines were considered for LCH_4/LO_2 and NTO/MMH. After close consideration, the options lessened to include LH_2 density and temperature requiring a large quantity of pressurant, along with the demonstrated throttling, pump-fed RL10-A5 engines on DC-X. For the large 13.6 to 22.7 mt (15 to 25 t) cargo being landed, the LH_2/LO_2 pump-fed propulsion provided the lowest system mass, followed by pump-fed LCH_4/LO_2. The pressure-fed, Earth-storable NTO/MMH had the highest initial mass in Low Earth Orbit and propellant mass, due to its lower Isp and the pressurization system. The combinations with LO_2 would have allowed use of lunar in-situ O_2, whereas the NTO combinations would not.
Telecommunications	EM/L_1 Lagrange Point/EML_2 relay satellites were selected for the baseline architecture because they provided the highest level of coverage per satellite, thus leading to a more affordable overall system.
Structures	Propellant tanks were Al/Li with dual-wall common bulkheads, whereas the structure was composite.

Orbital Sciences Corporation Human Lunar Lander: 0503-CE&R-6

The Orbital Sciences Corporation Human Lunar Lander was a reusable one-stage vehicle, with a pressure-fed LO_2/CH_4-fueled propulsion system. Both the lander and the CEV used a common Earth departure stage for Trans-Lunar Injection (TLI) and Lunar Orbit Insertion (LOI). The habitable volume of the lander held a crew of four astronauts and provided life support sufficient for 4 days on the Moon's surface, plus transit and contingency. It also provided 3 m³ (94 ft³) of habitable volume per crew member. The mass empty was 5,663 kg (12,485 lbm) and the gross mass was 27,021 kg (59,571 lbm). Electrical power for the lander was generated with fuel cells and stored in batteries. Reaction control was provided by a bipropellant system using MMH/N_2O_4.

Mass Breakdown		
Subsystem	**lbm**	**kg**
1.0 Structure	5,382	2,441
2.0 Protection	126	57
3.0 Propulsion	2,167	983
4.0 Power	1,634	741
5.0 Control	0	0
6.0 Avionics	143	65
7.0 Environment	1,243	564
8.0 Other	240	109
9.0 Growth	1,550	703
Dry Mass w/Growth	**12,485**	**5,663**
10.0 Non-cargo	0	0
11.0 Cargo	1,724	782
Inert Mass	**14,209**	**6,445**
12.0 Non-propellant	1,241	563
13.0 Propellant	44,121	20,013
Gross Mass	**59,571**	**27,021**

Raytheon Lunar Surface Access Module: 0503-CE&R-7

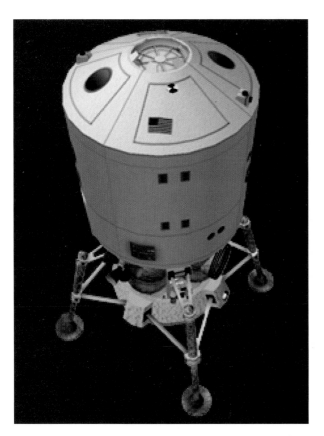

The Raytheon LSAM Block 2 lander was an intermediate-class single-mission generic lander (rovers, power/cargo, and cargo only, no refueling assumed from ISRU). It delivered cargo to the lunar surface and used cryo-propulsion, although a reusable cargo tug (Solar Electric Propulsion/Nuclear Electric Propulsion) could have been justified by Cost As an Independent Variable analysis, and reuse depended on ISRU propellants. A single Evolved Expendable Launch Vehicle-heavy launch injected the pre-positioned lander to a high-energy near-escape trajectory with a total cargo capacity of 4,500 kg (9,920.8 lbm), or to an early spiral 3 with a total cargo capacity of 8,500 kg (18,739.3 lbm), with ~2,000 kg (4,409.2 lbm) available for non-Environmental Control and Life Support System mass.

Descent Stage	
Structures	Based on earlier material trade studies, it was assumed the crew cabin was to be constructed of 8091-T6 Al-Li, and the same material was to be used for the airlock structure. The combined weight of this LL-4 cabin and airlock structure was 588 kg (1,296.3 lbm), including a 25% margin. The habitable volumes (excluding floor space) of the cabin and airlock were 16.9 m³ (595.8 ft³) and 4.7 m³ (166.3 ft³). Three internal pressure load cases were analyzed: 1) cabin and airlock at 55.2 kPa (8 psi); 2) cabin only at 55.2 kPa (8 psi); and 3) airlock only at 55.2 kPa (8 psi). The lowest stress margin of safety (+0.43) was generated by load case 3.

SAIC Lunar Module/Lunar Lander: 0503-CE&R-8

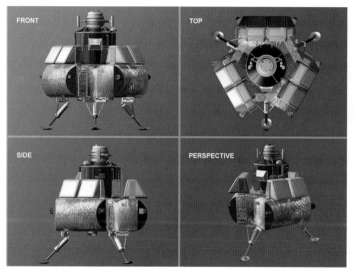

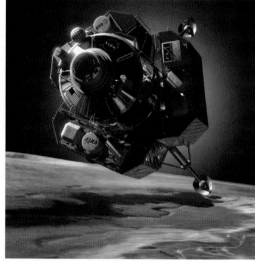

The Lunar Module (LM)/Lunar Lander (LL) consisted of a pressurized LM and an unpressurized LL stage, and fulfilled the role of Apollo's LEM and LSAM. The LM/LL was to travel to the Moon atop TLI stages, which were jettisoned when they were exhausted. It then waited, in a low-power Dormant Mode, for the crew's arrival in LLO while being monitored and controlled by ground controllers. It was to be reconfigured for Inhabited Mode and checked out prior to the crew's launch in the CEV. This provided an opportunity to verify its readiness to accept the crew. If an issue occurred, the crew launch could be aborted, rather than having the crew travel all the way there only to find out the LM/LL could not fulfill its mission.

Each four-person LM/LL was to be equipped with dual two-person unpressurized rovers similar to the Apollo Lunar Roving Vehicle and a science package similar to the Apollo Lunar Surface Experiments Package. The six-person lander version carried three unpressurized rovers. The LM/LL also carried 3 to 4 days of consumables and a lunar surface Extravehicular Activity (EVA) suit for each crew member.

The LL was responsible for carrying payloads from LLO to the lunar surface, as well as the crew and LM back to LLO. This was accomplished with a chemical propulsion system derived from the RL-10 engine using LOX/methane propellants.

Descent Stage (Lunar Lander)	
Power	Solar arrays and batteries, with the batteries providing continuous power when the sun was shaded.
Propulsion	The following performance assumptions were made for engine types and propellant types: RL-10 derived engine thrust: 99,190 N (22,298.8 lbf) LOX/methane Specific Impulse: 379 sec The Lander also provided an engine-out capability, needing only two of three engines to safely land. Aluminum tanks were used for fuel and oxidizer tanks as a conservative measure.
Ascent Stage (Lunar Module)	
Power	Solar arrays and batteries powered the LM. The batteries were to supply power during ascent and descent operations when the solar arrays were retracted and in LLO when the Moon shadowed the LM. This limited the operation of the LM to daylight only. For missions that extended into the lunar night, the LM needed power from the Nuclear Surface Power system after landing to keep it powered in Dormant Mode. The Baseline LM required about 5 kW during Inhabited Mode and 3.8 kW in Dormant Mode. The Modularity, Reusability, and Technology trade study LMs required about the same amount of power. All studies included a 15% power margin.

Ascent Stage (Lunar Module) continued	
Propulsion	Orbital Maneuvering System (OMS)-derived pressure-fed engines, NTO/Hydrazine propellant OMS-derived engine thrust: 26,700 N (6,002.4 lbf) NTO/Hydrazine Specific Impulse: 344 sec
Thermal	The Thermal Control System (TCS) was a dual-loop, heat exchange system. The internal thermal control system used water as the working fluid and the external thermal control system used a 60% propylene glycol/water mix. The radiators were mounted on the body of the LM.
Structures	The LM was nestled into the LL so that only the pressure vessel extended over the top surface of the LL. As with the Baseline CEV Crew Capsule, it was considered to be a larger version of the Apollo command module, and its structure mass was estimated by using the algorithm developed at NASA Johnson Space Center. The Baseline LM structure was estimated to be 1,939 kg (4,274.8 lbm) and the Modularity/Technology trade study LM was estimated to be 2,104 kg (4,638.5 lbm). The six-person version's structure was estimated to be 3,139 kg (6,920.3 lbm). The hatches and other mechanisms were grossly estimated to be 8% of the dry mass of the LM.
Environmental Control and Life Support System	The LM systems operated at full capacity for only a relatively short period. The majority of its operational life was expected to be spent in a standby mode – waiting in lunar orbit for the crew to arrive in the CEV or parked on the lunar surface while the crew was residing in the Habitat Module. Therefore, the ECLSS demands were not great. The oxygen and nitrogen supplies were stored in high-pressure bottles. The nitrogen tanks were assumed to have 10% residual and oxygen tanks were assumed to have an 8% residual, according to Space Shuttle and International Space Station data. Carbon dioxide was removed using LiOH canisters. The modest water supply was contained in shuttle-like bellowed tanks. Fire detectors and halon fire extinguishers were provided. The leakage rate was set at 0.5 kg/day (1.1 lbm/day).

Mass Breakdown

Subsystem	Lunar Capsule with Ascent/Descent Lunar Lander		Lunar Capsule with Service-Module-Based Ascent Propulsion		Descent-Only Lunar Lander	
	lbm	kg	lbm	kg	lbm	kg
1.0 Structure	6,255	2,837	1,400	635	6,221	2,822
2.0 Protection	0	0	0	0	0	0
3.0 Propulsion	5,192	2,355	1,802	818	3,856	1,749
4.0 Power	451	204	0	0	451	204
5.0 Control	659	299	255	116	584	265
6.0 Avionics	1,802	818	0	0	1,802	818
7.0 Environment	0	0	0	0	0	0
8.0 Other	0	0	0	0	0	0
9.0 Growth	0	0	0	0	0	0
Dry Mass w/Growth	**14,359**	**6,513**	**3,458**	**1,568**	**12,915**	**5,858**
10.0 Non-cargo	0	0	0	0	0	0
11.0 Cargo	13,890	6,300	13,890	6,300	36,290	16,461
Inert Mass	**28,249**	**12,813**	**17,348**	**7,869**	**49,205**	**22,319**
12.0 Non-propellant	0	0	0	0	0	0
13.0 Propellant	86,795	39,369	18,942	8,592	49,608	22,502
Gross Mass	**115,043**	**52,183**	**36,290**	**16,461**	**98,813**	**44,821**

SPACEHAB Lunar Surface Access Module: 0503-CE&R-10

The SPACEHAB LSAM was a modular system that could be launched on commercial Expendable Launch Vehicles from optimal launch sites. It used common vehicle crew and modular augmentation, along with standardized multifunctional mating interfaces, to support assembly and reassembly of elements, thus providing multiple resource transfer capabilities and the ability to economize on net resource requirements. Its CEV provided the capability to support three crew for a round trip to the lunar surface and to return up to 100 kg (220 lbm) of lunar samples, whereas the cargo version was able to return up to 700 kg (1,543 lbm) of lunar samples to Earth.

Mission State	Events	Delta-v Required (km/s)	Crew Mission	Cargo Mission
1	Ground Segment	0	✔	✔
2	Earth Ascent	7.78	✔	✔
3	Low Earth Orbit Operations	0.20	✔	✔
4	Trans-Lunar Injection	3.20	✔	✔
5	Lunar Orbit	1.00	✔	✔
6	Lunar Descent	2.07	✔	✔
7	Surface Operations	0	✔	✔
8	Lunar Ascent	1.90	✔	Autonomous LEV and CEV missions parallel crew missions to enable return of 700 kg (1,543 lbm) of lunar samples to Earth
9	Direct Return	1.00	✔	

Properties		
Properties	**Lunar Descent Module**	**Lunar Excursion Vehicle**
Pressurized Volume	0	9.6 m³ (339 ft³)
Passive Mission States	1-5	1-5
Active Mission States	6-7	6-8
Major Subsystems		
Propulsion	Yes	Yes
Attitude Control	Yes	Yes
Automated Rendezvous and Proximity Operations	No	Yes
Docking	Mates with LEV returning to state 5	Yes
Environmental Control and Life Support System	No	Yes
Communications	No	Yes

Mass Breakdown				
Subsystem	**lbm**	**kg**	**lbm**	**kg**
Dry/Empty Mass	2,646	1,200	1,587	720
Propellant Mass (max)	13,228	6,000	5,071	2,300
Cargo Mass (max)	10,582	4,800	3,924	1,780
Gross Mass	**26,456**	**12,000**	**10,582**	**4,800**

Transformational Space Corporation Lunar Surface Access Module: 0503-CE&R-11

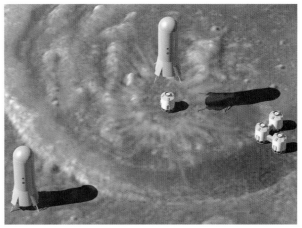

Transformational Space Corporation (t/Space) developed a two- to six-person Crew Transfer Vehicle (CXV) to carry crew to a space-based CEV. Because CXV was small, it could affordably perform many launches to help demonstrate its safety. CXV carried approximately 4 days of consumables, and a cargo variant could have carried propellants and supplies to CEVs, enhancing competition and economies of scale. The CXV would have been launched on a booster carried on the underside of a 747-200.

The CEV was designed to carry four to six people, and to be space-based. It was to travel from LEO to lunar

orbit, be refueled there, and then land, lift off and return to LEO. In later iterations of the architecture, if traffic levels were high enough to warrant the investment, the bottom section of the CEV could have become the basis for a Lunar Surface Access Module. In the configuration shown, the fuel tanks are enclosed within the upper cylindrical section of the lander with the habitation section and airlock section within the conical section at the bottom, just above the engines.

The propellant tanker used the same airframe/avionics/ propulsion technology as CXV, and a cargo vehicle used the same mold line and engine technology as the CEV.

Descent Stage	
Power	Vapak Integrated Power and Propulsion
Propulsion	6,880 kg (15,000 lbm) empty; 4,540 kg (10,000 lbm) payload to 5.5 km/s (18,000 ft/s), 28,800 kg (63,493.1 lbm) total propellant (LH$_2$, LOX) exploration, 56,700 kg (125,002.1 lbm) total propellant (LH$_2$, LOX). Tanker Pump Feed: Vacuum operation rendered high-pressure engines unnecessary to obtain high Isp, since high area ratio nozzles could be used without high chamber pressures (pumped systems have the additional complexity of a tank pressurization system). Pressure Feed: Stored gas with catalytic heating was selected for trade based on previous experience and its relatively high performance when compared to other stored gas systems. Vapak pressurization used the internal energy of a liquid stored in a closed container to perform the work required to expel the liquid from the container. Before starting, the bulk liquid temperature was adjusted so that the vapor pressure equaled the desired tank pressure. The liquid was in thermal equilibrium with the saturated vapors present in the tank ullage (other gasses were excluded). When the tank valve was opened, draining either liquid or vapor, the tank pressure dropped, upsetting the vapor-liquid equilibrium. The rate at which the tank pressure decreased was a function of the thermodynamic properties of the liquid and the relative volume of the liquid remaining in the tank.
Structures	6.7 m (22.0 ft) wide habitat

Ascent Stage	
Power	Batteries (two redundant). Diode isolated for automatic redundancy. Operated down to 50% depth of discharge for maximum cycle life as secondary cell. Operated down to 20% depth of discharge in contingency as primary cell. Each battery was capable of supporting an entire CXV mission as the primary cell in an emergency return scenario. Photovoltaic Cell Array (Deployable/Retractable). Array Power Shunt (Resistive Load) Power Buses (two redundant). Switch-Selected Redundant Battery and Regulator Strings Charge/Discharge Controller for Each Battery. Regulator for Each Power Bus.
Propulsion	The OMS provided axial impulse up to 113,398 kg-sec (250,000 lb-sec). Area ratio was 100:1, Isp was 380 seconds, thrust was 445.2 N (100 lbf) per engine, Mixture Ratio =3.0:1. Pc = 689.5 kPa (100 psi), tank feed pressure was 31,026.4 kPa (4500 psi), 340.2 kg (750 lbm) total propellant. Dual engines and tank subsystem with cross feed and isolation ("A" side and "B" side); could be refueled on orbit.
Thermal	Heat rejection; capability of approximately 2 kW was available through the use of commercial telecommunications spacecraft radiators and heat pipe cooling system. Temperature was actively controlled to 20°C to 30°C (68°F to 86°F) throughout orbital operations. No power was required to operate the system. The system was fully redundant.

Exploration System Architecture Study

In 2005, NASA's new administrator, Dr. Michael Griffin, established the Exploration Systems Architecture Study (ESAS) team at NASA Headquarters to execute the following four tasks during May, June, and July of that year:

1) Complete assessment of the top-level Crew Exploration Vehicle (CEV) requirements and plans to enable the CEV to provide crew transport to the International Space Station and to accelerate the development of the CEV and crew-launch system to reduce the gap between Space Shuttle retirement and CEV Initial Operating Capability,

2) Define top-level requirements and configurations for crew and cargo launch systems to support the lunar and Mars exploration programs,

3) Develop a reference lunar exploration architecture concept to support sustained human and robotic lunar exploration operations, and

4) Identify key technologies required to enable and significantly enhance these reference exploration systems and a reprioritization of near-term and far-term technology investments.

More than 20 core team members were selected from various NASA field centers and industry, and they co-located at NASA Headquarters for the 3-month study duration. Along with various CEV and Launch Vehicle configurations, a number of different configurations were examined for the lunar lander, or Lunar Surface Access Module (LSAM). Trade studies for the LSAM included the number of stages, stage propellant, engine type, level of engine-out capability, airlock approaches, cargo capacity, and abort options. The NASA administrator announced the ESAS results during a press conference held at NASA Headquarters in Washington, D.C., on September 19, 2005. These results became the foundation of NASA's Constellation Program.

2004 NASA Exploration logo.

Exploration System Architecture Study "Baseline Lander" – Single Volume, LOX/CH$_4$ Ascent Stage: 0507-ESAS-A

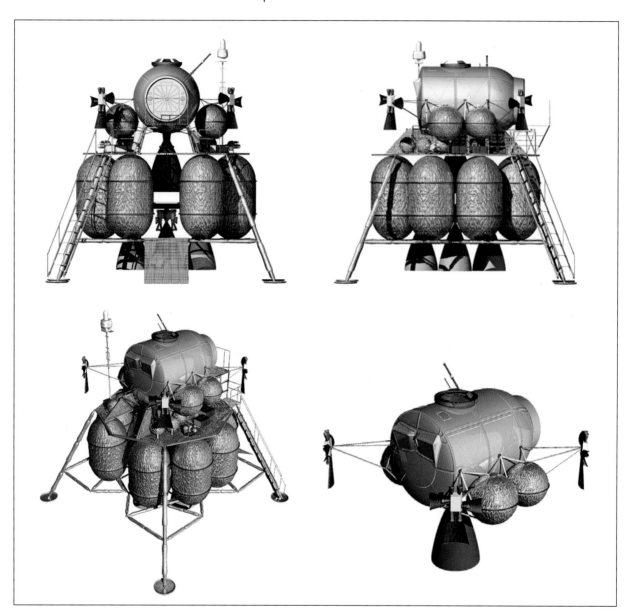

The LSAM, consisting of the ascent and descent stages, had a total mass of 45,862 kg (101,108 lbm). It was capable of landing and supporting four crew members for 7 days on the lunar surface and then transporting the crew from the surface back to lunar orbit. The LSAM descent stage was used in crewed lunar exploration missions to insert the CEV into Low Lunar Orbit, land the ascent stage and cargo on the surface, and provide the vehicle's life support and power generation capabilities during an assumed 7-day lunar surface stay. The ascent stage performed coplanar ascent to a 100-km (54 nmi) circular lunar orbit, rendezvous and docking with the CEV, and self-disposal following separation from the CEV.

Descent Stage	
Power	Four Rechargeable Li-ion batteries Three Proton Exchange Membrane (PEM) fuel cells on the descent stage provided LSAM power generation from Earth launch to lunar ascent. Oxygen reactant for the fuel cells was stored in the oxygen propellant tanks, while hydrogen reactant was stored in the hydrogen propellant tanks.
Propulsion	The descent stage used a pump-fed LOX/H_2 descent propulsion system to perform Lunar Orbit Insertion (LOI) and coplanar descent from a 100-km (54 nmi) circular lunar orbit. Four 66.7-kN (15,000-lbf) descent propulsion systems derived from the RL-10 engine family provided vehicle maneuvering; the descent propulsion system engines were arranged symmetrically around the vehicle centerline at the base of the descent stage. Six cylindrical hydrogen and two cylindrical oxygen descent stage tanks were included on the LSAM to store the propellant needed to perform up to 1,100 m/s (3,609 ft/s) of LOI delta-v, with the CEV and ascent stage attached, and 1,900 m/s (6,233.6 ft/s) of descent delta-v with only the ascent stage attached. Isp: 451 sec
Telecommunications	S-band
Structures	The eight LSAM propellant tanks were mounted around the descent stage in a ring arrangement, leaving two open bays on opposite sides of the stage exterior for surface access and cargo stowage, and a circular opening along the vehicle centerline for housing the single ascent stage engine nozzle. In addition to supporting its own propulsion system, the descent stage structure also served as a support system and launch platform for the ascent stage, provided attachment for a four-leg landing gear system, provided for crew access to the surface, and served as the attachment point to the Earth Departure Stage (EDS).
Guidance, Navigation & Control	None – the ascent stage Reaction Control System (RCS) was used for combined-vehicle attitude control.
Environmental Control and Life Support System	90% closed loop / 10% open loop
Ascent Stage	
Power	Power generation for all other LSAM operations prior to liftoff was provided by the descent stage.
Propulsion	Pressure-fed LOX/methane propulsion system, similar to the CEV Service Module, to perform coplanar ascent to a 100-km (54 nmi) circular lunar orbit, rendezvous and docking with the CEV, and self-disposal following separation from the CEV. A single 44.5-kN (10,000-lbf) ascent propulsion system engine and spherical ascent stage propellant tanks were sized to perform up to 1,866 m/s (6,122 ft/s) of main engine and 22 m/s (72.2 ft/s) of RCS delta-v. Isp: 310 sec
Structures	The LSAM pressure vessel was a horizontal short cylinder 3.0 m (9.8 ft) in diameter and 5.0 m (16.4 ft) long, providing 31.8 m³ (1,123 ft³) of pressurized volume for the crew during lunar operations. It was planned to have a nominal internal atmospheric pressure for the ascent stage of 65.5 kPa (9.5 psi) with an assumed 30% oxygen composition.
Guidance Navigation & Control	Sixteen 445-N (100-lbf) RCS thrusters were used for vehicle maneuvering and attitude control.

Mass Breakdown					
Subsystem	Descent Stage			Ascent Stage	
	lbm	kg		lbm	kg
1.0 Structure	2,454	1,113		2,260	1,025
2.0 Protection	194	88		249	113
3.0 Propulsion	5,207	2,362		1,969	893
4.0 Power	1,032	468			
5.0 Control	203	92		0	0
6.0 Avionics	152	69		849	385
7.0 Environment	619	281		1,975	896
8.0 Other	1,411	640		842	382
9.0 Growth	2,255	1,023		1,885	855
Dry Mass w/Growth	**13,527**	**6,136**		**11,305**	**5,128**
10.0 Non-cargo	2,277	1,033		1,839	834
11.0 Cargo	5,058	2,294		0	0
Inert Mass	**20,862**	**9,463**		**13,144**	**5,962**
12.0 Non-propellant	1,071	486		289	131
13.0 Propellant	55,347	25,105		10,395	4,715
Gross Mass	**77,280**	**35,054**		**23,828**	**10,808**

Exploration System Architecture Study Vertical 2-Stage, Crew Exploration Vehicle-to-Surface: 0507-ESAS-B

A CEV-to-Surface concept was analyzed to minimize the development of crew capsules, using just the CEV command module for lunar lander crew delivery. The vehicle concept combined the CEV command module and the LSAM ascent and descent propulsive stages (airlock assumed required for crewed), and included a LOX/LH_2 descent stage and a LOX/methane ascent stage for primary concepts. The ascent stage provided direct return to Earth for human missions. The ESAS Initial Reference Architecture (EIRA) 5.5 m (15 ft) CEV provided habitation throughout the mission and a Space Shuttle-derived inline payload capability to Low Earth Orbit (LEO) equal to 90.7 mt (100 t) assumed (net).

Command Module	
Power	4.5 kW CEV average power, Li-Mn-O_2 28 V batteries
Propulsion	Tridyne RCS system (gaseous N_2/H_2/O_2 at 34,473.8 kPa (5,000 psi), 12 thrusters Delta-v (OMS/RCS): 2,841/10 m/s (9,321/33 ft/s) Propellant: Integrated O_2/methane Orbital Maneuvering System (OMS)/RCS Isp: 350.3/315 sec Number of OMS Engines: 4 Engine Length: 2.14 m (7.04 ft) Engine Exit Diameter: 1.13 m (3.70 ft) Cant Angle: 10° Gimbal Angle: ±10° Thrust per Engine / T/W_eff: 34.0 kN (7.64 klbf)/0.32 (g's) Chamber Pressure: 1206.6 kPa (175 psi) Mixture Ratio: 3.8 Area Ratio: 70, Throttle: 22.0%
Telecommunications	Space-to-space, space-to-ground, video
Thermal	Carbon/phenolic ablator heat shield, insulation
Structures	The 0507 ESAS-B pressure vessel was made from AL6061 and had IM7 carbon fiber composite skin panels. Other structures of the ESAS were crushable ribs for landing impact loads, a Low Impact Docking System (LIDS), a window and hatch, three round chutes, two drogue chutes, a pilot chute, water "righting" airbags, and land landing airbags. Stage Diameter: 7.5 m (24.6 ft) Stage Total Length: 7.4 m (24.2 ft) Stage Structural Length: 5.8 m (19.0 ft) Tank Pressure: 1,896.1 kPa (275 psi) Tank Diameter: 1.6 m (5.2 ft) Tank Length: 2.82 m (9.2 ft)
Guidance Navigation & Control	Flight computers, data recorders, displays and switch panels, space navigation/Inertial Navigation System (INS)/star trackers, Laser Detection and Ranging (LADAR), health monitoring and sensors

Command Module (continued)	
Environmental Control and Life Support System	The ECLSS consisted of the following integrated sections: regenerative CO_2/moisture removal system (amine bed), O_2/N_2 storage, atmosphere monitoring, potable water/waste water storage, fire detection and suppression, cold plates, cabin heat exchanger, water evaporator, 60% propylene glycol/40% H_2O single-phase fluid loop.
Total Mass in Low Earth Orbit	32,073 kg (70,709 lbm)
Active/Passive Duration	11.7 days/180 days
Up Payload	Crew plus 100 kg (220.5 lbm) lunar samples
Major Maneuvers	Ascent and Trans-Earth Injection (TEI) (Earth direct)
Descent Stage	
Propulsion	Delta-v (OMS/RCS): 2,745 / 17 m/s (9,006/56 ft/s) Propellant: LOX/LH_2 OMS/RCS Isp: 451/401 sec Number of OMS Engines: Three RL-10A-4-2 engines Engine Length: 2.29 m (7.5 ft) Engine Exit Diameter: 1.17 m (3.84 ft) Cant Angle: 0° Gimbal Angle: ±4° Thrust per Engine / T/W_eff: 99.2 kN (22.3 klbf)/0.28 (g's) Chamber Pressure: 3,902.4 kPa (566 psi) Mixture Ratio: 5.5 Area Ratio: 84 Throttle: 27.4% Tank Pressure: 275.8 kPa (40 psi), LOX tank diameter (ea.) 3.45 m (11.3 ft); LH_2 tank diameter (ea.) 4.91 m (16.1 ft)
Structures	Stage Diameter: 4.5 m (14.8 ft) Stage Structural Length: 13.6 m (44.5 ft) Stage Total Length: 18.5 m (60.6 ft)
Total Mass in Low Earth Orbit	61,790 kg (136,224 lbm) Dry Mass Growth: 20%
Active/Passive Duration	4.0 days/180 days
Down Payload	Crew plus 500 kg (1,102.3 lbm) science equipment
Extravehicular Activity Mode	LIDS plus tunnel plus airlock
Major Maneuvers	LOI descent and landing Staging Orbit: 100 by 100 km (54 by 54 nmi)

EDS Performs LOI	
Power	3 x 28 Vdc distribution buses, 13.5 kW-hr LiMnO$_2$ batteries, power control unit
Propulsion	The propulsion system had 3 x 99,195.2 N (22,300 lbf) RL-10A-4-2 LOX/LH$_2$ engines operating at a Specific Impulse (Isp) of 451 seconds. The reaction control system had 16 x 445.2 N (100 lbf) LOX/LH$_2$ engines operating at an Isp of 401 sec Delta-v (OMS/RCS): 1,900 / 17 m/s (6,234/54 ft/s) Propellant: LOX/LH$_2$ OMS/RCS Isp: 451/401 sec Number of OMS Engines: 3 x RL-10A-4-2 engines Engine Length: 2.29 m (7.5 ft) Engine Exit Diameter: 1.17 m (3.84 ft) Cant Angle: 0°, gimbal angle: ±4° Thrust per Engine / T/W_eff: 99.2 kN (22.3 klbf)/0.36 (g's) Chamber Pressure: 3902.4 kPa (566 psi) Mixture Ratio: 5.5 Area Ratio: 84 Throttle: 29.5% Tank Pressure: 275.8 kPa (40 psi), LOX
Telecommunications	The K-band was to be used to transmit video (high-definition television)
Thermal	Multi-Layer Insulation (MLI)
Structures	Structures included a graphite epoxy composite primary structure landing gear, Pyro separation mechanisms, LIDS, a tunnel, and airlock Stage Diameter: 4.5 m (14.8 ft) Stage Structural Length: 11.8 m (38.7 ft) Stage Total Length: 16.0 m (52.3 ft) Tank Diameter (ea.): 2.94 m (9.62 ft) LH$_2$ Tank Diameter (ea.): 4.17 m (13.7 ft)
Guidance Navigation & Control	Altimetry and surface topography mapping, health monitoring, and sensors
Total Mass in Low Earth Orbit	40,863 kg (90,088 lbm) Dry Mass Growth: 20%
Active/Passive Duration	4.0 days/180 days
Down Payload	Crew plus 500 kg (1,102.3 lbm) science equipment
Major Maneuvers	Descent and landing Staging Orbit: 100 by 100 km (54 by 54 nmi)
Extravehicular Activity Mode	LIDS plus tunnel plus airlock

Ascent Stage	
Power	4.5 kW LSAM average power, PEM fuel cells, hydrogen reactant storage, power distribution cables, remote control units, one 28 Vdc distribution bus
Propulsion	The propulsion system had 4 x 35,048 N (7,879 lbf) pressure-fed LOX/CH_4 that operated at an Isp of 350.3 sec. The RCS had 16 x 445.2 N (100 lbf) LOX/CH_4 engines that operated at an Isp of 315 sec. There were eight Al 7075 graphite-wrapped common-bulkhead LOX/CH_4 tanks pressurized to 1,896.1 kPa (275 psi). There was also a shared fuel cell/RMS/OM LOX storage. Delta-v (OMS/RCS): 2,841/10 m/s (9,321/ 33 ft/s) Propellant: Integrated O_2/methane Engine Length: 2.14 m (7.04 ft) Engine Exit Diameter: 1.13 m (3.70 ft) Cant Angle: 10° Gimbal Angle: ±10° Thrust per Engine / T/W_eff: 34.0 kN (7.64 klbf)/0.32 (g's) Chamber Pressure: 1,206.6 kPa (175 psi) Mixture Ratio: 3.8 Area Ratio: 70 Throttle: 22.0%
Thermal	MLI
Structures	Graphite epoxy primary structure Stage Diameter: 7.5 m (24.6 ft) Stage Total Length: 7.4 m (24.2 ft) Stage Structural Length: 5.8 m (19.0 ft) Tank Pressure: 1,896.1 kPa (275 psi) Tank Diameter: 1.6 m (5.2 ft) Tank Length: 2.82 m (9.2 ft), Dry Mass Growth: 20%
Environmental Control and Life Support System	60% propylene glycol/40% H_2O single-phase fluid loop and body-mounted radiator
Total Mass in Low Earth Orbit	32,073 kg (70,709 lbm)
Active/Passive Duration	11.7 days/180 days
Up Payload	Crew plus 100 kg (220.5 lbm) lunar samples
Major Maneuvers	Ascent and TEI (Earth direct)

Mass Breakdown						
Subsystem	**CEV**		**Descent Stage**		**Ascent Stage**	
	lbm	kg	lbm	kg	lbm	kg
1.0 Structure	5,501	2,495	5,362	2,432	3,362	1,525
2.0 Protection	2,108	956	353	160	467	212
3.0 Propulsion	368	167	4,026	1,826	6,277	2,847
4.0 Power	1,030	467	741	336	1,093	496
5.0 Control	0	0	0	0	0	0
6.0 Avionics	1,415	642	320	145	194	88
7.0 Environment	2,213	1,004	2,222	1,008	390	177
8.0 Other	2,381	1,080	3,926	1,781	0	0
9.0 Growth	3,003	1,362	3,391	1,538	2,357	1,069
Dry Mass w/Growth	**18,019**	**8,173**	**20,341**	**9,226**	**14,140**	**6,414**
10.0 Non-cargo	4,321	1960	1,102	500	0	0
11.0 Cargo	633	287	326	148	450	204
Inert Mass	**22,973**	**10,420**	**21,769**	**9,874**	**14,590**	**6,618**
12.0 Non-propellant	633	287	326	148	450	204
13.0 Propellant	183	83	65,629	29,769	54,031	24,508
Gross Mass	**23,789**	**10,790**	**87,724**	**39,791**	**69,071**	**31,330**

ESAS Vertical 2-Stage, CEV-to-Surface Mass Breakdown: EDS Performs LOI						
Subsystem	**CEV**		**Descent Stage**		**Ascent Stage**	
	lbm	kg	lbm	kg	lbm	kg
1.0 Structure	5,501	2,495	5,362	2,432	3,362	1,525
2.0 Protection	2,108	956	353	160	467	212
3.0 Propulsion	368	167	4,026	1,826	6,277	2,847
4.0 Power	1,030	467	741	336	1,093	496
5.0 Control	0	0	0	0	0	0
6.0 Avionics	1,415	642	320	145	194	88
7.0 Environment	2,213	1,004	2,222	1,008	390	177
8.0 Other	2,381	1,080	3,926	1,781	0	0
9.0 Growth	3,003	1,362	3,391	1,538	2,357	1,069
Dry Mass w/Growth	**18,019**	**8,173**	**20,341**	**9,226**	**14,140**	**6,414**
10.0 Non-cargo	4,321	1960	1,102	500	0	0
11.0 Cargo	633	287	326	148	450	204
Inert Mass	**22,973**	**10,420**	**21,769**	**9,874**	**14,590**	**6,618**
12.0 Non-propellant	633	287	326	148	450	204
13.0 Propellant	183	83	65,629	29,769	54,031	24,508
Gross Mass	**23,789**	**10,790**	**87,724**	**39,791**	**69,071**	**31,330**

Exploration System Architecture Study Vertical, 1-Stage, 4-Engine, Pressure-Fed, Crewed Lander: 0507-ESAS-C

The ESAS vertical, 1-stage, 4-Engine, Pressure-Fed, Crewed lander included structures made of 7075 pressure vessels, LIDS docking system, window, docking hatch, an EVA hatch, and cabin. Its supporting launch vehicle infrastructure was equipped with 4 x 31,480.3 N (7,077 lbf) pressure-fed LOX/methane OMS engines, and was the upper-bound example of a lunar lander at the time of its design. Its concept of operations included a 95-day sized LEO period to Trans-Lunar Injection, which increased the size of the lander significantly due to the amount of cryogenic propellant needed.

Descent Stage	
Power	PEM fuel cells (FCs) provided 4.5 kW LSAM average power generation. The fuel cells utilized a hydrogen reactant.
Propulsion	4 x 31,480.3 N (7,077 lbf) pressure-fed LOX/methane OMS engines at 362.2 sec Isp, 16 x 445.2 N (100 lbf) LOX/methane RCS engines at 315 sec Isp, 4 x Al 7075 graphite-wrapped common-bulkhead LOX/methane tanks at 1,723.7 kPa (250 psi), shared LOX storage and gaseous helium pressurization for FC/ECLSS/RCS/OMS
	Delta-v (OMS/RCS): 3,772 / 27 m/s (12,374/87 ft/s)
	Tank Pressure: 1,723.7 kPa (250 psi)
	Propellant: Integrated O_2/methane
	OMS/RCS Isp: 362.2/315 sec
	Number of OMS Engines: 4
	Engine Length: 2.99 m (9.81 ft)
	Engine Exit Diameter: 1.69 m (5.54 ft)
	Cant Angle: 29°; Gimbal Angle: ±9°
	Thrust per Engine/Thrust-to-Weight (T/W)_eff: 1.5 kN (7.07 klbf) / 0.32 (Earth g's)
	Chamber Pressure: 1,034.2 kPa (150 psi), Area Ratio: 150
	Throttle: 27.4%
Telecommunications	S-band and Ultra-High Frequency (UHF) voice/video/data, K-band video (high-definition television)
	Telecommunications media for information transmission included S-band, UHF for voice/video/data transmission, and K-band for video (high definition television)
Thermal	MLI
Structures	Structures included the following: an Al 7075 pressure vessel, LIDS, window and docking hatch, and an EVA hatch, cabin
	FC, ECLSS, RC, OMS, and LOX shared a common storage
	Graphite epoxy composite primary structure and landing gear
	Pressurized Volume: 29.2 m³ (1,031 ft³)
	Stage Diameter: 6.76 m (22.2 ft)
	Tank Diameter (ea.): 2.21 m (7.25 ft)
	Tank Length: 3.3 m (10.83 ft)

Descent Stage (continued)	
Guidance Navigation & Control	The GN&C system included flight computers, data recorders, displays and switch panels, space navigation/INS/star trackers, LADAR, health sensors and monitoring, altimetry and surface topography mapping.
Environmental Control and Life Support System	The ECLSS had a habitat with a 65.5 kPa (9.5 psi) cabin pressure (consisting of 30% O_2). The ECLSS also had a regenerative CO_2/moisture removal system (amine bed), atmosphere monitoring, fire detection and suppression, gaseous nitrogen storage, potable/waste water storage, avionics, crew cabin conditioning with cold plates and cabin/external heat exchangers, water evaporator for peak loads, and 60% propylene glycol/40% H_2O single-phase fluid loop, radiators.
Total Mass in Low Earth Orbit	37,495 kg (82,663 lbm) Dry Mass Growth: 20%
Active/Passive Duration	4.7 days/180 days
Down Payload	Crew plus 500 kg (1,102.3 lbm) science equipment
Major Maneuvers	Ascent Docking with CEV Staging Orbit: 100 by 100 km (54 by 54 nmi)
Extravehicular Activity Mode	Full cabin depress
Crew Size/Number of Extravehicular Activities	4/4
Ascent Stage	
Up Payload	Crew plus 100 kg (220.5 lbm) lunar samples

Mass Breakdown		
Subsystem	**lbm**	**kg**
1.0 Structure	4,442	2,015
2.0 Protection	650	295
3.0 Propulsion	5,346	2,425
4.0 Power	1,219	553
5.0 Control	0	0
6.0 Avionics	1,310	594
7.0 Environment	1,713	777
8.0 Other	1,947	883
9.0 Growth	3,325	1,508
Dry Mass w/Growth	**19,952**	**9,050**
10.0 Non-cargo	3,889	1,764
11.0 Cargo	1,102	500
Inert Mass	**24,943**	**11,314**
12.0 Non-propellant	1,530	694
13.0 Propellant	56,187	25,486
Gross Mass	**82,660**	**37,494**

Exploration System Architecture Study Vertical, 1-Stage, 4-Engine Pressure-Fed, Cargo Lander: 0507-ESAS-D

A cargo-only variant of the Vertical, 1-stage, 4-Engine, Pressure-Fed lander, this lander used the same engines as the descent stage of the crewed version, with a thrust-to-weight engine efficiency of 31.5 kN (7.08 klbf)/0.21 (Earth g's) and specifications as described below.

Descent Stage	
Power	PEM fuel cells provided LSAM average power of 2.0 kW. This power generation involved fuel cell utilization of a hydrogen reactant.
Propulsion	The propulsion system was comprised of 4 x 31,480.3 N (7,077 lbf) pressure-fed LOX/methane OMS engines that operated at an Isp of 362 sec. The RCS had 16 x 445.2 N (100 lbf) LOX/methane engines rated for operation at an Isp of 315 sec. In addition, Al 7075 graphite-wrapped common-bulkhead LOX/methane tanks were pressurized to 1,723.7 kPa (250 psi). The fuel cell/RCS/OMS storage was shared. Delta-v (OMS/RCS): 1,900 / 17 m/s (6,234/54 ft/s) Propellant: Integrated O_2/methane OMS/RCS Isp: 362.2/315 sec Number of OMS Engines: 4 Engine Length: 2.99 m (9.81 ft) Engine Exit Diameter: 1.69 m (5.54 ft) Cant Angle: 29°, Gimbal Angle: ±9° Thrust per Engine / T/W_eff: 31.5 kN (7.08 klbf)/0.21 (Earth g's) Chamber Pressure: 1,034.2 kPa (150 psi) Area Ratio: 150 Throttle: 45.8%
Telecommunications	The S-band and UHF band were used to transmit information
Thermal	MLI
Structures	Included a graphite epoxy composite structure and landing gear. Stage Diameter: 6.76 m (22.2 ft) Tank Pressure: 1,723.7 kPa (250 psi) Tank Diameter (ea.): 2.11 m (6.92 ft) Tank Length: 3.15 m (10.34 ft)
Guidance Navigation & Control	GN&C systems included flight computers, space navigation/INS/star trackers, altimetry, surface topography mapping and health sensors
Environmental Control and Life Support System	The ECLSS included cold plates, heat exchangers, a water evaporator, 60% propylene glycol/40% H_2O, and a single-phase fluid loop
Total Mass in Low Earth Orbit	Maximum: 60,935 kg (134,340 lbm) Nominal: 37,377 kg (82,402 lbm) Dry Mass Growth: 20%
Down Payload	Maximum: 28,475 kg (62,777 lbm) Nominal: 15,000 kg (33,069 lbm)
Major Maneuvers	Descent and landing Staging Orbit: 100 by 100 km (54 by 54 nmi)

Exploration System Architecture Study Vertical, 1-Stage, 1-Engine, Pressure-Fed, Crewed Lander: 0507-ESAS-E

Version E of the ESAS lander was a single-engine variant of 0507-ESAS-C designed to carry a crew of four with four expected EVAs, with the full cabin depressurized when in EVA mode. Designed to operate in a 100 by 100 km (54 by 54 nmi) staging orbit, the only planned major on-orbit maneuvers consisted of ascent docking with the CEV. It had a planned down payload of 500 kg (1,102.3 lbm) of science equipment in addition to the crew, and an up payload of crew + 100 kg (220 lbm) of lunar samples. Expected operational duration was 4.7 days active and 180 days in passive mode. Total mass in LEO was 35,688 kg (78,634 lbm), with a dry mass growth of 20%.

Descent Stage	
Power	4.5 kW LSAM average power, PEM fuel cells, hydrogen reactant storage, power distribution cables, remote control units, 1 x 28 Vdc distribution bus
Propulsion	The propulsion system had 1 x 112,615.6 N (25,317 lbf) pressure-fed LOX/methane OMS engine operating at an Isp of 351.5 sec. The RCS had 16 x 445.2 N (100 lbf) LOX/methane engines operating at an Isp of 315 sec. It also had 4 x Al 7075 graphite-wrapped common-bulkhead LOX/methane tanks that were helium pressurized to 1,896.1 kPa (275 psi). Delta-v (OMS/RCS): 3,772 / 27 m/s (12,374/87 ft/s) Propellant: Integrated O2/methane OMS/RCS Isp: 351.5/315 sec Number of OMS Engines: 4 Engine Length: 4.00 m (13.1 ft) Engine Exit Diameter: 2.12 m (6.96 ft) Cant Angle: 0° Gimbal Angle: ±9° Thrust per Engine / T/W_eff: 112.6 kN (25.3 klbf)/0.32 (Earth g's) Chamber Pressure: 1,206.6 kPa (175 psi) Area Ratio: 75 Throttle: 29.7%
Telecommunications	S-band and UHF voice/video/data, K-band video
Thermal	MLI
Structures	Structures included an Al 7075 pressure vessel, LIDS, window and docking hatch, and an EVA hatch. Graphite epoxy composite primary structure and landing gear Pressurized Volume: 29.2 m³ (1,031 ft³) Stage Diameter: 6.63 m (21.8 ft) Tank Pressure: 1,896.1 kPa (275 psi) Tank Diameter (ea.): 2.17 m (7.11 ft) Tank Length: 3.23 m (10.61 ft)
Guidance Navigation & Control	Flight computers, data recorders, displays and switch panels, space navigation/INS/star trackers, LADAR, health sensors and monitoring, altimetry and surface topography mapping
Environmental Control and Life Support System	The habitat cabin was pressurized at 65.5 kPa (9.5 psi), consisting of 30% O_2. In addition, the ECLSS system had a regenerative CO_2/moisture removal system (amine bed), atmospheric monitoring, fire detection and suppression, gaseous nitrogen.
Ascent Stage	
Up Payload	Crew plus 100 kg (220.5 lbm) lunar samples

ESAS Vertical, 1-Stage, 1-Engine, Pressure-Fed (Crew Variant) Mass Breakdown		
Subsystem	lbm	kg
1.0 Structure	4,376	1,985
2.0 Protection	637	289
3.0 Propulsion	5,174	2,347
4.0 Power	1,219	553
5.0 Control	0	0
6.0 Avionics	1,310	594
7.0 Environment	1,713	777
8.0 Other	1,911	867
9.0 Growth	3,269	1,483
Dry Mass w/Growth	**19,609**	**8,895**
10.0 Non-cargo	3,838	1,741
11.0 Cargo	1,102	500
Inert Mass	**24,549**	**11,136**
12.0 Non-propellant	1,539	698
13.0 Propellant	52,543	23,833
Gross Mass	**78,631**	**35,667**

Exploration System Architecture Study Vertical, 1-Stage, 1-Engine, Pressure-Fed, Cargo Lander: 0507-ESAS-F

Version F was a cargo-only version of the 1-stage, 1-engine lander. Total mass in LEO for this lander was 56,989 kg (125,640 lbm), with a maximum down payload of 26,357 kg (58,107 lbm). As with the other versions, its planned staging orbit was 100 by 100 km (54 by 54 nmi).

Descent Stage	
Power	2.0 kW LSAM average power, PEM fuel cell, hydrogen reactant storage, power distribution cables, power control units. 2.0 kW of LSAM average power was provided by PEM fuel cell(s) which utilized a hydrogen reactant.
Propulsion	The propulsion system had 1 x 112,615.6 N (25,317 lbf) pressure-fed LOX/methane OMS engine with an Isp of 351.5 sec. The RCS had 16 x 445.2 N (100 lbf) LOX/methane engines with an Isp of 315 sec. Al 7075 graphite-wrapped common-bulkhead LOX/methane tanks helium pressurized to 1,896.1 kPa (275 psi). Deltav (OMS/RCS): 1,900 / 17 m/s (6,234/54 ft/s) Propellant: Integrated O_2 /methane OMS/RCS Isp: 351.5/315 sec Number of OMS Engines: 4 Engine Length: 4.00 m (13.1 ft) Engine Exit Diameter: 2.12 m (6.96 ft) Cant Angle: 0° Gimbal Angle: ±9° Thrust per Engine / T/W_eff: 112.6 kN (25.3 klbf)/0.20 (Earth g's) Chamber Pressure: 1,206.6 kPa (175 psi) Area Ratio: 75 Throttle: 47.9% Tank Pressure: 1,896.1 kPa (275 psi)
Telecommunications	S-band UHF
Thermal	MLI
Structures	Graphite epoxy composite primary structure and landing gear Stage Diameter: 6.63 m (21.8 ft) Tank Diameter (ea.): 2.17 m (7.11 ft) Tank Length: 3.23 m (10.61 ft)
Guidance Navigation & Control	Flight computers, space navigation/INS/star trackers, altimetry and surface topography mapping, health sensors
Environmental Control and Life Support System	Cold plates, heat exchangers, water evaporator, 60% propylene glycol/40% H_2O single-phase fluid loop
Total Mass in Low Earth Orbit	Maximum: 56,989 kg (125,640 lbm) Nominal: 37,134 kg (81,866 lbm) Dry Mass Growth: 20%
Down Payload	Maximum: 26,357 kg (58,107 lbm) Nominal: 15,000 kg (33,069 lbm)
Major Maneuvers	Descent and landing Staging Orbit: 100 by 100 km (54 by 54 nmi)

Exploration System Architecture Study Vertical, 1-Stage, 4-Engine, Pump-Fed, Crewed Lander: 0507-ESAS-G

This variant used pump-fed instead of pressure-fed engines featured in 0507-ESAS-C, but was otherwise very similar to that previously described versions. Detailed specifications are shown in the table below.

Descent Stage	
Power	4.5 kW LSAM average power, PEM fuel cells, hydrogen reactant storage, power distribution cables, remote control units, 1 x 28 Vdc distribution bus PEM fuel cells, which utilized a hydrogen reactant.
Propulsion	The propulsion system had 4 x 23,308.4 N (5,240 lbf) pump-fed LOX/methane OMS engines with an Isp of 363.4 sec. There were 16 x 445.2 N (100 lbf) LOX/methane RCS engines with an Isp of 315 sec. 4 x Al 7075 graphite-wrapped common-bulkhead LOX/methane tanks pressurized at 275.8 kPa (40 psi) were also a part of the propulsion system. Delta-v (OMS/RCS): 3,772 / 27 m/s (12,374/87 ft/s) Propellant: Integrated O_2/methane OMS/RCS Isp: 363.4/315 sec Number of OMS Engines: 4 Engine Length: 1.41 m (4.63 ft) Engine Exit Diameter: 0.80 m (2.61 ft) Cant Angle: 18.5° Gimbal Angle: ±6.5° Thrust per Engine / T/W_eff: 23.3 kN (5.24 klbf)/0.32 (Earth g's) Chamber Pressure: 3,447.4 kPa (500 psi) Area Ratio: 150 Throttle: 29.3%
Telecommunications	The UHF was used to send voice/video/data. The K-band was used as the carrier for video (high-definition television).
Thermal	MLI
Structures	Al 7075 pressure vessel, LIDS, window and docking hatch, EVA hatch, cabin design pressure 65.5 kPa (9.5 psi) Graphite epoxy composite primary structure and landing gear Pressurized Volume: 29.2 m³ (1,031 ft³) Stage Diameter: 6.17 m (20.25 ft) Tank Pressure: 275.8 kPa (40 psi) Tank Diameter (ea.): 2.01 m (6.61 ft) Tank Length: 3.0 m (9.84 ft)

Descent Stage (continued)	
Guidance Navigation & Control	Flight computers, data recorders, displays and switch panels, space navigation/INS/star trackers, LADAR, health sensors and monitoring, altimetry and surface topography mapping
Environmental Control and Life Support System	The ECLSS system had a habitat that was pressurized to 65.5 kPa (9.5 psi), with 30% O_2. Other features of the ECLSS were a regenerative CO_2/moisture removal system (amine bed), atmosphere monitoring, fire detection and suppression, gaseous nitrogen storage, potable/waste water storage, avionics and crew cabin conditioning with cold plates and cabin/external heat exchangers, a water evaporator for peak loads, 60% propylene glycol/40% H_2O single-phase fluid loop, and radiators.
Total Mass in Low Earth Orbit	28,819 kg (63,535 lbm) Dry Mass Growth: 20%
Active/Passive Duration	4.7 days/180 days
Down Payload	Crew plus 500 kg (1,102.3 lbm) science equipment
Major Maneuvers	Ascent, Docking with CEV Staging Orbit: 100 by 100 km (54 by 54 nmi)
Extravehicular Activity Mode	Full cabin depress
Crew Size/Number of Extravehicular Activities	4/4
Ascent Stage	
Up Payload	Crew plus 100 kg (220.5 lbm) lunar samples

Mass Breakdown		
Descent Stage		
Subsystem	lbm	kg
1.0 Structure	4,138	1,877
2.0 Protection	600	272
3.0 Propulsion	2,480	1,125
4.0 Power	1,219	553
5.0 Control	0	0
6.0 Avionics	1,310	594
7.0 Environment	1,713	777
8.0 Other	1,702	772
9.0 Growth	2,632	1,194
Dry Mass w/Growth	**15,794**	**7,164**
10.0 Non-cargo	2,835	1,286
11.0 Cargo	1,102	500
Inert Mass	**19,731**	**8,950**
12.0 Non-propellant	1,581	717
13.0 Propellant	42,223	19,152
Gross Mass	**63,535**	**28,819**

Exploration System Architecture Study Vertical, 1-Stage, 4-Engine, Pump-Fed, Cargo Lander: 0507-ESAS-H

The cargo-only variation of the 4-engine pump-fed lander (0507-ESAS-D) consisted of a single stage that was similar to the descent stage of the 0507-ESAS-G crewed version, with a total mass in LEO of 45,807 kg (100, 988 lbm) and a nominal mass of 33,519 kg (73,897 lbm). Its maximum down payload was 22,028 kg (48,654 lbm), with a nominal down payload of 15,000 kg (33,069 lbm).

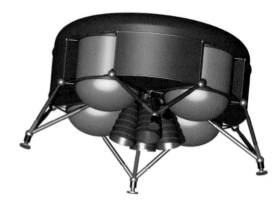

Descent Stage	
Propulsion	Delta-v (OMS/RCS): 1,900 / 17 m/s (6,234/54 ft/s) Propellant: Integrated O₂/methane OMS/RCS Isp: 363.4/315 sec Number of OMS Engines: 4 Engine Length: 1.41 m (4.63 ft) Engine Exit Diameter: 0.80 m (2.61 ft) Cant Angle: 18.5° Gimbal Angle: ±6.5° Thrust per Engine / T/W_eff: 23.3 kN (5.24 klbf)/0.32 (Earth g's) Chamber Pressure: 3,447.4 kPa (500 psi) Area Ratio: 150 Throttle: 46.4%
Structures	Stage Diameter: 6.17 m (20.25 ft) Tank Pressure: 275.8 kPa (40 psi) Tank Diameter (ea.): 2.01 m (6.61 ft) Tank Length: 3.0 m (9.84 ft)
Total Mass in Low Earth Orbit	Maximum: 45,807 kg (100,988 lbm) Nominal: 33,519 kg (73,897 lbm) Dry Mass Growth: 20%
Down Payload	Maximum: 22,028 kg (48,564 lbm) Nominal: 15,000 kg (33,069 lbm)
Major Maneuvers	Descent and landing Staging Orbit: 100 by 100 km (54 by 54 nmi)

Exploration System Architecture Study Vertical, 1-Stage, 1-Engine, Pump-Fed, Crewed Lander: 0507-ESAS-I

As with 0507-ESAS-E, this 1-engine version of the vertical, 1-stage pump-fed lander was designed to carry four crew, with four planned EVAs for an active duration of 4.7 days (passive duration – 180 days). Its habitat pressurized volume was 29.2 m³ (1,031 ft³), and, as with the previous crewed lander, had a down payload capacity of crew + 500 kg (1,102.3 lbm) of science equipment, and an up payload of crew + 100 kg (220.5 lbm) of lunar samples.

Descent Stage	
Power	4.5 kW LSAM average power, PEM fuel cells, hydrogen reactant storage, power distribution cables, remote control units, 1 x 28 Vdc distribution bus
Propulsion	The propulsion system had 1 x 88,288.3 N (19,848 lbf) pump-fed LOX/methane OMS engine with an Isp of 363.4 sec. There were 16 x 445.2 N (100 lbf) LOX/methane engines with an Isp of 315 sec that were in the RCS. Delta-v (OMS/RCS): 3,772 / 27 m/s (12,374/87 ft/s) Propellant: Integrated O_2/methane OMS/RCS Isp: 363.4/315 sec Number of OMS Engines: 4 Engine Length: 2.75 m (9.01 ft) Engine Exit Diameter: 1.55 m (5.09 ft) Cant Angle: 0° Gimbal Angle: ±9° Thrust per Engine / T/W_eff: 88.3 kN (19.8 klbf)/0.32 (Earth g's) Chamber Pressure: 3,447.4 kPa (500 psi) Area Ratio: 150 Throttle: 30.3%
Telecommunications	S-band and UHF voice/video/data, K-band video (high-definition television)
Thermal	MLI
Structures	Structures included an Al 7075 pressure vessel, LIDS, window and docking hatch, and EVA hatch. Pressurized Volume: 29.2 m³ (1,031 ft³) Stage Diameter: 6.09 m (19.98 ft) Tank Pressure: 275.8 kPa (40 psi) Tank Diameter (ea.): 1.99 m (6.52 ft) Tank Length: 2.96 m (9.71 ft)
Guidance Navigation & Control	The GN&C systems included flight computers, data recorders, displays, switch panels, space navigation/INS/star trackers, LADAR, health sensors and monitoring, altimetry and surface topography mapping.

Descent Stage	
Environmental Control and Life Support System	The ECLSS was composed of a habitable cabin pressurized to 65.5 kPa (9.5 psi), with 30% O_2, a regenerative CO_2 moisture removal system (amine bed), atmosphere monitoring, fire detection and suppression, gaseous nitrogen, potable/waste water storage, avionics and crew cabin conditioning with cold plates, cabin/external heat exchangers, a water evaporator for peak loads, a 60% propylene glycol/40% H_2O single-phase fluid loop and radiators.
Total Mass in Low Earth Orbit	27,890 kg (61,486 lbm) Dry Mass Growth: 20%
Active/Passive Duration	4.7 days/180 days
Down Payload	Crew plus 500 kg (1,102.3 lbm) science equipment
Major Maneuvers	Ascent Docking with CEV Staging Orbit: 100 by 100 km (54 by 54 nmi)
Extravehicular Activity Mode	Full cabin depress
Crew Size/Number of Extravehicular Activities	4/4
Ascent Stage	
Up Payload	Crew plus 100 kg (220.5 lbm) lunar samples

Mass Breakdown		
Subsystem	**lbm**	**kg**
1.0 Structure	4,101	1,860
2.0 Protection	593	269
3.0 Propulsion	2,414	1,095
4.0 Power	1,219	553
5.0 Control	0	0
6.0 Avionics	1,310	594
7.0 Environment	1,713	777
8.0 Other	1,684	764
9.0 Growth	2,606	1,182
Dry Mass w/Growth	**15,640**	**7,094**
10.0 Non-cargo	2,787	1,264
11.0 Cargo	1,102	500
Inert Mass	**19,529**	**8,858**
12.0 Non-propellant	1,585	719
13.0 Propellant	40,371	18,312
Gross Mass	**61,485**	**27,889**

Exploration System Architecture Study Vertical, 1-Stage, 1-Engine, Pump-Fed, Cargo Lander: 0507-ESAS-J

The cargo-only version had a maximum down payload of 20,956 kg (46,200 lbm) and consisted of the descent stage of the crewed variant (see 0507-ESAS-I). Detailed specifications are described in the table below.

Descent Stage	
Power	PEM fuel cells provided 4.5 kW of average power to the LSAM.
Propulsion	The propulsion system had 1 x 88,288.3 N (19,848 lbf) pressure-fed LOX/methane OMS engine that operated at an Isp of 363.4 sec. The RCS had 16 x 446.2 N (100 lbf) LOX/methane engines that operated at an Isp of 315 sec. Al 7075 graphite-wrapped common bulkhead LOX/methane tanks were pressurized to 275.8 kPa (40 psi). There was a shared fuel cell/RCS/OMS LOX storage. Delta-v (OMS/RCS): 1,900 / 17 m/s (6,234/54 ft/s) Propellant: Integrated O_2/methane OMS/RCS Isp: 363.4/315 sec Number of OMS Engines: 4 Engine Length: 2.75 m (9.01 ft) Engine Exit Diameter: 1.55 m (5.09 ft) Cant Angle: 0° Gimbal Angle: ±9° Thrust per Engine / T/W_eff: 88.3 kN (19.8 klbf)/0.21 (Earth g's) Chamber Pressure: 3447.4 kPa (500 psi) Area Ratio: 150 Throttle: 46.9%
Telecommunications	S-band and UHF voice/video/data, K-band video (high-definition television)
Structures	Structures included an Al 7075 pressure vessel, LIDS, window and docking hatch, and an EVA hatch. The material of the primary structure and landing gear was graphite epoxy. Stage Diameter: 6.09 m (19.98 ft) Tank Pressure: 275.8 kPa (40 psi) Tank Diameter (ea.): 1.99 m (6.52 ft) Tank Length: 2.96 m (9.71 ft)
Guidance Navigation & Control	The GN&C system had flight computers, data recorders, displays, switch panels, space navigation/INS/star trackers, LADAR, health sensors and monitoring, altimetry and surface topography mapping.
Environmental Control and Life Support System	The ECLSS had a habitable cabin pressurized to 65.5 kPa (9.5 psi), with 30% O_2, a regenerative CO_2/moisture removal system (amine bed), atmosphere monitoring, fire detection and suppression, gaseous nitrogen storage, potable/waste water storage, avionics and crew cabin conditioning with cold plates and cabin/external heat exchangers, a water evaporator for peak loads, 60% propylene glycol/40% H_2O single-phase fluid loop, and radiators.
Total Mass in Low Earth Orbit	Maximum: 43,803 kg (96,570 lbm) Nominal: 33,391 kg (73,615 lbm) Dry Mass Growth: 20%
Down Payload	Maximum: 20,956 kg (46,200 lbm) Nominal: 15,000 kg (33,069 lbm)
Major Maneuvers	Descent and landing Staging Orbit: 100 by 100 km (54 by 54 nmi)

Lunar Surface Access Module Pre-Project

In December 2005, the Lunar Surface Access Module (LSAM) Pre-Project Office became the organizational focal point for lunar lander activity within NASA. A number of different configurations were examined, with trade studies performed on the number of stages, stage propellant, engine types, level of engine-out capability, airlock approaches, cargo capacity, and abort options. This continued through the creation of the LSAM/Altair Project in January 2007 and included the Lunar Lander Preparatory Study and the Lunar Architecture Team-1 study activities.

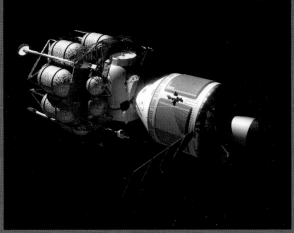

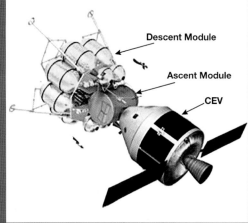

Crew Exploration Vehicle and NASA Lunar Surface Access Module, late 2005.

Lunar Lander Preparatory Study

The Lunar Lander Preparatory Study (LLPS) was a large-scale, in-house NASA effort to challenge NASA center teams to develop multiple innovative design concepts that fulfilled the human lunar lander requirements of the Constellation Program. The LLPS explored the implications of various architectural implementations (e.g., incremental deployment of outpost elements), broadened the number of viable lander concepts in anticipation of Lunar Strategy Team/Lunar Architecture Team output, and completed two 8-week study phases, with Phase 1 purposely exploring new lander design concepts and Phase 2 concentrating on further refinement of selected concepts. Phase 1 was conducted from March through May of 2006. During this time, the teams were encouraged to develop multiple inventive lander design concepts (designated as 0605-LLPS-1 through 30). The teams began by brainstorming creative ideas for the integration of the lander and surface systems (e.g., deployment of surface outpost habitation). The teams then developed several different vehicle concepts to present to the review board. The process

concluded by assessing performance of their vehicle concepts, performing sensitivity studies, and planning for Phase 2. In parallel to the in-house NASA LLPS study, six concepts were developed by outside sources in response to a NASA Request for Information. These concepts were designated as 0606-LLPS-RFI-1 through -6. Phase 2 of the LLPS was conducted from June to mid-September of 2006. The in-house teams refined their design concepts during this period, assessing vehicle performance characteristics and trade/sensitivity studies at the next level of detail. These concepts were designated 0609-LLPS-1 through -7. The teams identified technological drivers and flight experiments/technology demonstrations for precursor robotic missions. They also developed inputs for common cost estimating activities and common risk analysis activities. At the conclusion of Phase 2, the Constellation Program Office/Advanced Project Office had multiple lander concepts to evaluate against the lunar surface strategies and architectures under development at NASA Headquarters.

Langley Research Center Hybrid Global Lander (Crew, Habitat, Cargo): 0605-LLPS-LaRC-1

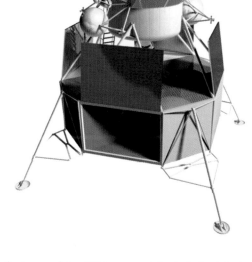

The Hybrid Global Lander (HGL) was a "lower bound" concept that was defined to explore a revised "minimum" mission concept for lunar exploration. For this lander concept, the HGL Crew Lander with minimal pressurized volume supported two-crew, 7-day "mini-sortie" missions. The Crew Lander and a separate Habitat Lander supported four-crew, 28-day "super-sortie" missions. A Cargo Lander configuration was also defined based on the HGL Descent Stage.

Key features of the HGL concept included: global landing capability for mini-sortie missions, common elements used across the three lander configurations, and landers that left behind reusable assets for follow-on missions to the same location. Numerous trades were performed, including those on Lunar Orbit Insertion (LOI) vehicles, propellants, power system configurations, and crew cabin and habitat layouts.

Descent Stage	
Power	4.5 kW Photo-Voltaic (PV) array/Li-ion batteries (including 2.0 kW portable and reusable power unit), power distribution cables, remote control units, 1 x 28 Vdc distribution bus
Propulsion	1 x 66,723.5 N (15,000 lbf) pressure-fed NTO/MMH Orbital Maneuvering System (OMS) engine at 323 sec Isp; spherical Al 7075 graphite-wrapped tanks at 1,723.7 kPa (250 psi)
Structures	Al-Li pressure vessel, Low-Impact Docking System (LIDS), window and docking hatch, Extravehicular Activity (EVA) hatch, cabin design pressure 65.5 kPa (9.5 psi); Al-Li primary structure and landing gear
Ascent Stage	
Propulsion	One 44,482 N (10,000 lbf) pressure-fed NTO/MMH OMS ascent engine at 323 sec Isp; 16 x 445.2 N (100 lbf) NTO/MMH RCS engines at 315 sec Isp; spherical Al 7075 graphite-wrapped tanks at 1,723.7 kPa (250 psi)

Crewed HGL All Hypergolic Mass Breakdown, Lander Performs LOI				
Subsystem	LSAM Descent Stage		LSAM Ascent Stage	
	lbm	kg	lbm	kg
1.0 Structure	2,229	1,011	1,078	489
2.0 Protection	357	162	156	71
3.0 Propulsion	3,563	1,616	1,270	576
4.0 Power	675	306	1,104	501
5.0 Control	203	92	0	0
6.0 Avionics	152	69	836	379
7.0 Environment	273	124	999	453
8.0 Other	1,224	555	842	382
9.0 Growth	1,735	787	1,257	570
Dry Mass w/Growth	10,411	4,722	7,542	3,421
10.0 Non-cargo	1,444	655	1,040	472
11.0 Cargo	3,505	1,590*	221	100
Inert Mass	15,360	6,967	8,804	3,993
12.0 Non-propellant	209	95	99	45
13.0 Propellant	60,499	27,442	8,195	3,717
Gross Mass	76,068	34,504	17,098	7,755

* 7-day Low Lunar Orbit (LLO) Loiter, 1,000 kg (2,204.6 lbm) "Down" Science Payload, 590 kg (1,300.7 lbm) portable PV/battery power trainer

Crewed HGL All LOX/CH$_4$ Mass Breakdown, Lander Performs LOI				
Subsystem	LSAM Descent Stage		LSAM Ascent Stage	
	lbm	kg	lbm	kg
1.0 Structure	2,987	1,355	1,078	489
2.0 Protection	311	141	157	71
3.0 Propulsion	4,438	2,013	1,594	723
4.0 Power	675	306	1,105	501
5.0 Control	203	920	0	0
6.0 Avionics	152	69	836	379
7.0 Environment	273	124	999	453
8.0 Other	1,288	584	842	382
9.0 Growth	2,066	937	1,323	600
Dry Mass w/Growth	12,393	5,621	7,934	3,598
10.0 Non-cargo	4,339	1,968	1,616	733
11.0 Cargo	3,505	1,590*	220	100
Inert Mass	20,237	9,179	9,770	4,431
12.0 Non-propellant	209	95	99	45
13.0 Propellant	54,551	24,744	7,355	3,336
Gross Mass	74,997	34,018	17,224	7,812

* 7-day LLO Loiter, 1,000 kg (2,204.6 lbm) "Down" Science Payload, 590 kg (1,300.7 lbm) portable PV/battery power trainer

Crewed HGL All Hypergolic Mass Breakdown, Earth Departure Stage (EDS) Performs LOI				
Subsystem	LSAM Descent Stage		LSAM Ascent Stage	
	lbm	kg	lbm	kg
1.0 Structure	994	451	1,078	489
2.0 Protection	190	86	157	71
3.0 Propulsion	1,493	677	1,268	575
4.0 Power	675	306	1,105	501
5.0 Control	203	92	0	0
6.0 Avionics	152	69	836	379
7.0 Environment	273	124	999	453
8.0 Other	1,093	496	842	382
9.0 Growth	1,014	460	1,257	570
Dry Mass w/Growth	**6,087**	**2,761**	**7,542**	**3,420**
10.0 Non-cargo	551	250	1,038	471
11.0 Cargo	3,505	1,590*	220	100
Inert Mass	**10,143**	**4,601**	**8,800**	**3,991**
12.0 Non-propellant	209	95	99	45
13.0 Propellant	23,056	10,458	8,159	3,701
Gross Mass	**33,408**	**15,154**	**17,058**	**7,737**

7-day LLO Loiter, 1,000 kg (2,204.6 lbm) "Down" Science Payload, 590 kg (1,300.7 lbm) portable PV/battery power trainer

Crewed HGL All LOX/CH₄ Mass Breakdown, EDS Performs LOI				
Subsystem	LSAM Descent Stage		LSAM Ascent Stage	
	lbm	kg	lbm	kg
1.0 Structure	1,581	717	1,078	489
2.0 Protection	209	95	157	71
3.0 Propulsion	2,105	955	1,420	644
4.0 Power	675	306	1,105	501
5.0 Control	203	92	0	0
6.0 Avionics	152	69	836	379
7.0 Environment	273	124	999	453
8.0 Other	1,124	510	842	382
9.0 Growth	1,265	574	1,288	584
Dry Mass w/Growth	**7,587**	**3,442**	**7,725**	**3,503**
10.0 Non-cargo	2,194	995	1,658	752
11.0 Cargo	3,505	1,590*	220	100
Inert Mass	**13,286**	**6,027**	**9,603**	**4,355**
12.0 Non-propellant	209	95	99	45
13.0 Propellant	20,613	9,350	7,203	3,267
Gross Mass	**34,108**	**15,472**	**16,905**	**7,667**

7-day LLO Loiter, 1,000 kg (2,204.6 lbm) "Down" Science Payload, 590 kg (1,300.7 lbm) portable PV/battery power trainer

Habitat HGL All Hypergolic Mass Breakdown, EDS Performs LOI

Subsystem	LSAM Descent Stage		LSAM Surface Habitat	
	lbm	kg	lbm	kg
1.0 Structure	994	451	1,964	891
2.0 Protection	190	86	284	129
3.0 Propulsion	1,493	677	366	166
4.0 Power	675	306	2,110	957*
5.0 Control	203	92	0	0
6.0 Avionics	152	69	758	344
7.0 Environment	273	124	4,213	1,911
8.0 Other	1,093	496	428	194
9.0 Growth	1,014	460	2,024	918
Dry Mass w/Growth	**6,087**	**2,761**	**12,147**	**5,510**
10.0 Non-cargo	551	250	2,804	1,272
11.0 Cargo	0	0	2,542	1,153
Inert Mass	**6,638**	**3,011**	**17,493**	**7,935**
12.0 Non-propellant	209	95	3,499	1,587
13.0 Propellant	23,056	10,458	172	78
Gross Mass	**29,903**	**13,564**	**21,164**	**9,600**

* Includes a 491 kg (1,082.5 lbm) 5 kW Sterling Radioisotope Generator

Habitat HGL All LOX/CH₄ Mass Breakdown, EDS Performs LOI

Subsystem	LSAM Descent Stage		LSAM Surface Habitat	
	lbm	kg	lbm	kg
1.0 Structure	1,581	717	1,964	891
2.0 Protection	209	95	284	129
3.0 Propulsion	2,105	955	366	166
4.0 Power	675	306	2,110	957*
5.0 Control	203	92	0	0
6.0 Avionics	152	69	758	344
7.0 Environment	273	124	4,213	1,911
8.0 Other	1,124	510	428	194
9.0 Growth	1,265	574	2,024	918
Dry Mass w/Growth	**7,587**	**3,442**	**12,147**	**5,509**
10.0 Non-cargo	2,194	995	2,804	1,272
11.0 Cargo	0	0	1,916	869
Inert Mass	**9781**	**4,437**	**16,867**	**7,650**
12.0 Non-propellant	209	95	3,499	1,587
13.0 Propellant	20,613	9,350	168	76
Gross Mass	**30,603**	**13,882**	**20,534**	**9,313**

* Includes a 491 kg (1,082.5 lbm) 5 kW Sterling Radioisotope Generator. Note: Polar location (> 87° latitude)

Habitat HGL Hypergolic Solutions with and without LOI Mass Breakdown, EDS Performs LOI				
Subsystem	LSAM Descent Stage		LSAM Surface Habitat	
	lbm	kg	lbm	kg
1.0 Structure	994	451	1,964	891
2.0 Protection	190	86	284	129
3.0 Propulsion	1,493	677	366	166
4.0 Power	675	306	2,110	957*
5.0 Control	203	92	0	0
6.0 Avionics	152	69	758	344
7.0 Environment	273	124	4,213	1,911
8.0 Other	1,093	496	428	194
9.0 Growth	1,014	460	2,024	918
Dry Mass w/Growth	**6,087**	**2,761**	**12,147**	**5,510**
10.0 Non-cargo	551	250	2,804	1,272
11.0 Cargo	0	0	2,542	1,153
Inert Mass	**6,638**	**3,011**	**17,493**	**7,935**
12.0 Non-propellant	209	95	3,499	1,587
13.0 Propellant	23,056	10,458	172	78
Gross Mass	**29,903**	**13,564**	**21,164**	**9,600**

Includes a 491 kg (1,082.5 lbm) Sterling Radioisotope Generator. Note: Polar location (> 87° latitude)

Habitat HGL Hypergolic Solutions with and without LOI Mass Breakdown, Habitat Lander Performs LOI				
Subsystem	LSAM Descent Stage		LSAM Surface Habitat	
	lbm	kg	lbm	kg
1.0 Structure	2,242	1,017	1,964	891
2.0 Protection	357	162	284	129
3.0 Propulsion	3,580	1,624	370	168
4.0 Power	675	306	2,110	957*
5.0 Control	203	92	0	0
6.0 Avionics	152	69	758	344
7.0 Environment	273	124	602	273
8.0 Other	1,224	555	2,701	1,225
9.0 Growth	1,742	790	3,840	1,742
Dry Mass w/Growth	**10,448**	**4,739**	**12,629**	**5,729**
10.0 Non-cargo	1,451	658	2,806	1,273
11.0 Cargo	0	0	12,657	5,741
Inert Mass	**11,899**	**5,397**	**28,092**	**12,743**
12.0 Non-propellant	210	95	3,499	1,587
13.0 Propellant	60,792	27,575	267	121
Gross Mass	**72,901**	**33,067**	**31,858**	**14,451**

Includes a 491 kg (1,082.5 lbm) Sterling Radioisotope Generator. Note: Polar location (> 87° latitude)

Habitat All Hypergolic Mass Breakdown, Lander Performs LOI				
Subsystem	LSAM Descent Stage		LSAM Surface Habitat	
	lbm	kg	lbm	kg
1.0 Structure	2,242	1,017	1,964	891
2.0 Protection	357	162	284	129
3.0 Propulsion	3,580	1,624	370	168
4.0 Power	675	306	2,110	957*
5.0 Control	203	92	0	0
6.0 Avionics	152	69	758	344
7.0 Environment	273	124	4,213	1,911
8.0 Other	1,224	555	428	194
9.0 Growth	1,742	790	2,024	918
Dry Mass w/Growth	**10,448**	**4,739**	**12,151**	**5,512**
10.0 Non-cargo	1,451	658	2,806	1,273
11.0 Cargo	0	0	12,657	5,741
Inert Mass	**11,899**	**5,397**	**27,614**	**12,526**
12.0 Non-propellant	209	95	3,499	1,587
13.0 Propellant	60,792	27,575	267	121
Gross Mass	**72,900**	**33,067**	**31,380**	**14,234**

Includes a 491 kg (1,082.5 lbm) Sterling Radioisotope Generator. Note: Polar location (> 87° latitude)

Habitat All LOX/CH$_4$ Mass Breakdown, Lander Performs LOI				
Subsystem	LSAM Descent Stage		LSAM Surface Habitat	
	lbm	kg	lbm	kg
1.0 Structure	3,007	1,364	1,964	891
2.0 Protection	313	142	284	129
3.0 Propulsion	4,469	2,027	370	168
4.0 Power	675	306	2,110	957*
5.0 Control	203	92	0	0
6.0 Avionics	152	69	758	344
7.0 Environment	273	124	4,213	1,911
8.0 Other	1,299	589	428	194
9.0 Growth	2,077	942	2,024	918
Dry Mass w/Growth	**12,468**	**5,655**	**12,151**	**5,512**
10.0 Non-cargo	4,367	1,981	2,806	1,273
11.0 Cargo	0	0	13054	5,921
Inert Mass	**16,835**	**7,636**	**28,011**	**12,706**
12.0 Non-propellant	209	95	3,499	1,587
13.0 Propellant	55,047	24,969	269	122
Gross Mass	**72,091**	**32,700**	**31,779**	**14,415**

Includes a 491 kg (1,082.5 lbm) Sterling Radioisotope Generator. Note: Polar location (> 87° latitude)

Langley Research Center Unpressurized Crew Transport with Surface Habitat: 0605-LLPS-LaRC-2

This was a two-stage lander that incorporated unique, dockable rear-entry space suits for a crew of four on an unpressurized ascent stage. The ascent stage mission was designed for a nominal surface stay time of 7 days, and a return payload capacity of 100 kg (220 lbm).

Descent Stage	
Power	The descent stage carried oxygen-hydrogen fuel cells for primary power; total peak power required by descent stage (when active) = 4.0 kW; total peak power required by descent stage (when inactive) = 500 W.
Propulsion	The propulsion system had three LOX/LH$_2$ descent engines that operated at an Isp of 459.7 sec. The engine thrust was 31.1 kN (7,000 lb). Oxygen boil-off was estimated to be at 1.2% per month and hydrogen boil-off was estimated to be at 4.3% per month. Descent delta-v: 1,900 m/s (6,233 ft/s)
Structures	The baseline primary structural material was aluminum 2024 or similar. There were two oxidizer tanks/four fuel tanks; The landing structures made up 3.3% of the total mass to be landed.
Environmental Control and Life Support System	Standard ECLSS in pressurized habitat; 13.2 m^3 (466 ft^3) total habitable volume; 3.3 m^3 (116.5 ft^3) habitable volume per crew member; 14.2 m^3 (500 ft^3) total pressurized volume.
Down Payload	500 kg (1,100 lbm)
Surface Stay Time	7 days
Nominal Descent and Low Lunar Orbit Loiter Duration	7 days
Low Earth Orbit Loiter Duration	95 days
Guidance Navigation & Control	RCS Cluster (x4)

Ascent Stage	
Power	Ascent stage carried Li-ion batteries for primary power during ascent; total peak power required by ascent stage = 1.0 kW
Propulsion	There were four NTO/MMH ascent engines rated for operation at an Isp of 332.5 sec. The propulsion system provided a thrust of 11.1 kN (2,500 lb). Thrusters were initially gimballed out to avoid damaging the habitat (which could be reused on a future mission or as part of an outpost). Ascent delta-v: 1,889 m/s (6,197 ft/s)
Structures	Aluminum 2024 or similar. There were two oxidizer tanks/two fuel tanks.
Environmental Control and Life Support System	Nominal life support was to be provided by the Extravehicular Activity (EVA) suits.
Up Payload	100 kg (220 lb)
Surface Stay Time	7 days
Nominal Ascent Duration	3 hours

Mass Breakdown				
Subsystem	**Descent Stage**		**Ascent Stage**	
	lbm	**kg**	**lbm**	**kg**
1.0 Structure	2,535	1,150	507	230
2.0 Protection	132	60	44	20
3.0 Propulsion	1,653	750	1,036	470
4.0 Power	1,389	630	309	140
5.0 Control	0	0	44	20
6.0 Avionics	176	80	794	360
7.0 Environment	1,631	740	375	170
8.0 Other	970	440	882	400
9.0 Growth	1,852	840	970	440
Dry Mass w/Growth	**10,340**	**4,690**	**4,960**	**2,250**
10.0 Non-cargo	2,183	990	1,102	500
11.0 Cargo	1,102	500	0	0
Inert Mass	**13,625**	**6,180**	**6,063**	**2,750**
12.0 Non-propellant	2,094	950	44	20
13.0 Propellant	15,212	6,900	6,129	2,780
Gross Mass	**30,931**	**14,030**	**12,236**	**5,550**

Langley Research Center Horizontal, 1-Stage Crew Lander: 0605-LLPS-LaRC-3

This concept was a single-stage crew lander with an underslung horizontal crew transport module, and provided propulsion for descent from orbit, ascent, and docking with the Crew Exploration Vehicle (CEV) (no LOI). It was capable of transporting four crew and supporting four EVAs, and it could remain on the surface in active mode for over 4.7 days, or in passive mode for 180 days.

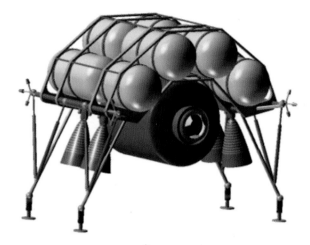

Descent Stage	
Power	4.5 kW LSAM average power, Proton Exchange Membrane (PEM) fuel cells, hydrogen reactant storage, power distribution cables, remote control units, 1 x 28 Vdc distribution bus
Propulsion	There were 4 x 30,265.3 N (6,804 lbf) pressure-fed LOX/methane OMS engines that operated at an Isp of 350 sec. The Reaction Control System (RCS) had 16 x 445.2 N (100 lbf) LOX/methane engines that operated at an Isp of 315 sec. The cylindrical Al 7075 graphite-wrapped LOX and methane tanks were pressured to 1,896.1 kPa (275 psi). Delta-v (OMS/RCS): 3,772/27 m/s (12,374/87 ft/s) Propellant: Integrated O_2/methane OMS/RCS Isp: 350.3/315 sec Number of OMS Engines: 4 Engine Length: 2.02 m (6.64 ft) Engine Exit Diameter: 1.06 m (3.49 ft) Cant Angle: 10° Thrust per Engine / T/W_eff: 30.2 kN (6.8 klbf)/0.32 (Earth g's) Chamber Pressure: 1,206.6 kPa (175 psi) Area Ratio: 70 Throttle: 29.0%
Telecommunications	S-band and Ultra-High Frequency (UHF) were the telecommunications media used to transmit information including voice, video, and data. The K-band was used to transmit high-definition television video.
Thermal	65.5 kPa (9.5 psi) cabin pressure with 30% O_2, regenerative CO_2/moisture removal system (amine bed), atmosphere monitoring, fire detection and suppression, gaseous nitrogen storage, potable/waste water storage; avionics and crew cabin conditioning with cold plates and cabin/external heat exchangers, water evaporator for peak loads, 60% propylene glycol/40% H_2O single-phase fluid loop, radiators
Structures	The following structures were a part of the descent stage: Al 7075 pressure vessel, LIDS, window and docking hatch, EVA hatch. The primary structure and landing gear were composed of graphite-epoxy. Pressurized Volume: 29.2 m³ (1,031 ft³) Stage Diameter: 7.5 m (24.6 ft) Stage Length: 4.9 m (16.0 ft) Tank Pressure: 1,896.1 kPa (275 psi) Tank Diameter (ea.): 1.6 m (5.24 ft) Fuel Tank Length: 2.57 m (8.43 ft) Oxidizer Tank Length: 3.39 m (11.13 ft)

Descent Stage (continued)	
Guidance, Navigation & Control	Flight computers, data recorders, displays and switch panels, space navigation/INS/star trackers, LADAR, health sensors and monitoring, altimetry and surface topography mapping
Environmental Control and Life Support System	The cabin design pressure was 65.5 kPa (9.5 psi) consisting of 30% O_2. Other features/systems of the ECLSS were a regenerative CO_2/moisture removal system (amine bed); atmospheric monitoring; fire detection and suppression; avionics and crew cabin conditioning with cold plates; cabin/external heat exchangers; water evaporation for peak loads; a 60% propylene glycol/40% H_2O single-phase fluid loop, and radiators.
Total Mass in Low Earth Orbit	37,848 kg (83,441 lbm) Dry Mass Growth: 20%
Active/Passive Duration	4.7 days/180 days
Down Payload	The crew plus 500 kg (1,102.3 lbm) of science equipment
Major Maneuvers	Descent, ascent and docking with the CEV Staging Orbit: 100 by 100 km (54 by 54 nmi)
Extravehicular Activity Mode	Full cabin depress
Crew Size/Number of Extravehicular Activities	4/4
Ascent Stage	
Up Payload	The crew plus 100 kg (220.5 lbm) of lunar samples

Mass Breakdown		
Subsystem	lbm	kg
1.0 Structure	5,432	2,464
2.0 Protection	234	106
3.0 Propulsion	5,340	2,422
4.0 Power	1,219	553
5.0 Control	0	0
6.0 Avionics	1,310	594
7.0 Environment	1,713	777
8.0 Other	1,967	892
9.0 Growth	3,441	1,561
Dry Mass w/Growth	20,656	9,369
10.0 Non-cargo	4,156	1,885
11.0 Cargo	1,102	500
Inert Mass	25,914	11,754
12.0 Non-propellant	1,327	602
13.0 Propellant	56,200	25,492
Gross Mass	83,441	37,848

Langley Research Center Horizontal, 1-Stage Cargo Lander: 0605-LLPS-LaRC-4

The Horizontal, 1-Stage Lander is a concept that is optimized for lunar surface cargo delivery. The horizontal design facilitates crew egress/ingress and cargo unloading/deployment (i.e., minimizes travel distance to the lunar surface). Additionally, analysis performed jointly with the Jet Propulsion Laboratory demonstrated that this lander configuration is uniquely suited for the deployment of a 9 mt (10 t) surface fission power system proposed for a permanently crewed lunar outpost. Another benefit of the horizontal lander configuration is that the LOX/CH$_4$ propellant tank location provides inherent radiation protection during in-space transit and on the lunar surface. Similar to several other lander concepts, the EDS performs the LOI maneuver sequence for this lander concept.

Descent/Ascent Stage	
Power	The descent stage was powered by PEM fuel cells, which provided 2.0 kW LSAM average power.
Propulsion	The propulsion system had 4 x 30,265.3 N (6,804 lbf) pressure-fed LOX/methane OMS engines that were rated for operation at an Isp of 350 sec. The RCS had 16 x 445.2 N (100 lbf) LOX/methane engines rated for operation at an Isp of 315 sec. The system had cylindrical Al 7075 graphite-wrapped LOX and methane tanks pressurized to 1,896.1 kPa (275 psi) in addition to having a shared fuel cell/RCS/OMS and LOX storage. Delta-v (OMS/RCS): 1,900 / 17 m/s (6,234/54 ft/s) Propellant: Integrated O$_2$/methane OMS/RCS Isp: 350.3/315 sec Number of OMS Engines: 4 Engine Length: 2.02 m (6.64 ft) Engine Exit Diameter: 1.06 m (3.49 ft) Cant Angle: 10° Thrust per Engine / Thrust-to-Weight (T/W)_eff: 30.2 kN (6.8 klbf)/0.21 (Earth g's) Chamber Pressure: 1206.6 kPa (175 psi) Area Ratio: 70 Throttle: 44.7%
Telecommunications	S-band UHF are used to transmit voice, data, and video
Thermal	Cold plates, heat exchangers, water evaporator, 60% propylene glycol/40% H$_2$O single-phase fluid loop; Multi-Layer Insulation (MLI)
Structures	The primary structure was composed of graphite epoxy. Stage Diameter: 7.5 m (24.6 ft) Stage Length: 4.9 m (16.0 ft) Tank Pressure: 1,896.1 kPa (275 psi) Tank Diameter (ea.): 1.6 m (5.24 ft) Fuel Tank Length: 2.57 m (8.43 ft) Oxidizer Tank Length: 3.39 m (11.13 ft)
Guidance Navigation & Control	Made up of flight computers, space navigation/INS/star trackers, altimetry and surface topography mapping and health sensors
Environmental Control and Life Support System	Crew cabin conditioning was to be achieved using cold plates and cabin/external heat exchangers.
Total Mass in Low Earth Orbit	Maximum: 58,862 kg (129,768 lbm) Nominal: 39,062 kg (86,117 lbm) Dry Mass Growth: 20%
Down Payload	Maximum: 26,013 kg (57,349 lbm) Nominal: 15,000 kg (33,069 lbm)
Major Maneuvers	Descent and landing Staging Orbit: 100 by 100 km (54 by 54 nmi)

Langley Research Center Dual-Stage, Split Habitat Lander: 0605-LLPS-LaRC-5

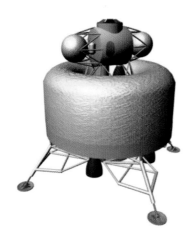 

A dual-stage, split habitat lander reduced system mass through use of a nested, toroidal descent stage propellant tank. Features: minimum volume ascent stage designed to reduce lander gross mass; "front porch" designed to facilitate crew egress/ingress; toroidal tank designed to provide inherent radiation protection and minimize thermal and power variances; ability to support four crew members for 7 days; lunar lander performed LOI.

Descent Stage	
Power	PEM fuel cells provided 4.5 kW of average power to the descent stage.
Propulsion	The propulsion system had 4 x 57,826.9 N (13,000 lbf) pump-fed LOX/LH$_2$ OMS engines rated for operation at an Isp of 459 sec. The RCS had LOX/LH$_2$ engines rated for operation at an Isp of 459 sec.
Telecommunications	S-band and UHF were the frequency bands used for communicating information, including voice, video, and data.

Ascent Stage	
Propulsion	The ascent stage had a 1 x 19,572.1 N (4,400 lbf) pressure-fed NTO/MMH OMS engine rated for operation at an Isp of 312 sec. The RCS had 16 x 222.6 N (50 lbf) NTO/MMH engines rated to operate at an Isp of 312 sec.
Structures	There was a nested LOX/LH$_2$ toroidal tank with other structural features including an Al 7075 pressure vessel, LIDS, a window and docking hatch.

	Crew Lander	Cargo Lander
Total Vehicle Mass	41,862 kg (92,290 lbm)	47,601 kg (104,942 lbm)
Total Mass to Lunar Surface	17,940 kg (39,551 lbm)	24,412 kg (53,819 lbm)
Total Cargo to Lunar Surface	2,300 kg (5,060 lbm)	17,605 kg (38,812 lbm)
Fuel Type	LOX/LH$_2$	LOX/LH$_2$
Thrust per Engine	13 klbf	13 klbf
Shroud Diameter	7.5 m (24.6 ft)	7.5 m (24.6 ft)

Langley Research Center Descent Assisted Split Habitat Lander: 0605-LLPS-LaRC-6

The Langley Research Center (LaRC) Descent Assisted Split Habitat (DASH) Lander was a split habitat crew lander that used a descent assisting Retro Module and was reconfigurable to accommodate a dual habitat or cargo mission. The split habitat design facilitated crew egress/ingress and cargo unloading deployment. It supported four crew members for 7 days. The total habitable volume was 32 m³ (1,130 ft³). The Retro Module performed an LOI maneuver of 1,100 m/s (3,608.9 ft/s) and a partial descent delta-v of 1,700 m/s (5,577.4 ft/s). After staging, the lander performed the remaining 200 m/s (656 ft/s) of terminal descent and the complete 2,000 m/s (6,562 ft/s) ascent to LLO. The suit port concept for EVA eliminated the need for an airlock and mitigated lunar dust/habitable volume contamination issues.

Descent Stage	
Power	PEM fuel cells provided an average power of 4.5 kW to the descent stage.
Propulsion	The propulsion system had 3 x 111,205.4 N (25,000 lbf) pump-fed RL-10B-2 LOX/LH₂ engines that operated at an Isp of 459.8 sec.
Structures	The descent stage included an Al 7075 pressure vessel, LIDS, a window and docking hatch, a suit port concept for EVA, cabin design pressure 65.5 kPa (9.5 psi); 2 x ~1.5 m³ (54 ft³) unpressurized cargo bays.
Ascent Stage	
Propulsion	The ascent stage had 4 x 14,457 N (3,250 lbf) pressure-fed NTO/MMH engines that operated at an Isp of 319 sec. The RCS had 16 x 222.6 N (50 lbf) NTO/MMH engines.

Mass Breakdown						
Subsystem	Payload Module		Lander Module		Retro Module	
	lbm	kg	lbm	kg	lbm	kg
1.0 Structure	2,709	1,229	996	452	1,184	537
2.0 Protection	132	60	172	78	0	0
3.0 Propulsion	0	0	1,612	731	4,504	2,043
4.0 Power	1,581	717	1,041	472	284	129
5.0 Control	0	0	0	0	0	0
6.0 Avionics	176	80	977	443	501	227
7.0 Environment	2,123	963	320	145	0	0
8.0 Other	1,678	761	1,056	479	677	307
9.0 Growth	1,680	762	1,235	560	1,102	500
Dry Mass w/Growth	10,079	4,572	7,409	3,360	8,252	3,743
10.0 Non-cargo	1,459	662	750	340	3,256	1,477
11.0 Cargo	1,933	877	220	100	0	0
Inert Mass	13,471	6,111	8,379	3,800	11,508	5,220
12.0 Non-propellant	1,605	728	15	7	0	0
13.0 Propellant	0	0	9,740	4,418	54,717	24,819
Gross Mass	15,076	6,839	18,134	8,225	66,225	30,039

Glenn Research Center Split Habitat Lander: 0605-LLPS-GRC-1

The Glenn Research Center (GRC) Split Habitat Lander performed capture and most of the de-orbit burn by a disposable single crew/cargo stage, and used the spent stage as an impactor. The Split Habitat put the Sortie Habitat and Cargo on the bottom for ready surface access, leaving the Crew Taxi on top. A 9 m (30 ft) pressurized crew tunnel, used only at the beginning and end of the sortie mission, facilitated crew transfer between the Taxi and Habitat. This lander combined the best of the baseline mission with the split lander configuration.

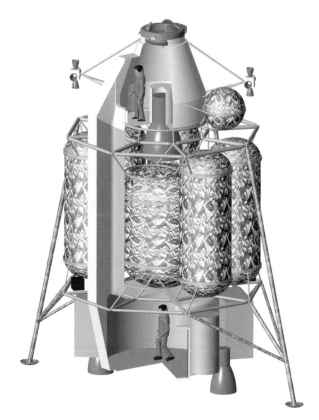

STAGING

Descent Stage: Performs lunar orbit capture with descent stage, then descent stage performs descent burn.

Ascent Taxi Landed by Descent Stage: Crew access of Sortie Habitat by pressurized tunnel.

Descent Stage: LOX/LH$_2$ propellants and fuel cells for power (with 95-day LEO loiter and zero boil-off). Cargo variant concept developed using LOX/LH$_2$ and fuel cells (no 95-day LEO loiter).

Ascent Stage (Crew Taxi) Trades: (1) MMH/NTO and fuel cells, (2) Pressurized LOX/CH$_4$ and fuel cells, (3) Pumped LOX/CH$_4$ and fuel cells.

Descent Stage	
Power	3-hr Li-ion batteries (4 batteries are redundant)
Propulsion	Throttleable LOX/CH$_4$ unconstrained, pump-fed
Thermal	Flash water evaporator
Structures	Aluminum Pressure Vessel
Guidance Navigation & Control	Scaled from Exploration System Architecture Study (ESAS)
Ascent Stage	
Power	Fuel Cells, 3 Li-ion batteries
Propulsion	LOX/LH$_2$ descent tanks and feed system only
Thermal	Radiators, Propylene-glycol/H$_2$O
Structures	Aluminum Truss
Guidance Navigation & Control	Scaled ESAS

Mass Breakdown				
Subsystem	**Descent Stage**		**Ascent Stage**	
	lbm	kg	lbm	kg
1.0 Structure	9,841	4,464	2,756	1,250
2.0 Protection	1,504	682	853	387
3.0 Propulsion	1,426	647	710	322
4.0 Power	710	322	1,087	493
5.0 Control	0	0	0	0
6.0 Avionics	611	277	1,109	503
7.0 Environment	2,522	1,144	1,067	484
8.0 Other	3,364	1,526	1,025	465
9.0 Growth	0	0	0	0
Dry Mass w/Growth	**19,978**	**9,062**	**8,607**	**3,904**
10.0 Non-cargo	Details Not Available			
11.0 Cargo				
Inert Mass	**82,323**	**37,341**	**16,883**	**7,658**

Glenn Research Center Split Lander: 0605-LLPS-GRC-2

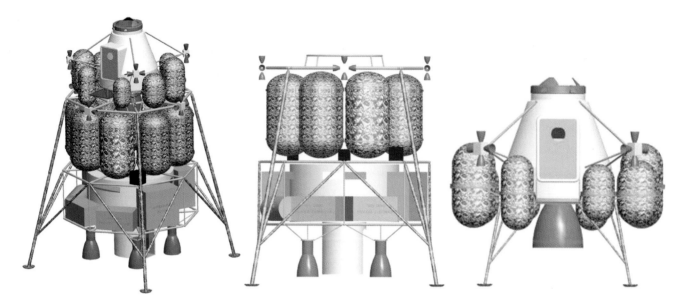

The GRC Split Lander was a single-stage cargo/habitat lander with a Crew Taxi. The lander provided excellent surface access for both crew and cargo by putting the cargo and the bottom of the cargo lander and landing crew directly on the surface in the Taxi. The ascent and descent stages separated before landing as follows:

(1) Descent stage performed lunar orbit capture for Taxi and CEV, landing cargo and habitat autonomously;

(2) Descent stage and Taxi stage separated in LLO, with the descent stage landing before the Taxi began flight; and

(3) Taxi stage descended and ascended for crew surface access. The fixed descent stage (cargo/habitat), with a 95-day LEO loiter with zero boil-off, used LOX/LH$_2$ propellants for power. Ascent stage (crew taxi) trades, with 95-day LEO loiter, and zero boil-off, included:

A. MMH/NTO Solar Array/Battery

B. Pressurized LOX/CH$_4$ Solar Array/Battery

C. Pumped LOX/CH$_4$ Solar Array/Battery

D. LOX/H$_2$ and fuel cells. Cargo variant concept developed using LOX/LH$_2$ and fuel cells (no 95-day LEO loiter).

Descent Stage	
Power	Fuel cells, 3 Li-ion batteries
Propulsion	LOX/LH$_2$ descent tanks and feed system only
Thermal	Radiators, Propylene-glycol/H$_2$O
Structures	Aluminum truss
Guidance, Navigation & Control	Scaled from ESAS
Ascent Stage	
Power	3-hr Li-ion batteries (four batteries, one redundant), fuel cells provided power to the ascent stage.
Propulsion	Throttleable LOX/LH$_2$ unconstrained, pressure fed
Thermal	Flash water evaporator
Structures	Aluminum pressure vessel
Guidance Navigation & Control	Scaled from ESAS lander concepts

Mass Breakdown						
Subsystem	Descent Stage		Discarded Stage		Ascent Stage	
	lbm	kg	lbm	kg	lbm	kg
1.0 Structure	7,758	3,519	1,303	591	2,652	1,203
2.0 Protection	1,321	599	234	106	615	279
3.0 Propulsion	1,836	833	0	0	710	322
4.0 Power	710	322	0	0	710	322
5.0 Control	0	0	0	0	0	0
6.0 Avionics	1,351	613	185	84	1,138	516
7.0 Environment	2,465	1,118	121	55	996	452
8.0 Other	2,862	1,298	999	453	1,243	564
9.0 Growth	0	0	0	0	0	0
Dry Mass w/Growth	**18,303**	**8,302**	**2,842**	**1,289**	**8,064**	**3,658**
10.0 Non-cargo	Details Not Available					
11.0 Cargo						
Inert Mass	**71,492**	**32,428**	**13,506**	**6,126**	**14,202**	**6,442**

Glenn Research Center Split Descent Lander: 0605-LLPS-GRC-3

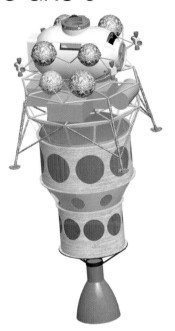

The GRC Split Descent Lander featured propellant tanks on the top with the habitat/cargo and airlock below – it could have also incorporated a tunnel or the ability to lower down or tilt for surface access.

Split Descent Stages:

The Lunar Capture and Descent Stage (LCADS) performed lunar orbit capture and some portion of descent. The LSAM performed the remainder of descent and all of ascent with the ascent stage.

Baseline Concept for Ascent Stage: MMH/NTO propellants and fuel cells for power (with 95-day LEO loiter and zero boil-off).

Trades Conducted on Ascent Stage:

- MMH/NTO with fuel cells
- MMH/NTO with solar array/battery
- Pressurized LOX/CH_4 with fuel cells
- Pressurized LOX/CH_4 with solar array/battery
- Pumped LOX/CH_4 with solar array

Descent Stage	
Power	Four solar arrays, three Li-ion batteries
Propulsion	LOX/CH_4 descent tanks and feed system only LCADS Propulsion: LOX/LH_2, zero boil-off, all lunar capture, 3/4 lunar descent
Thermal	Radiators, Propylene-glycol/H_2O
Structures	Aluminum Truss
Guidance Navigation & Control	none

Ascent Stage	
Power	3-hr Li-ion batteries (four batteries, one redundant)
Propulsion	Throttleable LOX/CH_4 unconstrained, pump fed
Thermal	Flash water evaporator
Structures	Aluminum pressure vessel
Guidance Navigation & Control	Scaled from ESAS

Mass Breakdown				
Subsystem	Descent Stage		Ascent Stage	
	lbm	kg	lbm	kg
1.0 Structure	2,604	1,181	4,652	2,110
2.0 Protection	474	215	1,144	519
3.0 Propulsion	0	0	710	322
4.0 Power	1,537	697	1,120	508
5.0 Control	0	0	0	0
6.0 Avionics	0	0	1,138	516
7.0 Environment	941	427	2,544	1,154
8.0 Other	1,537	697	1,124	510
9.0 Growth	0	0	0	0
Dry Mass w/Growth	7,093	3,217	12,432	5,639
10.0 Non-cargo	Details Not Available			
11.0 Cargo				
Inert Mass	17,659	8,010	23,528	10,672

Goddard Space Flight Center Ascent-Airlock Lander: 0605-LLPS-GFSC-1

Sortie Configuration

This configuration featured an ascent stage that was to be used as an airlock, and cargo was to be unloaded by hand. In preparation for ascent, the airlock/ascent stage hatch was sealed and EVA suits were discarded, with 15 mt (16.5 t) left on the lunar surface.

Key Features:

A. Modular airlock
B. Simplified ascent stage
C. Compact lander
D. Maximized landed mass
E. Extended Apollo concept

Dimensions	
Descent Stage/Sortie Mission	
Unpressurized Structure	Graphite epoxy composite; Volume = 88.9 m³ (3,139 ft³)
Habitat Pressure Vessel	Volume = 23.8 m³ (840 ft³); Area = 47.47 m² (511 ft²)
Ascent Stage	
Pressure Vessel Structure	Al-Li 2090, 9.5 psi internal pressure; Volume = 8.0 m³ (282 ft³); Area = 22.2 m² (239 ft²)
Windows	Double-paned fused silica; 0.5 m² (5.4 ft²)
Docking Adapter Hatch	81-cm (32-in.) diameter; Volume = 0.083 m³ (2.9 ft³)
Umbilical and Servicing Panels	Interfaces for launch prep; Volume = 0.061 m³ (2.1 ft³)

Mass Breakdown				
Subsystem	Descent Stage/Sortie Mission		Ascent Stage	
	lbm	kg	lbm	kg
1.0 Structure	4,260	1,932	984	446
2.0 Protection	194	88	25	11
3.0 Propulsion	4,936	2,239	1,814	823
4.0 Power	1,032	468	252	114
5.0 Control	201	91	0	0
6.0 Avionics	674	306	619	281
7.0 Environment	2,467	1,119	522	237
8.0 Other	1,411	640	842	382
9.0 Growth	3,035	1,377	1,012	459
Dry Mass w/Growth	18,210	8,260	6,070	2,753
10.0 Non-cargo	3,751	1,701	780	354
11.0 Cargo	10,261	4,654	220	100
Inert Mass	32,222	14,615	7,070	3,207
12.0 Non-propellant	1,071	486	90	41
13.0 Propellant	54,467	24,706	4,287	1,945
Gross Mass	87,760	39,807	11,447	5,193

Goddard Space Flight Center Swing Habitat: 0605-LLPS-GSFC-2

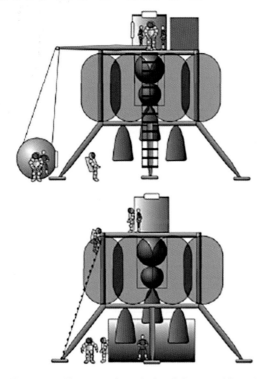

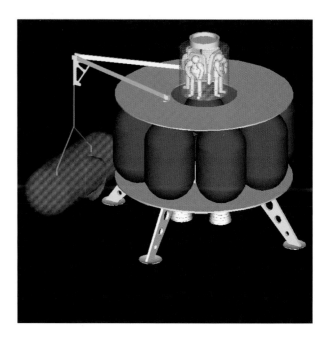

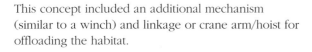

Habitat concept with crane arm in use (top), and when stowed (bottom).

This concept included an additional mechanism (similar to a winch) and linkage or crane arm/hoist for offloading the habitat.

The crane arm was driven up via a ball screw mechanism at the base of each leg, and was stowed just above the habitat for initial launch. It also protected the habitat during mating with the CEV.

Dimensions	
Descent Stage/Sortie Mission	
Unpressurized Structure	Graphite epoxy composite; Volume = 88.9 m³ (3,139 ft³)
Habitat Pressure Vessel	Volume = 23.8 m³ (840 ft³); Area = 47.47 m² (511 ft²)
Ascent Stage	
Pressure Vessel Structure	Al-Li 2090, 9.5 psi internal pressure; Volume = 8.0 m³ (282 ft³); Area = 22.2 m² (239 ft²)
Windows	Double-paned fused silica; 0.5 m² (5.4 ft²)
Docking Adapter Hatch	81-cm (32-in.) diameter; Volume = 0.083 m³ (2.9 ft³)
Umbilical and Servicing Panels	Interfaces for launch prep; Volume = 0.061 m³ (2.1 ft³)

Mass Breakdown				
Subsystem	Descent Stage/Sortie Mission		Ascent Stage	
	lbm	kg	lbm	kg
1.0 Structure	4,976	2,257	983	446
2.0 Protection	194	88	24	11
3.0 Propulsion	4,936	2,239	1,814	823
4.0 Power	1,032	468	251	114
5.0 Control	201	91	0	0
6.0 Avionics	675	306	619	281
7.0 Environment	2,467	1,119	668	303
8.0 Other	1,521	690	842	382
9.0 Growth	3,199	1,451	1,041	472
Dry Mass w/Growth	19,201	8,709	6,242	2,832
10.0 Non-cargo	3,492	1,584	780	354
11.0 Cargo	9,356	4,244	220	100
Inert Mass	32,049	14,537	7,242	3,286
12.0 Non-propellant	1,071	486	90	41
13.0 Propellant	54,467	24,706	4,288	1,945
Gross Mass	87,587	39,729	11,620	5,272

Goddard Space Flight Center Suit² Tubelock: 0605-LLPS-GSFC-3

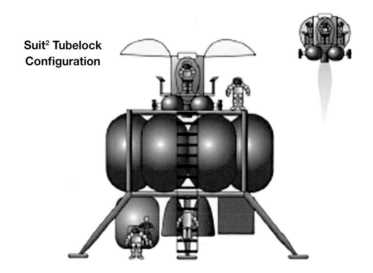

Suit² Tubelock Configuration

Key features included a minimal ascent stage and a suit lock/airlock, based on an Orlan or Krechet suit. Although it was possible to use the ascent stage as lunar transport, separable ascent and lander modules maximized the flexibility of landed elements and minimized damage to the landed element.

This configuration utilized a Tube Ascent Stage with shields to protect the crew. The habitat, with suit locks, allowed the crew to move back and to the ascent stage from the habitat, leaving ~15 mt (16.5 t) on the lunar surface.

Dimensions	
Descent Stage/Sortie Mission	
Habitat Pressure Vessel	Volume = 23.8 m³ (840 ft³); Area = 47.47 m² (511 ft²)
Ascent Stage	
Pressure Vessel Structure	Al-Li 2090, 9.5 psi internal pressure; Volume = 8.0 m³ (282 ft³); Area = 22.2 m² (239 ft²)
Windows	Double-paned fused silica; 0.5 m² (5.4 ft²)
Docking Adapter Hatch	81-cm (32-in.) diameter; Volume = 0.083 m³ (2.9 ft³)
Umbilical and Servicing Panels	Interfaces for launch prep; Volume = 0.061 m³ (2.1 ft³)

Mass Breakdown				
Subsystem	**Descent Stage/Sortie Mission**		**Ascent Stage**	
	lbm	**kg**	**lbm**	**kg**
1.0 Structure	4,857	2,203	470	213
2.0 Protection	194	88	25	11
3.0 Propulsion	4,936	2,239	1,814	823
4.0 Power	1,032	468	252	114
5.0 Control	201	91	0	0
6.0 Avionics	674	306	619	281
7.0 Environment	2,434	1,104	702	318
8.0 Other	1,521	690	842	382
9.0 Growth	3,170	1,438	945	429
Dry Mass w/Growth	**19,019**	**8,627**	**5,669**	**2,571**
10.0 Non-cargo	3,311	1,502	960	436
11.0 Cargo	10,330	4,686	220	100
Inert Mass	**32,660**	**14,815**	**6,849**	**3,107**
12.0 Non-propellant	1,071	486	90	41
13.0 Propellant	54,467	24,706	4,070	1,846
Gross Mass	**88,198**	**40,007**	**11,009**	**4,994**

Goddard Space Flight Center Sky Crane: 0605-LLPS-1GSFC-4

In this configuration, the sky crane remained joined to the ascent stage, habitat, and toroidal fuel tank through the descent burn, with engines canted. At 100 m (328.1 ft), the sky crane lowered the habitat, ascent stage, and cargo to the surface, the 100 m (328.1 ft) tethers were cut, and the propulsion stage departed. The crew performed EVAs through an airlock. EVA suits were discarded when the crew returned to the ascent stage (15 mt [16.5 t] were left on surface). Key features included a minimal ascent stage and separable ascent and lander modules, which maximized flexibility of the landed elements. Additionally, landing structure mass was minimized, and assets were soft-landed.

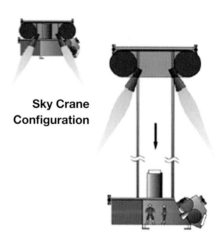

Sky Crane Configuration

Dimensions	
Descent Stage/Sortie Mission	
Unpressurized Structure	Graphite epoxy composite; Volume = 88.9 m³ (3,139 ft³)
Habitat Pressure Vessel	Volume = 23.8 m³ (840 ft³); Area = 47.47 m² (511 ft²)
Ascent Stage	
Pressure Vessel Structure	Al-Li 2090, 9.5 psi internal pressure; Volume = 8.0 m³ (282 ft³); Area = 22.2 m² (239 ft²)
Windows	Double-paned fused silica; 0.5 m² (5.4 ft²)
Docking Adapter Hatch	81 cm (32 in) diameter; Volume = 0.083 m³ (2.9 ft³)
Umbilical and Servicing Panels	Interfaces for launch prep; Volume = 0.061 m³ (2.1 ft³)

Mass Breakdown				
Subsystem	**Descent Stage/Sortie Mission**		**Ascent Stage**	
	lbm	kg	lbm	kg
1.0 Structure	5,047	2,289	984	446
2.0 Protection	194	88	25	11
3.0 Propulsion	4,936	2,239	1,814	823
4.0 Power	1,032	468	285	129
5.0 Control	201	91	0	0
6.0 Avionics	780	354	619	281
7.0 Environment	2,434	1,104	522	237
8.0 Other	567	257	842	382
9.0 Growth	3,038	1,378	1,018	462
Dry Mass w/Growth	**18,229**	**8,268**	**6,109**	**2,771**
10.0 Non-cargo	3,491	1,583	780	354
11.0 Cargo	10,442	4,736	220	100
Inert Mass	**32,162**	**14,587**	**7,109**	**3,225**
12.0 Non-propellant	1,071	486	90	41
13.0 Propellant	54,467	24,706	4,308	1,954
Gross Mass	**87,700**	**39,779**	**11,507**	**5,220**

Jet Propulsion Laboratory Option 1b Stack Lander: 0605-LLPS-JPL-1

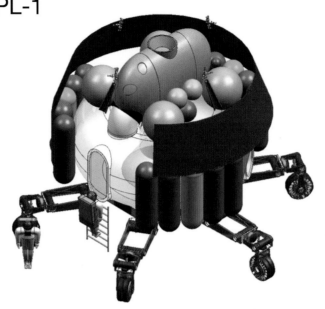

The Option 1b LSAM was comprised of an ascent stage, descent stage, and LOI Stage (LOIS). The ascent stage was a minimal volume structure (13.6 m³ [480.3 ft³] crew module) that housed the crew during descent and ascent. The descent stage included an annular habitat with cylindrical propellant tanks about its outer periphery, an axially mounted, gimballed RL-10 engine, and an ATHLETE mobility platform. The LOIS was a 7.5-m (24.6-ft) diameter propulsion stage with a restartable, modified RL-10 engine, which was jettisoned after performing the LOI burn and part of the descent burn. The habitat had an interior volume of 56 m³ (1,977.6 ft³), a rooftop connection to the ascent stage and three side ports, one of which was an airlock exit. The descent stage engine extended into the lower portion of the load-bearing habitat core, with its nozzle projected 0.8 m (2.6 ft) below the floor. The ascent stage engine extended 0.9 m (3 ft) into the upper part of the core. A refractory shield protected the Habitat roof and core. The ATHLETE mobility system was a hexagonal package ~6 m (19.7 ft) across and 0.5 m (1.6 ft) high in its folded configuration. With legs extended for walking, it lifted the habitat base 3.3 m (10.8 ft) above the surface. Restowable ultra flex arrays provided power.

Descent Stage	
Power	Main power was provided to the descent stage by ultra-flex solar arrays and was load leveled by large Li-ion secondary batteries. The arrays could retract and shield themselves during ascent stage firing. A small regenerative fuel cell provided power throughout the lunar night.
Propulsion	The descent stage performed the LOI burn of 1,100 m/s (3,608.9 ft/s) for the entire CEV/LSAM stack and the descent/landing burn of 1,900 m/s (6,233.6 ft/s) for the LSAM stack. The ascent stage performed the ascent burn, rendezvous, docking, and disposal of 1850 m/s (6,069.6 ft/s). It contained RL-10 LOX-LH₂ pump driven engine(s), which were throttleable from 10% to 100% of nominal thrust, and had electric gimbal(s) drives. The RL 10 Isp was 460 seconds and Mixture Ratio (MR) was 6 seconds. Tanks were sized assuming 25 days of boil-off (1,750 kg [3,858.1 lbm]). LOX tank pressurization helium was stored cryogenically in the LH₂ tanks. All tanks were to be made of 2219 aluminum.
Thermal	Cryogenic propellants (LOX/LH₂) provided passive thermal control using insulation and an MLI boil-off. A sun/Earth shade was used to minimize boil-off during LEO (assumed 25 days). Thermal radiators for Environmental Control and Life Support (ECLS) and fuel cell heat exchangers were mounted on the descent stage.
Guidance Navigation & Control	Radar altimeter provided altitude and horizontal and vertical velocity relative to the surface. LN-200S and Mars Exploration Rover (MER) heritage navigation and hazard cams provided surface navigation and hazard avoidance. A gimbal provided both pitch and yaw control. Thrusters on the ascent stage provided roll control. Each leg carried a stereo pair of MER heritage navigation cameras. Hazard cams were used to see obstacles while mobile.

Ascent Stage	
Power	A primary Li-CFx battery was to be used to support a 3-hour ascent and docking phase. Minimal charge control electronics were used to minimize mass.
Thermal	The outer surface was covered with foam insulation in addition to a 60-layer MLI. MMH/NTO was space storable (+10 °C). Internal thermal control elements were fluid lines, pumps, cold plates, heat exchangers, instrumentation/controls, fluids, fluid evaporator, a water tank and a feed system made up of radiators mounted to the descent stage. Thrusters on the ascent stage provided torque control and translation capability.
Guidance Navigation & Control	Star trackers and gyros for stellar inertial attitude determination, accelerometers for position determination during descent and ascent, scanning LIght Detection And Ranging (LIDAR) for rendezvous (couple of kilometers to tens of meters), and a wide angle camera used during terminal rendezvous.

Mass Breakdown						
Subsystem	**LOI Stage**		**Descent Stage**		**Ascent Stage**	
	lbm	**kg**	**lbm**	**kg**	**lbm**	**kg**
1.0 Structure	2,950	1,338	7,161	3,248	3,051	1,384
2.0 Protection	1,250	567	1,224	555	205	93
3.0 Propulsion	3,128	1,419	1,404	637	1,140	517
4.0 Power	448	203	1,660	753	511	232
5.0 Control	150	68	0	0	0	0
6.0 Avionics	15	7	379	172	452	205
7.0 Environment	0	0	2,884	1,308	743	337
8.0 Other	1,047	475	3,314	1,503	913	414
9.0 Growth	1,797	815	3,247	1,473	1,378	625
Dry Mass w/Growth	**10,785**	**4,892**	**21,273**	**9,649**	**8,393**	**3,807**
10.0 Non-cargo	0	0	1,230	558	560	254
11.0 Cargo	0	0	1,102	500	1,041	472
Inert Mass	**10,785**	**4,892**	**23,605**	**10,707**	**9,994**	**4,533**
12.0 Non-propellant	0	0	904	410	90	41
13.0 Propellant	49,657	22,524	9,797	4,444	8,852	4,015
Gross Mass	**60,442**	**27,416**	**34,306**	**15,561**	**18,936**	**8,589**

Jet Propulsion Laboratory Option 1c Side-by-Side: 0605-LLPS-JPL-2

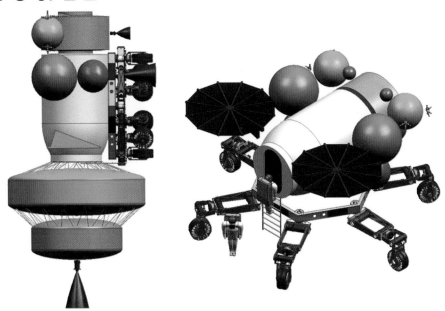

The Option 1c LSAM was comprised of an ascent stage, a descent stage, and LOIS. The ascent stage was a minimal volume structure (13.6 m³ [480.3 ft³]) that housed the crew during descent and ascent. The descent stage included a cylindrical habitat with spherical propellant tanks, a gimbaled RL-10 engine, and an ATHLETE mobility platform. The LOIS was a 7.5-m (24.6-ft) diameter propulsion stage with a restartable, modified RL-10 engine, which was jettisoned after performing the LOI insertion and part

of the descent burn. The habitat had an interior volume of 22 m³ (776.9 ft³), a side connection to the ascent stage, and an airlock at the opposite side. The descent stage engine was mounted below the habitat core. The ATHLETE mobility system was a hexagonal package ~6 m (19.7 ft) across and 0.5 m (1.6 ft) high in its folded configuration. With legs extended for walking, it was designed to lift the habitat base 3.3 m (10.8 ft) above the surface.

Descent Stage	
Power	Main power was provided to the descent stage from two ultra-flex solar arrays that were load leveled by a large Li-ion secondary battery. The arrays could retract and shield themselves during ascent stage firing. Small regenerative fuel cell(s) provided power through the lunar night. The propellant tanks attached to the descent stage were used to store gaseous H_2 and O_2 for nighttime use at 1,379 to 2,757.9 kPa (200 to 400 psi). The power control system could have also been used to support cryo-cooling of propellant tanks during the LEO loiter phase.
Propulsion	The LOIS portion of the descent stage performed the LOI burn of 1,100 m/s (3,608.9 ft/s) for the entire CEV/LSAM stack, and the descent/landing burn of 1,900 m/s (6,233.6 ft/s) for the LSAM stack. Electric gimbal(s) drives were to be used, as well as RL 10 engines with an Isp of 460 sec and MR with an Isp of 6 sec. Tanks were sized assuming 25 days of boil-off (1,750 kg [3,858.1 lbm]). LOX tank pressurization helium was to be stored cryogenically in the LH_2 tanks. All tanks were to be made of 2219 aluminum.
Thermal	Cryogenic propellants – LOX/LH_2 passive thermal control using insulation and MLI, thermal isolating structure, and boil-off utilization. Sun/Earth shade minimized boil-off during LEO (assumed 25 days). Thermal radiators for ECLS and fuel cell heat exchangers were mounted on the descent stage.
Guidance Navigation & Control	The GN&C system had a radar altimeter that provided altitude, horizontal and vertical velocity relative to the surface, LN-200S and MER heritage navigation cams and hazard cams for surface navigation and hazard avoidance, and a gimbal for pitch and yaw control. In addition, there were thrusters in the ascent stage that provided roll control. Each leg carried a stereo pair of MER heritage navigation cameras to see obstacles while mobile.

Ascent Stage	
Power	Li-CFx primary batteries were used to support 3-hour ascent and docking phase. Minimal charge control electronics were used to minimize mass.
Propulsion	Contained one fixed 45,000 N (10,116 lbf) NTO-MMH main engine with an Isp of 317 sec at a MR of 1.65 and two branches of RCS thrusters, each containing eight 490 N (110 lbf) NTO-MMH thrusters, with an Isp of 300 sec at an MR of 1.65. The ascent stage RCS engines also provided attitude control during descent. The tanks were titanium.
Thermal	The outer surface was covered with foam insulation in addition to a 60-layer MLI. MMH/NTO was space storable (+10 °C). Internal thermal control elements included fluid lines, pumps, cold plates, heat exchangers, instrumentation/controls, fluids, fluid evaporator, water tank, and feed system (radiators were mounted to descent stage). The thrusters on the ascent stage provided control torque and translation capability.
Guidance Navigation & Control	The GN&C system included star trackers and gyros for stellar inertial attitude determination, accelerometers for position determination during descent and ascent, scanning LIDAR for rendezvous (couple of kilometers to tens of meters), and a wide-angle camera used during terminal rendezvous (tens of meters).

Jet Propulsion Laboratory Option 2 Habitank: 0605-LLPS-JPL-3

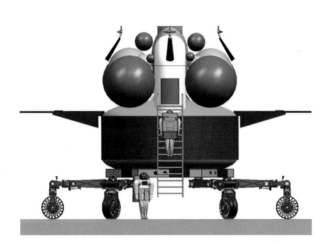
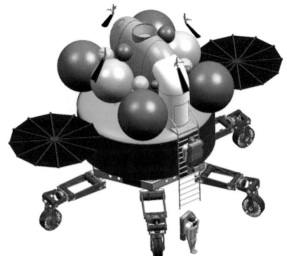

The Option 2 LSAM consisted of an ascent stage and a descent stage. The ascent stage was a minimal volume structure (13.6 m³ [480.3 ft³]) crew module plus a small hypergolic propulsion stage that housed the crew during descent and ascent. The ascent stage had a rooftop LIDS for docking with the CEV and an airlock mounted between the ascent stage and descent stage. The descent stage contained a large, cylindrical LH_2 tank with three LOX tanks above; an axially mounted, restartable, gimballed RL-10 engine; and an ATHLETE mobility platform. The descent stage engine performed both LOI and descent maneuvers. The ATHLETE was a hexagonal package ~6 m (19.7 ft) across and 0.5 m (1.6 ft) high in its folded configuration. With legs extended for landing and walking, it lifted the LH_2 tank 3.3 m (10.8 ft) above the surface. The LH_2 tank had a volume of 55.3 m³ (1,952.9 ft³) and was designed to serve as a habitat after venting its contents on the lunar surface. The "habitank" had a rooftop hatch for access to the ascent stage and three side hatches for cluster buildup.

Descent Stage	
Power	Main power was provided by two ultra-flex solar arrays and was load-leveled by a large Li-ion secondary battery. The arrays could retract and shield themselves during the ascent stage firing. A small regenerative fuel cell provided power through the lunar night. The propellant tanks were attached to the descent stage and were used to store gaseous phase H_2 and O_2 for nighttime use at 1,379 to 2,757.9 kPa (200 to 400 psi). The power control system could be used to support cryo-cooling of propellant tanks during LEO Loiter phase.
Propulsion	The descent stage performed the LOI burn for the entire CEV/LSAM stack at 1,100 m/s (3,608.9 ft/s) and the descent/landing burn of 1,900 m/s (6,233.6 ft/s) for the LSAM stack. The ascent stage performed the ascent burn, rendezvous, docking, and disposal of 1,850 m/s (6,069.6 ft/s). The propulsion system contained RL-10 LOX-LH_2 pump driven engine(s), which were throttleable from 10% to 100% of nominal thrust. Electric gimbal(s) drives were also used. The RL-10 was rated to operate at an Isp of 460 sec and MR of 6 sec. Tanks were sized assuming 25 days of boil-off (1,750 kg [3,858.1 lbm]). The LOX tank pressurization helium was stored cryogenically in the LH_2 tanks. All tanks were made of 2219 aluminum.
Thermal	Cryogenic propellants – LOX/LH_2 passive thermal control using insulation and MLI, thermal isolating structure, and boil-off utilization. There was a sun/Earth shade to minimize boil-off during LEO (assumed 25 days). Thermal radiators were used for ECLS and fuel cell heat exchangers were mounted on the descent stage.
Guidance Navigation & Control	The radar altimeter provided altitude and horizontal and vertical velocity relative to the surface, LN-200S and MER heritage navigation cams and hazard cams for surface navigation and hazard avoidance. The gimbal provided pitch and yaw control, and thrusters on the ascent stage provided roll control. Each leg carried a stereo pair of MER heritage navigation cameras. Hazard cams were used to see obstacles while mobile.

Ascent Stage	
Power	Three power bus architecture; the Li-CFx primary battery was used to support the 3-hour ascent and docking phase. Minimal charge control electronics were used to minimize mass.
Propulsion	The propulsion system contained one fixed 45,000 N (10,116 lbf) NTO-MMH main engine rated to operate at an Isp of 317 sec at an MR of 1.65 sec, and two branches of RCS thrusters, each containing eight 490 N (110 lbf) NTO-MMH thrusters with an Isp of 300 sec at an MR of 1.65 sec. The ascent stage RCS engines also provided attitude control during descent. The tanks were made of titanium.
Thermal	The outer surface was covered with foam insulation plus a 60-layer MLI. MMH/NTO was space storable (+10°C). Internal thermal control elements included fluid lines, pumps, cold plates, heat exchangers, instrumentation/controls, fluids, fluid evaporator, a water tank, and a feed system (the radiators were mounted to the descent stage). Thrusters on the ascent stage provided control torque and translation capability.
Guidance Navigation & Control	GN&C systems included star trackers and gyros that provided stellar inertial attitude determination, accelerometers for position determination during descent and ascent, scanning LIDAR for rendezvous (couple of kilometers to tens of meters), and a wide-angle camera used during terminal rendezvous (tens of meters).

Mass Breakdown				
Subsystem	**Descent Stage**		**Ascent Stage**	
	lbm	kg	lbm	kg
1.0 Structure	2,954	1,340	3,031	1,375
2.0 Protection	851	386	205	93
3.0 Propulsion	5,401	2,450	1,140	517
4.0 Power	2,048	929	527	239
5.0 Control	150	68	0	0
6.0 Avionics	379	172	452	205
7.0 Environment	2,132	967	743	337
8.0 Other	3,455	1,567	908	412
9.0 Growth	3,142	1,425	1,378	625
Dry Mass w/Growth	**20,512**	**9,304**	**8,384**	**3,803**
10.0 Non-cargo	1,358	616	560	254
11.0 Cargo	1,102	500	1,041	472
Inert Mass	**22,972**	**10,420**	**9,985**	**4,529**
12.0 Non-propellant	904	410	90	41
13.0 Propellant	52,415	23,775	8,852	4,015
Gross Mass	**76,291**	**34,605**	**18,927**	**8,585**

Jet Propulsion Laboratory Option 3 Sky Crane: 0605-LLPS-JPL-4

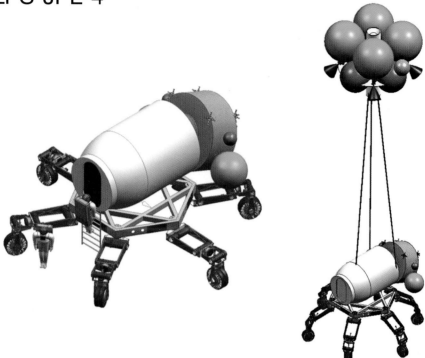

The Option 3 LSAM consists of an ascent stage, mobile habitat, and a sky crane stage. The ascent stage was a minimal volume structure (13.6 m³ [480.3 ft³]) used to house the crew during descent and ascent. The mobile habitat was a cylindrical crew station mounted on an ATHLETE mobility platform. The sky crane was a propulsion stage derived from the Mars Science Lab (MSL) concept, with four restartable new cryogenic engines and spherical tanks. It provided all of the propulsion for LOI, lander descent, hovering while lowering the lander to the lunar surface on cables, and disposal after lander release. The CEV docked with the lander/sky crane in LEO, and the sky crane performed the LOI burn. The crew entered the lander through a long tunnel. The lander/sky crane separated and the sky crane performed deorbit.

Descent Stage	
Power	Main power was provided by two ultra-flex solar arrays and load leveled by a large secondary Li-ion battery. A small regenerative fuel cell provided power throughout the lunar night. The propellant tanks that were attached to the descent stage were used to store gaseous phase H_2 and O_2 for nighttime use at 1,379 to 2,757.9 kPa (200 to 400 psi). The power control system was also capable of supporting cryo-cooling of propellant tanks during LEO loiter phase.
Propulsion	The descent stage performed the LOI burn for the entire CEV/LSAM stack (1,100 m/s [3,608.9 ft/s]) and the descent/landing burn for the LSAM stack (1,900 m/s [6,233.6 ft/s]). The ascent stage performed the ascent burn, rendezvous, docking, and disposal at 1,850 m/s (6,069.6 ft/s). The propulsion system contained RL-10 LOX/LH_2 pump-driven engine(s), which were throttleable from 10% to 100% of nominal thrust. RL 10 engines performed at an Isp of 460 sec and MR of 6 sec. Tanks were sized assuming 25 days of boil-off (1,750 kg [3,858.1 lbm]).
Thermal	Cryogenic propellants – LOX/LH_2 passive thermal control using insulation and MLI, thermal isolating structure, and boil-off utilization, including sun/Earth shade to minimize boil-off during LEO (assumed 25 days). Thermal radiators for Environmental Control and Life Support (ECLS) and fuel cell heat exchangers were also mounted on the descent stage.
Guidance Navigation & Control	The radar altimeter provided altitude and horizontal and vertical velocity relative to surface. The LN-200S and MER heritage navigation cams and hazard cams provided surface navigation and hazard avoidance. A gimbal provided pitch and yaw control, and thrusters on the ascent stage provided roll control. Each leg carried a stereo pair of MER heritage navigation cameras.

Ascent Stage	
Power	Three power bus architecture – a primary Li-CFx battery was used to support a 3-hour ascent and docking phase. Minimal charge control electronics were used to minimize mass.
Propulsion	Contained one fixed 45,000 N (10,116 lbf) NTO-MMH main engine with an Isp of 317 sec at an MR of 1.65 sec and two branches of RCS thrusters, each containing eight 490 N (110 lbf) NTO-MMH thrusters that operated at an Isp of 300 sec at an MR of 1.65 sec. The ascent stage RCS engines also provided attitude control during descent. The tanks were titanium.
Thermal	The outer surface was covered with foam insulation plus 60-layer MLI. MMH/NTO was space storable (+10ºC). Internal thermal control elements included fluid lines, pumps, cold plates, heat exchangers, instrumentation/controls, fluids, a fluid evaporator, water tank and a feed system (radiators were mounted to the descent stage). Thrusters on the ascent stage provided control torque and translation capability.
Guidance Navigation & Control	Included star trackers and gyros for stellar inertial attitude determination, accelerometers for position determination during descent and ascent, scanning LIDAR for rendezvous (couple of kilometers to tens of meters), and a wide-angle camera used during terminal rendezvous (tens of meters).

Mass Breakdown						
Subsystem	**LOI Stage**		**Descent Stage**		**Ascent Stage**	
	lbm	kg	lbm	kg	lbm	kg
1.0 Structure	4,526	2,053	5,346	2,425	3,814	1,730
2.0 Protection	1,717	779	291	132	194	88
3.0 Propulsion	6,934	3,145	0	0	1,030	467
4.0 Power	1,127	511	1,448	657	500	227
5.0 Control	600	272	0	0	0	0
6.0 Avionics	229	104	379	172	452	205
7.0 Environment	0	0	2,758	1,251	743	337
8.0 Other	1,329	603	2,939	1,333	924	419
9.0 Growth	3,294	1,494	2,302	1,044	1,508	684
Dry Mass w/Growth	**19,756**	**8,961**	**15,463**	**7,014**	**9,165**	**4,157**
10.0 Non-cargo	0	0	1,358	616	560	254
11.0 Cargo	0	0	1,102	500	1,041	472
Inert Mass	**19,756**	**8,961**	**17,923**	**8,130**	**10,766**	**4,883**
12.0 Non-propellant	0	0	904	410	90	41
13.0 Propellant	82,676	37,501	0	0	9,667	4,385
Gross Mass	**102,432**	**46,462**	**18,827**	**8,540**	**20,523**	**9,309**

Johnson Space Center Hab-Lander: 0605-LLPS-JSC-1

The Johnson Space Center (JSC) Hab-Lander was a sortie crew lander that was to deliver four crew and 2,294 kg (5,057.4 lbm) of payload to the lunar surface for a 7-day mission or crew rotation, return four crew and 100 kg (220.5 lbm) of payload to LLO, and featured a two-person airlock. It could also be used as a logistics lander to deliver a pressurized logistics carrier and 2,294 kg (5,057.4 lbm) of payload to the lunar surface, or as a cargo lander to deliver large, uncrewed elements to the surface such as the habitat, laboratory, power stations, or ISRU plants. This lander provided optimal net habitable volume for lunar crew and reduced the number of large surface assets to be moved/manipulated and mated on the lunar surface. It facilitated a radiation protection strategy for the outpost and was compatible with ESAS Cargo Launch Vehicle (CaLV) and Crew Launch Vehicle architecture.

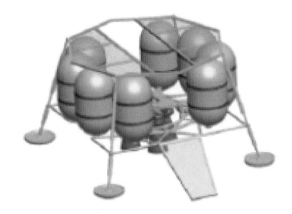

The airlock was close to the surface during outpost missions. It was a common Descent Module for all lunar missions and required minimal reconfiguration for habitability.

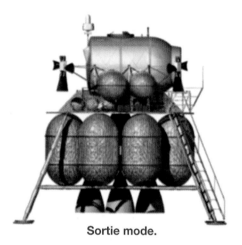

Sortie mode.

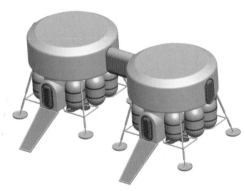

Outpost mode.

Mass Breakdown		
	lbm	kg
Payload to Surface	13,144	5,962
Lander Inert Mass	20,865	9,464
Descent Propellant	23,429	10,627
Ascent Propellant	10,395	4,715
LOI Propellant	31,010	14,066
Total Post-Trans-Lunar Injection Mass	143,226	64,966
Payload to Low Lunar Orbit	220	100
Logistics Cargo	5,057	2,294

Johnson Space Center Deployable Lander: 0605-LLPS-JSC-2

 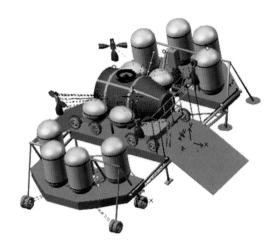

This lander was based on an LSAM design from the ESAS study. The bottom half of the structure separated, with one half rolling away from the other half to lower the upper payload platform between the split propulsion platforms so that payloads were close to the surface and could be driven down a ramp. The configuration in the launch vehicle shroud permitted a variety of payload sizes and shapes. An additional LOI stage could have increased payload capacity.

Subsystem	Descent Stage		Cargo Lander Descent Stage		Ascent Stage	
	lbm	kg	lbm	kg	lbm	kg
1.0 Structure	5,152	2,337	5,862	2,659	2,260	1,025
2.0 Protection	194	88	194	88	249	113
3.0 Propulsion	1,453	659	1,691	767	2,870	1,302
4.0 Power	1,032	468	1,032	468	1,276	579
5.0 Control	203	92	203	92	0	0
6.0 Avionics	152	69	152	69	849	385
7.0 Environment	619	281	619	281	1,975	896
8.0 Other	1,411	640	1,411	640	842	382
9.0 Growth	2,255	1,023	2,255	1,023	1,885	855
Dry Mass w/Growth	**12,471**	**5,657**	**13,419**	**6,087**	**12,206**	**5,537**
10.0 Non-cargo	2,277	1,033	2,277	1,033	1,839	834
11.0 Cargo	5,057	2,294	40,424	18,336	0	0
Inert Mass	**19,805**	**8,984**	**56,120**	**25,456**	**14,045**	**6,371**
12.0 Non-propellant	1,071	486	1,071	486	289	131
13.0 Propellant	48,868	22,166	60,975	27,658	11,147	5,056
Gross Mass	**69,744**	**31,636**	**118,166**	**53,600**	**25,481**	**11,558**

Table title: Mass Breakdown

Johnson Space Center Surface Mobile Lander: 0605-LLPS-JSC-3

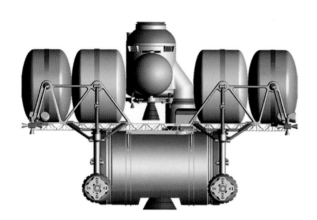 

The JSC Surface Mobile lander provided an evolvable architecture for all mission durations, from sorties to outpost missions. Its mobility allowed launch/landing away from the outpost, preventing ejecta damage to the outpost assets. The crew airlock was close to surface, providing simpler cargo unloading. It maximized use of mass brought to the Moon, and included cargo storage space at each end of the lander.

The lander had expandable modular habitat capability, allowing modular habitats left behind to be assembled into an outpost. The lander could also function as a mobile pressurized volume rover, since it could "squat" for lifting and surface handling. It operated on fuel cell power, with the fuel cells supplied by residual propellants.

Descent Stage	
Propulsion	One engine on center
Structures	Habitat: 3-m (9.8-ft) diameter by 5 m (16.4-ft) length
Down Payload	Node, mobile rover volume, cargo
Ascent Stage	
Propulsion	LO_2/CH_4; one engine on center
Structures	Minimum Ascent Stage: four crew standing
Surface Stay Time	7-day stay

Mass Breakdown					
Subsystem	Crew Lander			Cargo Lander	
	lbm	kg		lbm	kg
Ascent Stage					
1.0 Structure	1,100	499			
2.0 Protection	134	61			
3.0 Propulsion	0	0			
4.0 Power	265	120			
5.0 Control	0	0			
6.0 Avionics	531	241			
7.0 Environment	985	447			
8.0 Other	952	432		N/A	
9.0 Growth	794	360			
Dry Mass w/Growth	4,761	2,160			
10.0 Non-cargo (Fluids)	2,280	1,034			
11.0 Cargo	220	100			
Inert Mass	7,261	3,294			
12.0 Non-propellant	84	38			
13.0 Propellant	10,512	4,768			
Ascent Stage Mass	17,857	8,100			
Descent Stage					
Landing Gear	2,134	968		2,134	968
Prop Hardware (tanks, valves, etc.)	3,730	1,692		3,730	1,692
Structures	5,807	2,634		5,807	2,634
Dry Mass	11,671	5,294		11,671	5,294
Propellant	58,610	26,585		58,610	26,585
Descent Stage Mass	70,281	31,879		70,281	31,879
Payload					
7-day Habitat	11,464	5,200		11,464	0
Cargo	1,369	621		1,369	13,921
Total Payload	12,833	5,821		12,833	13,921
Total Gross Mass	100,971	45,800		100,971	45,800

Johnson Space Center Crew Taxi and Lunar Orbiter: 0605-LLPS-JSC-4

This lander was a fully reusable, single-stage lander with a separate LOI stage, and was designed for both crew and cargo. Its use could establish a transportation system for sustained exploration, since it provided extensive reuse of assets and an earlier transition to in-situ resource utilization, flexible manifesting for Earth launch and lunar landing payloads, and enhanced safety with safe-haven, rescue, and lifeboat capability. For high efficiency, an on-ramp was a part of the lander, allowing commercial and international partner cargo delivery to lunar orbit alternate launch vehicles (large and small) and to alternate orbit transfer systems, including low-thrust vehicles.

Mass Description	
Crew Taxi	The cargo mass included the crew module and all vehicle systems (except propulsion). Stage mass included tanks, engines, and some structure (32% of propellant mass).
Cargo Landers	Stage mass included all systems and structure (32% of propellant mass plus 800 kg [1,763.7 lbm]).

Mass Breakdown						
Subsystem	**Two-Way Crew Taxi**		**Reusable Cargo Lander**		**One-Way Cargo Lander**	
	lbm	**kg**	**lbm**	**kg**	**lbm**	**kg**
Stage Mass	6,173	2,800	7,937	3,600	7,937	3,600
Cargo Mass	8,378	3,800	19,842	9,000	35,274	16,000
Propellant Mass	20,283	9,200	20,283	9,200	20,283	9,200
Gross Mass	**34,834**	**15,800**	**48,062**	**21,800**	**63,494**	**28,800**

Johnson Space Center Split Lunar Crew/Cargo Vehicle: 0605-LLPS-JSC-5

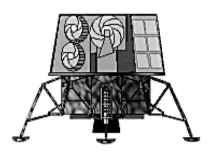

When configured as a dedicated crew lander with an ascent vehicle, the JSC Split Lunar Crew/Cargo Vehicle could deliver four crew members to the surface and remained in quiescent mode when not occupied. As a dedicated cargo lander, it could deliver large masses to the surface. The descent stage could be common between the two landers, and the ascent vehicle could land at a distance from surface

elements, so its departure would have less of an impact. A smaller, dedicated human lander could be specifically engineered to facilitate piloted landings, and the cargo lander could be engineered to provide support services unique to the payload that it carried. Performance requirements, which were similar to both landers, could employ common design solutions.

Mass Breakdown				
Descent Stage Propellant Type: Hypergolic (Isp = 320 s)				
Subsystem	Crew Lander		Cargo Lander	
	lbm	kg	lbm	kg
LOI Stage				
Propellant	23,658	10,731	27,670	12,551
Inert	5,915	2,683	6,918	3,138
Total Lunar Orbit Insertion Stage	**29,573**	**13,414**	**34,588**	**15,689**
Descent Stage				
Propellant	32,553	14,766	38,076	17,271
Inert	16,034	7,273	18,755	8,507
Total Descent Stage	**48,587**	**22,039**	**56,831**	**25,778**
Payload to the Surface				
Ascent Vehicle	17,968	8,150	0	0
Cargo	4,839	2,195	26,676	12,100
Total Payload to the Surface	**22,807**	**10,345**	**26,676**	**12,100**
Hypergolic Gross Mass	**100,967**	**45,798**	**118,095**	**53,567**

Descent Stage Propellant Type: Cryogenic (Isp = 420 s)				
Subsystem	**Crew Lander**		**Cargo Lander**	
	lbm	kg	lbm	kg
LOI Stage				
Propellant	23,664	10,734	27,677	12,554
Inert	5,915	2,683	6,918	3,138
Total Lunar Orbit Insertion Stage	**29,579**	**13,417**	**34,595**	**15,692**
Descent Stage				
Propellant	26,502	12,021	30,997	14,060
Inert	13,054	5,921	15,267	6,925
Total Descent Stage	**39,556**	**17,942**	**46,264**	**20,985**
Payload to the Surface				
Ascent Vehicle	17,968	8,150	0	0
Cargo	13,889	6,300	37,258	16,900
Total Payload to the Surface	**31,857**	**14,450**	**37,258**	**16,900**
Cryogenic Gross Mass	**100,992**	**45,809**	**118,117**	**53,577**

Johnson Space Center Retrofit H$_2$ Tanks into Habitat: 0605-LLPS-JSC-6

This configuration was an LSAM alternative in which the huge volume of the empty descent propellant tanks was accessed post landing as habitation volume. Its low mass as compared to other options allowed an outpost end-state to be reached with low total mass to the surface, and configuration variants were possible using its common lander base.

Reuse of hardware such as the propellant tanks meant much less hardware was discarded; therefore, using this lander configuration could result in a smaller "lunar junkyard." This design also made maximum use of airlocks, providing redundant outpost capabilities if multiple units were mated together for habitation. The inherent flexibility of this modular design meant the lander could be used for various exploration strategies, including sorties.

The airlock was mated to the ascent stage and to the descent tanks via hatchways. Tank hatchways were to be sealed during flight. The airlock porch was very close to the surface, providing simplified crew ingress/egress access for EVA activities.

Mass Breakdown						
Subsystem	Crew/Cargo Descent Stage		Cargo Only Descent Stage		Ascent Stage	
	lbm	kg	lbm	kg	lbm	kg
1.0 Structure	2,454	1,113	2,454	1,113	1,343	609
2.0 Protection	194	88	194	88	134	61
3.0 Propulsion	5,207	2,362	5,207	2,362	2,200	998
4.0 Power	1,032	468	1,032	468	1,001	454
5.0 Control	203	92	203	92	0	0
6.0 Avionics	152	69	152	69	531	241
7.0 Environment	619	281	619	281	650	295
8.0 Other	4,773	2,165	1,411	640	952	432
9.0 Growth	3,616	1,640	3,616	1,640	1,640	744
Dry Mass w/Growth	**18,250**	**8,278**	**14,888**	**6,753**	**8,451**	**3,834**
10.0 Non-cargo	2,277	1,033	2,277	1,033	1,360	617
11.0 Cargo	5,412	2,455	41,888	19,000	220	100
Inert Mass	**25,939**	**11,766**	**59,053**	**26,786**	**10,031**	**4,551**
12.0 Non-propellant	1,071	486	1,071	486	84	38
13.0 Propellant	55,991	25,397	58,138	26,371	7,851	3,561
Gross Mass	**83,001**	**37,649**	**118,262**	**53,643**	**17,966**	**8,150**

Easy Surface Access (Marshall Space Flight Center In-House Configuration 1): 0605-LLPS-MSFC-1

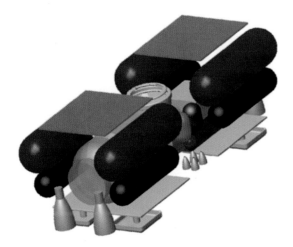 

This lander included a horizontal habitat and tanks with a central ascent stage between tank sets and four outboard descent engines with 450 sec Isp and 66.7 kN thrust per engine, fueled by LOX/LH$_2$. It also included two banks of four ascent engines with 315 sec Isp and 4 kN thrust per engine, fueled by

MMH/N$_2$O$_4$. Fuel tanks were composed of Al-Li. Two LIDs, one on top of the ascent stage and one on the outer end of the habitat, accommodated CEV docking. The concept plans were based on an 8.4 m (27.5 ft) CaLV shroud with a 7.5-m (24.6-ft) diameter payload dynamic envelope.

Mass Breakdown						
Subsystem	**Descent Stage**		**Ascent Stage Single Engine**		**Ascent Stage Multi-Engine**	
	lbm	**kg**	**lbm**	**kg**	**lbm**	**kg**
1.0 Structure	10,020	4,545	589	267	842	382
2.0 Protection	397	180	198	90	198	90
3.0 Propulsion	6,859	3,111	959	435	802	364
4.0 Power	2,059	934	780	354	780	354
5.0 Control	0	0	0	0	0	0
6.0 Avionics	972	441	556	252	556	252
7.0 Environment	344	156	344	156	344	156
8.0 Other	946	429	425	193	425	193
9.0 Growth	4,109	1,864	507	230	485	220
Dry Mass w/Growth	**25,706**	**11,660**	**4,358**	**1,977**	**4,432**	**2,011**
10.0 Non-cargo	8,093	3,671	1,182	536	1,182	536
11.0 Cargo	3,587	1,627	231	105	231	105
Inert Mass	**37,386**	**16,958**	**5,771**	**2,618**	**5,845**	**2,652**
12.0 Non-propellant	0	0	0	0	0	0
13.0 Propellant	61,824	28,043	5,187	2,353	5,187	2,353
Gross Mass	**99,210**	**45,001**	**10,958**	**4,971**	**11,032**	**5,005**

Single Engine Ascent (Marshall Space Flight Center In-House Configuration 2): 0605-LLPS-MSFC-2

 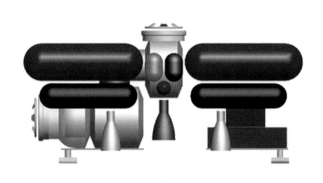

This lander concept also included a horizontal habitat and tanks with a central ascent stage between tank sets, but was raised up higher than Configuration 1 to accommodate a larger engine bell on the ascent stage. This modification necessitated an inflatable tunnel for transfer between the habitat and ascent stage. Its propulsion system consisted of four descent engines with 450 sec Isp and 66.7 kN thrust per engine, fueled

by LOX/LH_2, and one ascent engine with 315 sec Isp and 15.6 kN thrust, fueled by MMH/N_2O_4. As in the first configuration, fuel tanks were structured from Al-Li. Two LIDs, one on top of the ascent stage and one on the outer end of the habitat, accommodated CEV docking. Its design also planned on an 8.4 m (27.5 ft) CaLV shroud with a 7.5 m (24.6 ft) diameter payload dynamic envelope.

Descent Stage				
Structures	Two LIDS, 8.4 m (27.6 ft) diameter CaLV shroud. 7.5 m (24.6 ft) diameter payload dynamic envelope.			
Mass Breakdown				
Subsystem	**Descent Stage**		**Ascent Stage Single Engine**	
	lbm	**kg**	**lbm**	**kg**
1.0 Structure	9,766	4,430	589	267
2.0 Protection	397	180	198	90
3.0 Propulsion	7,015	3,182	959	435
4.0 Power	2,059	934	780	354
5.0 Control	0	0	0	0
6.0 Avionics	972	441	556	252
7.0 Environment	344	156	344	156
8.0 Other	946	429	425	193
9.0 Growth	3,739	1,696	507	230
Dry Mass w/Growth	**25,238**	**11,448**	**4,358**	**1,977**
10.0 Non-cargo	8,093	3,671	1,182	536
11.0 Cargo	4,054	1,839	231	105
Inert Mass	**37,385**	**16,958**	**5,771**	**2,618**
12.0 Non-propellant	0	0	0	0
13.0 Propellant	61,824	28,043	5,187	2,353
Gross Mass	**99,209**	**45,001**	**10,958**	**4,971**

Minimal Residuals and Boil-off (Marshall Space Flight Center In-House Configuration 3): 0605-LLPS-MSFC-3

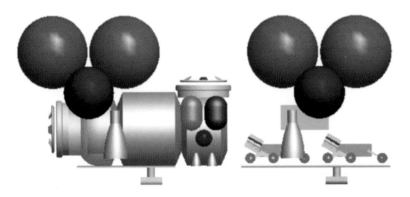

As in the other configurations, this lander had a horizontal habitat and a central ascent stage between tank sets. It used spherical tanks and four descent engines with 450 sec isp and 66.7 kN thrust per engine, fueled by LOX/LH$_2$, and four ascent engines with 315 sec Isp and 4 kN thrust per engine, fueled by MMH/N$_2$O$_4$. Two LIDs, one on top of the ascent stage and one on the outer end of the habitat, accommodated CEV docking, and the design assumed an 8.4 m (27.5 ft) CaLV shroud with a 7.5-m (24.6-ft) diameter payload dynamic envelope.

Descent Stage				
Propulsion	Boil-off: 705 kg (1,554 lb), 2%, spherical oxygen tanks (4) Boil-off: 678 kg (1,495 lb), 2% hydrogen tanks			
Mass Breakdown				
Subsystem	**Descent Stage**		**Ascent Stage Multi-Engine**	
	lbm	**kg**	**lbm**	**kg**
1.0 Structure	14,473	6,565	842	382
2.0 Protection	397	180	198	90
3.0 Propulsion	6,369	2,889	802	364
4.0 Power	2,059	934	780	354
5.0 Control	0	0	0	0
6.0 Avionics	972	441	556	252
7.0 Environment	344	156	344	156
8.0 Other	983	446	425	193
9.0 Growth	4,330	1,964	485	220
Dry Mass w/Growth	**29,927**	**13,575**	**4,432**	**2,011**
10.0 Non-cargo	5,390	2,445	1,182	536
11.0 Cargo	2,066	937	231	105
Inert Mass	**37,383**	**16,957**	**5,845**	**2,652**
12.0 Non-propellant	0	0	0	0
13.0 Propellant	61,824	28,043	5,187	2,353
Gross Mass	**99,207**	**45,000**	**11,032**	**5,005**

Easy Access to Cargo and Surface (Marshall Space Flight Center In-House Configuration 4): 0605-LLPS-MSFC-4

Configuration 4 switched to vertical tanks and included a single-engine ascent stage, radiator, inflatable nonstructural tunnel, extra cargo stowage, LOX/LH$_2$ tanks, easy access to cargo (and close to surface), and four clustered descent engines, in addition to an 8.4-m (27.6-ft) diameter CaLV and a 7.5-m (24.6-ft) diameter payload dynamic envelope.

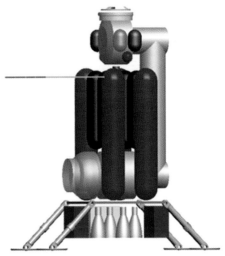

Descent Stage		
Propulsion	Propulsion: Hydrogen tanks (4) Material: AL-LI Boil-off: 950 kg (2,095 lb) Residual: 2%	Oxygen Tanks: 4; Material: AL-LI Boil-off: 876 kg (1,931 lb) Residual: 2%. Propellants: LOX/LH$_2$, 44.5 kN (10,000 lbf), Isp (450 sec)

Ascent Stage	
Propulsion	Propulsion: Single ascent engine, MMH/N$_2$O$_4$ Thrust: 15.6 kN (3,500 lb), Isp: 315 sec

Mass Breakdown				
	Descent Stage		**Ascent Stage Single Engine**	
Subsystem	**lbm**	**kg**	**lbm**	**kg**
1.0 Structure	4,092	1,856	589	267
2.0 Protection	397	180	198	90
3.0 Propulsion	5,684	2,578	959	435
4.0 Power	2,059	934	780	354
5.0 Control	0	0	0	0
6.0 Avionics	972	441	556	252
7.0 Environment	344	156	344	156
8.0 Other	1,556	706	425	193
9.0 Growth	2,822	1,280	507	230
Dry Mass w/Growth	**17,926**	**8,131**	**4,358**	**1,977**
10.0 Non-cargo	6,369	2,889	1,182	536
11.0 Cargo	13,089	5,937	231	105
Inert Mass	**37,384**	**16,957**	**5,771**	**2,618**
12.0 Non-propellant	0	0	0	0
13.0 Propellant	61,824	28,043	5,187	2,353
Gross Mass	**99,208**	**45,000**	**10,958**	**4,971**

Single Engine Ascent Stage (Marshall Space Flight Center In-House Configuration 5): 0605-LLPS-MSFC-5

The 0605-LLPS-MSFC-5 Configuration 5 concept included a single-engine ascent stage, a radiator, an inflatable nonstructural tunnel, extra cargo stowage, LOX/LH$_2$ tanks, and easy access to cargo (and close to surface). It had four engines moved outboard and 8.4-m (27.6-ft) diameter CaLV, with a 7.5-m (24.6-ft) payload dynamic envelope.

Descent Stage				
Propulsion	Propulsion: Hydrogen tanks (4) Material: AL-Li Boil-off: 950 kg (2,095 lb) Residual: 2%		Oxygen Tanks: 4 Boil-off: 876 kg (1,931 lb) Propellants: LOX/LH$_2$, 66.7 kN (15,000 lbf), Isp (450 sec)	
Ascent Stage				
Propulsion	Propulsion: Single ascent engine, MMH/N$_2$O$_4$ Thrust: 15.6 kN (3,500 lb), Isp: 315 sec			

Mass Breakdown				
	Descent Stage		**Ascent Stage Single Engine**	
Subsystem	**lbm**	**kg**	**lbm**	**kg**
1.0 Structure	4,092	1,856	589	267
2.0 Protection	397	180	198	90
3.0 Propulsion	6,268	2,843	959	435
4.0 Power	2,059	934	780	354
5.0 Control	0	0	0	0
6.0 Avionics	972	441	556	252
7.0 Environment	344	156	344	156
8.0 Other	1,583	718	425	193
9.0 Growth	2,873	1,303	507	230
Dry Mass w/Growth	**18,588**	**8,431**	**4,358**	**1,977**
10.0 Non-cargo	6,369	2,889	1,182	536
11.0 Cargo	12,430	5,638	231	105
Inert Mass	**37,387**	**16,958**	**5,771**	**2,618**
12.0 Non-propellant	0	0	0	0
13.0 Propellant	61,824	28,043	5,187	2,353
Gross Mass	**99,211**	**45,001**	**10,958**	**4,971**

Vertical Lander with Side Mount (Marshall Space Flight Center In-House Configuration 6): 0605-LLPS-MSFC-6

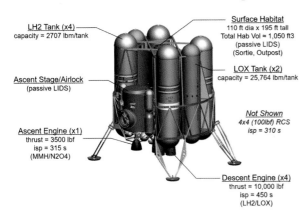

LH2 Tank (x4)
capacity = 2707 lbm/tank

Surface Habitat
110 ft dia x 195 ft tall
Total Hab Vol ≈ 1,050 ft3
(passive LIDS)
(Sortie, Outpost)

LOX Tank (x2)
capacity = 25,764 lbm/tank

Ascent Stage/Airlock
(passive LIDS)

Not Shown
4x4 (100lbf) RCS
isp = 310 s

Ascent Engine (x1)
thrust = 3500 lbf
isp = 315 s
(MMH/N2O4)

Descent Engine (x4)
thrust = 10,000 lbf
isp = 450 s
(LH2/LOX)

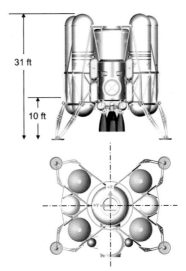

31 ft

10 ft

Configuration 6 was a vertical lander with a side-mount, minimum-ascent stage that was to be used as an airlock. It was designed to support four crew for a 7-day surface stay, with a vertical cylinder surface habitat in the center of the descent tanks.

Descent Stage	
Propulsion	Propulsion: 4 x 10,000 lbf pump-fed LOX/LH$_2$ engines @ 450 sec Isp; 16 x 100 lbf NTO/MMH RCS
Power	4.5 kW Lander average power. Two H$_2$-O$_2$ 5 kW fuel cell power plants (one primary, one backup).
Structure and Mechanisms	Truss construction
Crew Accommodations	9.6 m^3 (340 ft^3) pressurized volume
Ascent Stage	
Propulsion	1 x 3,500 lbf pressure-fed NTO/MMH engine @ 315 sec Isp; 16 x 100 lbf NTO/MMH RCS @310 sec Isp
Power	Two 3.5 kW fuel cell power plants (one primary, one backup)
Structure and Mechanisms	Aluminum sheet and stringer construction
Crew Accommodations	9.6 m^3 (340 ft^3) pressurized volume
Surface	
Crew Accommodations	29.7 m^3 (1,050 ft^3) total pressurized volume

Mass Breakdown				
	Descent Stage		Ascent Stage Single Engine	
Subsystem	lbm	kg	lbm	kg
1.0 Structure	3,611	1,638	589	267
2.0 Protection	397	180	198	90
3.0 Propulsion	5,734	2,601	959	435
4.0 Power	2,059	934	780	354
5.0 Control	0	0	0	0
6.0 Avionics	972	441	556	252
7.0 Environment	344	156	344	156
8.0 Other	1,208	548	425	193
9.0 Growth	2,639	1,197	507	230
Dry Mass w/Growth	**16,964**	**7,695**	**4,358**	**1,977**
10.0 Non-cargo	6,021	2,731	1,182	536
11.0 Cargo	14,401	6,532	231	105
Inert Mass	**37,386**	**16,958**	**5,771**	**2,618**
12.0 Non-propellant	0	0	0	0
13.0 Propellant	61,824	28,043	5,187	2,353
Gross Mass	**99,210**	**45,001**	**10,958**	**4,971**

Lunar Lander Preparatory Study Request for Information

The Lunar Lander Preparatory Study (LLPS) Request for Information (RFI) was a short, focused study with the objectives of widely releasing in-house LLPS study guidelines so that contractors, academia, or others could perform parallel studies and/or use this information to make decisions on how to focus their internal efforts. In addition to broadening the number of lander concepts, one of the main goals of this activity was to engage industry and academia in the Constellation Program Office activities beyond development of the Crew Exploration Vehicle (CEV) and Crew Launch Vehicle. To this end, the study was primarily concerned with Lunar Landers (i.e., Lunar Surface Access Modules [LSAMs]), which could, by themselves, provide transport between the lunar surface and Low Lunar Orbit (LLO), the Earth Moon Libration points L1 and L2, Low Earth Orbit (LEO) or Earth's surface (direct to lunar surface – as a component of a flight – without stopping in LLO or L1 or L2), or another location on the lunar surface and return (ballistic hopper mode).

The landers developed during this study were specified to provide the following capabilities:
- Crew transport from the flight origin point to any point on the illuminated portion of the lunar surface
- Crew transport from the lunar surface back to the flight origin point
- Cargo transport from the origin point to the lunar surface
  - Integral structures and vehicles (not components)
  - Unpressurized equipment, components, and supplies
  - Pressurized equipment, components, and supplies
- Tanker (fueled with hydrogen and/or methane) to the lunar surface
  - A modified cargo lander with propellant tank(s) as cargo
  - A special cargo lander with extra-large functional propellant tanks (connected to the engine)
- Oxidizer consisting of LOX from the surface transported to a fuel depot at the flight origin point.

Several corporations and universities responded to the RFI and submitted designs, include Alcatel Alenia Space /Italian Aerospace Research Center (CIRA), Boeing/ Northrop Grumman, Alliant Techsystems Incorporated (ATK), the University of Colorado, and Massachusetts Institute of Technology (MIT).

Alenia Alcatel Space/Italian Aerospace Research Center (CIRA)/ Microgravity Advanced Research and Support (MARS) Center EAGLE: 0606-LLPS-RFI-1

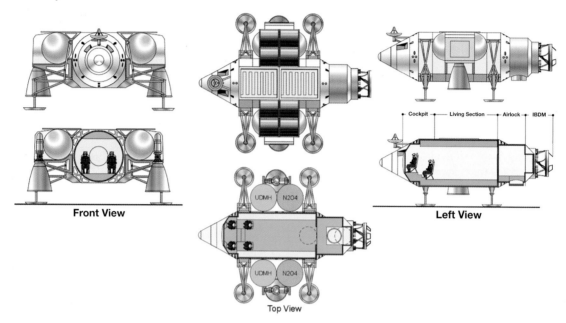

Front View

UDMH N2O4

UDMH N2O4

Top View

Cockpit — Living Section — Airlock — IBDM

Left View

Proposed by an Italian team consisting of engineers and scientists from the Italian firms of Alcatel Alenia Space, CIRA, and the Microgravity Advanced Research and Support (MARS) Center in Naples, Italy, the EAGLE lander was a single-stage fully reusable vehicle that also served as a temporary lunar surface outpost/ habitat for up to four crew members. It could be operated in an LLO parking orbit in automatic standby mode, and was capable of performing automatic refueling between crewed missions.

Six launches, performed as three coordinated pairs, were required to enable a lunar surface mission

with the EAGLE. The first two vehicles to launch to LLO were a Lunar Tug and an EAGLE, with 4,500 kg (1,170 gal) of fuel. The second pair of launches, also to LLO, consisted of a second Lunar Tug and a Lunar Tanker with 13,500 kg (3,510 gal) of fuel. The purpose of this pair was to perform refueling of the EAGLE. The third pair of launched vehicles were a third Lunar Tug and a crew vehicle, such as the ARIES-A/CEV, with up to four crew members. The crew would have transferred to the EAGLE from the CEV in LLO, then landed on the lunar surface, using the EAGLE as a temporary outpost.

Mass Breakdown		
	lbm	**kg**
Crew (4)	**882**	**400**
Payload:		
Oxygen (8 days + 20% safety margin)	71	32
Nitrogen	284	129
Water (8 days + 20% safety margin)	948	430
Food (8 days + 20% safety margin	53	24
Total Payload	**1,356**	**615**
Structural Mass:		
Cockpit	2,205	1,000
Forward Pressurized Section	2,646	1,200
Rear Pressurized Section	2,646	1,200
Airlock	2,646	1,200
Docking System (International Berthing Docking Mechanism – active)	992	450
External Protection Layers	1,102	500
Thermal Control	882	400
Telemetry, Tracking and Communications + Antennas	441	200
Landing Legs (4)	1,764	800
RCS Propellant (Hydrazine)	220	100
Engines (2) – Ref. Yangel RD-8	1,676	760
Fuel Tanks (4)	970	440
Batteries	220	100
Solar Panels	220	100
Avionics	441	200
Power	220	100
Total Structural Mass	**19,291**	**8,750**
Propellant N_2O_4/Unsymmetrical Di-Methyl Hydrazine	39,683	18,000
Total Mass	**60,330**	**27,365**
Total w/Crew	**61,212**	**27,765**

Massachusetts Institute of Technology Crasher-Bouncer: 0606-LLPS-RFI-2

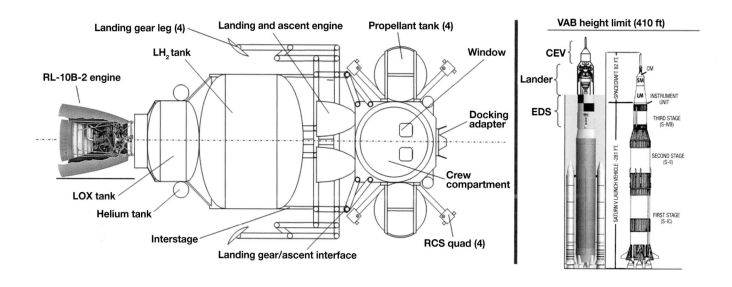

This architecture family is called "crasher-bouncer" because it involves one propulsion stage that is used for Lunar Orbit Insertions (LOI) (including the CEV as payload), and subsequently for part of the descent. It is then jettisoned and impacts the lunar surface downrange. After separation, a second propulsion stage is burned for the remainder of descent and landing. This stage carries the crew compartment, the landing gear, and any equipment for the surface mission. After the surface mission, the crew compartment and propulsion stage lift off the gear, which serves as a launch platform and is left on the surface. As a single stage performs both landing and ascent, it is considered to "bounce."

The crasher-bouncer concept provides some inherent advantages: as the LOI and descent stage does not have to land on the lunar surface, it can be built with a very efficient structure (much like an Earth launch vehicle upper stage) and can employ a non-throttleable, high-performance engine such as an RL-10B-2. Also, the landing gear needs to support less mass than for a traditional descent/ascent configuration (such as in the Exploration System Architecture Study [ESAS]), which leads to a further mass saving. On the other hand, the ascent stage needs to carry additional propulsion system mass in the form of tanks and, potentially, engines back to orbit, which results in a mass penalty. Analysis indicates that for the same performance

requirements on the mission, the overall effect is that of a significant Trans-Lunar Injection (TLI) mass saving compared to a traditional two-stage design; this mass reduction could enable a single-launch lunar mission. However, the concept also features a challenge: because the LOI and descent stage is jettisoned while the lander-ascender is on a ballistic impact trajectory, a propulsion failure would result in the vehicle impacting the lunar surface without rescue capability. This risk could, however, be mitigated by using several engines and including engine-out capability. Initial analysis for the concept presented in the figure above suggests that two throttleable Orbiter Main Engine (OME)-class engines or 4 10-kN class engines would be sufficient to provide abort capability to lunar orbit in case of engine failure. These engines could be common with the CEV propulsion system (one OME-class engine or two 10-kN class engines for the CEV, driven by Trans-Earth Injection thrust to weight requirements due to gravity loss).

Additional attractive features of the crasher-bouncer concept include:

- The lander/ascender vehicle might be suitable for reusability: if the landing gear could be transported back to orbit, the vehicle could be refueled with propellant brought from Earth, and could use the remaining propellant in the LOI stage for descent.

- The lander ascender could be easily converted into an uncrewed lander for cargo. In this configuration, the entire ascent propellant could be utilized for landing so that the cargo delivery capability would be increased compared to that of the ESAS concept.

- Only one new throttleable engine in the 10-20 kN class would need to be developed for both the CEV and lunar lander.

- The lander would be much smaller than the ESAS LSAM, easing crew surface access and cargo deployment.

If strong mitigation of the crashing risk is desired, a three-stage concept could be employed. Since the remainder of descent and landing would be carried out by a separate stage, the ascent stage could be used for abort to orbit during descent and landing. However, while this would decrease risk, it would also diminish the TLI benefit, adding both development and unit production cost (i.e., three propulsion stages instead of two).

University of Colorado Exploration System Architecture Study Lander: 0606-LLPS-RFI-3

The University of Colorado conducted a mass analysis of the LSAM using several different methods including historical analogues, a top-down approach, and a bottoms-up approach by subsystem.

The LSAM structural design was derived from the ESAS report and the Apollo Lunar Module (LM). The ascent geometry constraint was a 4.6-m (15-ft) long by 3-m (9.8-ft) diameter cylinder. The descent stage envelope was an 8.5-m (27.9-ft) maximum outer diameter by 4-m (13-ft) tall decagon. Descent stage cargo volume was approximately 17 m³ (600 ft³).

The ascent stage was comprised of a dual shell with wall thicknesses nearly identical to that of the Apollo LM. No vibration or system-level structural analysis was performed; however, it was believed that the structure mass still had significant growth potential. The figure above shows the general layout with two crew members included for relative scale. For easier viewing, the descent stage sidewalls and two of the descent stage propellant tanks are not shown.

Baseline Requirements	
Mission Requirements	• Four humans to the Moon • Sortie: 7 active/0 dormant LSAM days • Outpost: 4 active/180 dormant LSAM days • "1.5-launch" mission profile • Four crew members on every Extravehicular Activity (EVA)
Lunar Surface Access Module Requirements	• Mass: Wet = 44,900 kg (98,987.6 lbm) (Max Launch Capability); Dry = 9,056 kg (19,965.1 lbm) • Pressurized Volume 24.6 m³ (868.7 ft³); 9.5 psi, (65.5 kPa), 30% O$_2$ • Equivalent Habitable Volume 13.8 m³ (487.3 ft³)
Other Key Requirements	• Flash evaporators for ascent • LOX/LH$_2$ descent engine

Dry Mass Analysis Tabular Results								
	ESAS		Larson & Pranke, 2000		Bottoms-Up		Bottoms-Up w/Margin	
	lbm	kg	lbm	kg	lbm	kg	lbm	kg
Propellant	70,618	32,032	N/A	N/A	65,651	29,779	82,065	37,224
Structures	6,014	2,728	4,991	2,264	4,890	2,218	6,113	2,773
Propulsion	5,701	2,586	9,846	4,466	4,991	2,264	6,239	2,830
Crew Accommodations	933	423	1,605	728	1,354	614	1,693	768
Thermal	933	423	800	363	2,150	975	2,687	1,219
Power	N/A	N/A	2,996	1,359	3,693	1,675	4,616	2,094
Extravehicular Activities	N/A	N/A	1,874	850	1,689	766	2,112	958
C3	1,001	454	1,993	905	1,334	605	1,667	756
Environmental Control and Life Support System	933	423	800	363	937	425	1,171	531
Crew	N/A	N/A	N/A	N/A	397	180	N/A	N/A

Boeing/Northrop Grumman: Six Concepts: 0606-LLPS-RFI-4

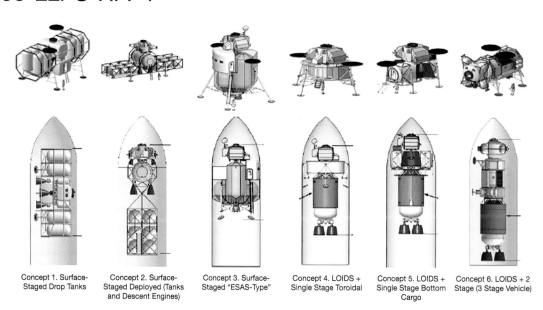

Concept 1. Surface-Staged Drop Tanks

Concept 2. Surface-Staged Deployed (Tanks and Descent Engines)

Concept 3. Surface-Staged "ESAS-Type"

Concept 4. LOIDS + Single Stage Toroidal

Concept 5. LOIDS + Single Stage Bottom Cargo

Concept 6. LOIDS + 2 Stage (3 Stage Vehicle)

In 2006, Boeing and Northrop Grumman responded to NASA's RFI by designing six different concepts, including a lander with its pressurized modules and propulsive staging, and how to package it within the Ares V payload fairing.

Concept 1: Surface-Staged Drop Tanks featured a semi-cubic Ascent Module on top of a semi-cubic Descent Module that included a surface habitat and airlock. A vertical hatch or tunnel connected the two pressurized modules. The unique feature of this concept was the drop tanks, which provided propellant for lunar orbit insertion (LOI) and initial descent burns. The drop tanks then separated from the Ascent Module and Descent Module to reduce the final landing mass. This design with the airlock in the Descent Module minimized the height above the lunar surface for extravehicular activities (EVAs). The Ascent Module without an airlock had an almost completely unobstructed pilot view angle over the long side of the Descent Module below and minimized the Ascent Module mass for ascent and aborts.

Concept 2: The Surface-Staged Deployed (Tanks and Descent Engines) featured a vertical cylindrical Ascent Module centered on top of a long horizontal Habitat and airlock on the Descent Module. The Ascent Module connected to the Habitat through a vertical tunnel. The unique feature of this design was the way the "wings" folded up inside the Ares V shroud to form a compact payload that could fly within a shroud diameter as

small as 7 m (23 ft), possibly resulting in a mass savings to LEO and throughout the mission architecture. This concept also put the airlock close to the surface. It combined the airlock and habitation cabin into the same module as in the ESAS Concept A.

Concept 3: The Surface-Staged "ESAS-Type" featured an Exploration System Architecture Study (ESAS) Type arrangement of its ascent and descent engines and propellant tankage. The Ascent Module was on center of the vertical thrust axis, with the Habitat Module and airlock below, off-center. Opposite this off-center pressurized section was the unpressurized cargo section. The Ascent Module connected to the Habitat through a protruding "nose tunnel" that secured to a hatch in the top of the Habitat. A major problem with this design was that the position and shape of the Habitat Module partially obstructed the pilot's sightline to the surface. However, the view angle could have been improved if the Ascent Module was turned 180 degrees, so that it looked out over the lower unpressurized payload compartment.

Concept 4: A LOIDS + Single Stage Toroidal design used the Lunar Orbit Insertion and Descent Stage (LOIDS) drop stage, so it staged during descent. It had essentially the same Ascent Module as Concept 3; however, the Descent Module contained a unique toroidal-shaped habitation zone. The Habitat, airlock, and unpressurized cargo were all sandwiched between the upper and lower decks as part of this toroidal envelope. The Ascent Module engine fired through the center opening of the toroid, serving as a single stage both for final descent to the surface and for ascent from the surface. In this design, the Ascent Module sat close to the surface and had a relatively unobstructed pilot sight line.

Concept 5: The LOIDS + Single Stage Bottom Cargo concept employed the LOIDS for descent staging. Its Ascent Module was a variant of those in Concepts 3 and 4, except that the vertical connection was right below it, so it did not need the "nose tunnel." As in Concept 4, the Ascent Module provided the terminal descent, landing propulsion, and ascent propulsion; however, unlike Concept 4, it had two engines offset to the sides of the Descent Module Habitat. The unique feature of this configuration was the provision of an unpressurized cargo compartment at the bottom of the lander structure. Otherwise, this Habitat and airlock configuration was similar to its counterpart in Concept 2. This design aligned the pilot station/flight deck to the long axis of the Habitat Module/airlock below; however, this alignment created the maximum interference with the pilot sight line. Rotating the Ascent Module 90 degrees so that it looked "over the side" of the cylinder, however, would have greatly improved the pilot's view angle, assuming that the

vehicle could fly and land on that vector.

Concept 6: The LOIDS + 2 Stage (3 Stage Vehicle) design used the LOIDS and the Descent Module for descent staging and the Ascent Module for surface staging. It took the long horizontal cylinder concept one step farther; it put the Ascent Module – a shallow cylinder on edge -- in line with the Habitat and airlock cylinder in a manner similar to the LAT-1 configuration. The difference was that the modules in this concept lay much closer to the surface upon landing. This concept was notated as the "LOIDS + 2" because, in addition to the LOIDS, it had both the separate Descent and Ascent Modules as stages. The Concept 6 design placed the Ascent Module closest to the surface of any of the six concepts. The pilot's view angle was completely clear and unobstructed except by the limitations of the front windows. This design raised a different question, which was that the abort-on-descent and ascent-from-surface vector was far removed from the conventional plus-nadir thrust axis through the center of the Descent Module. In fact, the ascent from surface vector was turned 90 degrees from the LOIDS thrust vector, so the guidance and navigation systems and the flight deck needed to be able to handle the spacecraft in different orientations during LOI and initial descent versus final descent, landing and ascent.

Mass Breakdown								
	Configuration 1: Surface Staged Horizontal				Configuration 2: Surface Staged Deployed Horizontal			
	Descent Stage O_2/H_2		Ascent Stage Storable		Descent Stage O_2/H_2		Ascent Stage Storable	
	lbm	kg	lbm	kg	lbm	kg	lbm	kg
Total Payloads	**-249**	**-113**	**10,836**	**4,915**	**8,944**	**4,057**	**6,074**	**2,755**
Tankage	3,955	1,794	417	189	3,955	1,794	280	127
Prop. Management	267	121	79	36	267	121	73	33
Engines and Thrust Vector Control (TVC)	1,087	493	190	86	1,087	493	126	57
Reaction Control System (RCS)	0	0	317	144	0	0	311	141
Structures	3,051	1,384	1,422	645	3,640	1,651	908	412
Structures Hinges	0	0	0	0	220	100	0	0
Thermal and Fluids	84	38	84	38	84	38	84	38
Avionics	269	122	937	425	269	122	937	425
Power	851	386	666	302	851	386	666	302
Cryo Coolers	247	112	0	0	247	112	0	0
Landing Legs	1,724	782	0	0	1,724	782	0	0
Dry Mass Growth	1,960	889	699	317	2,099	952	575	261
Stage Dry Mass	**13,495**	**6,121**	**4,811**	**2,182**	**14,443**	**6,551**	**3,960**	**1,796**

Mass Breakdown (Continued)								
	Configuration 1: Surface Staged Horizontal				Configuration 2: Surface Staged Deployed Horizontal			
	Descent Stage O_2/H_2		Ascent Stage Storable		Descent Stage O_2/H_2		Ascent Stage Storable	
	lbm	kg	lbm	kg	lbm	kg	lbm	kg
RCS	0	0	1,065	483	0	0	1,005	456
Residuals	851	386	187	85	851	386	121	55
Ascent	0	0	12,335	5,595	0	0	7,930	3,597
Descent	23,620	10,714	0	0	23,620	10,714	0	0
LOI	31,689	14,374	0	0	31,689	14,374	0	0
Boil-Off	567	257	0	0	567	257	0	0
Total Propellant	**56,727**	**25,731**	**13,587**	**6,162**	**56,727**	**25,731**	**9,056**	**4,108**
Total Wet Mass	**69,973**	**31,739**	**29,234**	**13,259**	**80,114**	**36,339**	**19,090**	**8,659**
Total Configuration Mass	44,998 kg (99,207 lbm)				44,998 kg (99,204 lbm)			
	Configuration 3: Surface Staged Vertical				Configuration 4: Descent Staged Vertical			
	Descent Stage O_2/H_2		Ascent Stage Storable		LOIDS Stage O_2/H_2		Descent/Ascent Stage Storable	
	lbm	kg	lbm	kg	lbm	kg	lbm	kg
Total Payloads	**9,233**	**4,188**	**6,074**	**2,755**	**0**	**0**	**15,778**	**7,157**
Tankage	3,955	1,794	280	127	3,710	1,683	445	202
Prop. Management	267	121	73	33	254	115	82	37
Engines and TVC	1,087	493	126	57	1,100	499	311	141
RCS	0	0	311	141	0	0	302	137
Structures	3,646	1,654	908	412	2,729	1,238	1,847	838
Structures Hinges	0	0	0	0	0	0	0	0
Thermal and Fluids	84	38	84	38	84	38	84	38
Avionics	269	122	937	425	161	73	937	425
Power	851	386	666	302	170	77	666	302
Cryo Coolers	247	112	0	0	247	112	0	0
Landing Legs	1,691	767	0	0	0	0	1,334	605
Dry Mass Growth	2,057	933	575	261	1,437	652	1,021	463
Stage Dry Mass	**14,154**	**6,420**	**3,960**	**1,796**	**9,892**	**4,487**	**7,029**	**3,188**
RCS	0	0	1,005	456	0	0	919	417
Residuals	851	386	121	55	783	355	201	91
Ascent	0	0	7,930	3,597	0	0	9,434	4,279
Descent	23,620	10,714	0	0	19,897	9,025	3,799	1,723
LOI	31,689	14,374	0	0	30,955	14,041	0	0

	Mass Breakdown (Continued)							
	Configuration 3: Surface Staged Vertical				Configuration 4: Descent Staged Vertical			
	Descent Stage O_2/H_2		Ascent Stage Storable		LOIDS Stage O_2/H_2		Descent/Ascent Stage Storable	
	lbm	kg	lbm	kg	lbm	kg	lbm	kg
Boil-Off	567	257	0	0	522	237	0	0
Total Propellant	56,727	25,731	9,056	4,108	52,157	23,658	14,353	6,510
Total Wet Mass	80,114	36,339	19,090	8,659	62,049	28,145	37,160	16,855
Total Configuration Mass	44,998 kg (99,204 lbm)				45,000 kg (99,209 lbm)			

	Configuration 5: Descent Staged Side Engine			
	LOIDS Stage O_2/H_2		Descent/Ascent Storable	
	lbm	kg	lbm	kg
Total Payloads	0	0	15,849	7,189
Tankage	3,710	1,683	445	202
Prop. Management	265	120	86	39
Engines and TVC	1,100	499	401	182
RCS	0	0	282	128
Structures	2,729	1,238	1,854	841
Structures Hinges	0	0	0	0
Thermal and Fluids	84	38	84	38
Avionics	161	73	937	425
Power	170	77	666	302
Cryo Coolers	247	112	0	0
Landing Legs	0	0	1,310	594
Dry Mass Growth	1,440	653	1,032	468
Stage Dry Mass	9,906	4,493	7,097	3,219
RCS	0	0	717	325
Residuals	783	355	203	92
Ascent	0	0	9,504	4,311
Descent	19,897	9,025	3,774	1,712
LOI	30,955	14,041	0	0
Boil-Off	522	237	0	0
Total Propellant	52,157	23,658	14,198	6,440
Total Wet Mass	62,063	28,151	37,144	16,848
Total Configuration Mass	44,999 kg (99,207 lbm)			

	Configuration 6: Descent Staged Horizontal						Configuration 7: Cargo Lander Descent Only	
Mass Breakdown (Continued)								
	LOIDS Stage O_2/H_2		Descent Stage Storable		Ascent Stage Storable		Descent Stage Storable	
	lbm	kg	lbm	kg	lbm	kg	lbm	kg
Total Payloads	0	0	9,848	4,467	6,074	2,755	29,366	13,320
Tankage	3,710	1,683	152	69	278	126	2,247	1,019
Prop. Management	265	120	68	31	75	34	190	86
Engines and TVC	1,100	499	192	87	179	81	1,312	595
RCS	0	0	258	117	227	103	282	128
Structures	2,729	1,238	981	445	873	396	5,525	2,506
Structures Hinges	0	0	0	0	0	0	0	0
Thermal and Fluids	84	38	84	38	84	38	84	38
Avionics	161	73	269	122	937	425	937	425
Power	170	77	851	386	666	302	851	386
Cryo Coolers	247	112	0	0	0	0	0	0
Landing Legs	0	0	1,325	601	0	0	1,870	848
Dry Mass Growth	1,440	653	710	322	564	256	2,260	1,025
Stage Dry Mass	9,906	4,493	4,890	2,218	3,883	1,762	15,558	7,057
RCS	0	0	472	214	161	73	725	329
Residuals	783	355	57	26	119	54	1,087	493
Ascent	0	0	0	0	7,866	3,568	0	0
Descent	19,897	9,025	3,774	1,712	0	0	37,468	16,995
LOI	30,955	14,041	0	0	0	0	33,964	15,406
Boil-Off	522	237	0	0	0	0	0	0
Total Propellant	52,157	23,658	4,303	1,953	8,146	3,695	73,244	33,223
Total Wet Mass	62,063	28,151	19,041	8,637	18,103	8,212	118,168	53,600
Total Configuration Mass	45,000 kg (99,207 lbm)						53,600 kg (118,168 lbm)	

ATK Solid Propulsion Lunar Surface Access Module: 0606-LLPS-RFI-5

Layout of Solid Propulsion LSAM Descent Stage

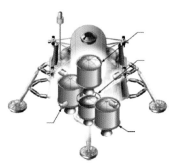

Layout of Solid Propulsion LSAM Ascent Stage

ATK's design fit within 8.4-, 10.0-, or 12.0-m (27.5-, 32.8-, or 39.4-ft) launch fairing, and used solid propellant motors as well as hydrazine monopropellant-based RCS engines on its descent stage, with a surface landing system based on variable control solid propulsion, exceeding both the delta-v and landing mass requirements. It also used staging of its motors, allowing inert mass to be dropped prior to lunar descent. This optimized mass fraction and reduced the overall height of the lander, easing

astronaut egress, and provided spent structures that could be filled with regolith for use in lunar bases. The ascent stage used a solid rocket motor for axial propulsion and hydrazine thrusters for RCS propulsion. This allowed the descent stage to both support the ascent stage on the lunar surface and provide a launching platform.

Sizing of the individual propulsion elements was based on the delta-v requirement for each portion of the mission, and is shown in the table below.

Delta-v Exceeds Requirements			
LSAM Descent Stage			
Maneuver	**Candidate Propulsion Components**	**ΔV Required, m/s**	**ΔV Provided, m/s**
Midcourse Correction	RCS	10	10
Lunar Orbit Insertion	Earth Departure Stage or CEV	1,100	1,100
Descent	STAR 75, STAR 63, and Proportional Control Landing System	1,900	2,231
Descent RCS	RCS	11	11
Total Descent ΔV		**3,021**	**3,352**
LSAM Ascent Stage			
Maneuver	**Candidate Propulsion Components**	**ΔV Required, m/s**	**ΔV Provided, m/s**
Ascent	STAR 75	1,850	2,431
Rendezvous	RCS	16	16
Disposal	RCS	23	23
Ascent RCS	RCS	21	21
Total Descent ΔV		**1,910**	**2,491**
Mass Breakdown			
	Descent Stage		**Ascent Stage Single Engine**	

Subsystem	**lbm**	**kg**	**lbm**	**kg**
Dry Weight	19,788	8,976	12,746	5,781
Propellant Weight	40,958	18,578	16,728	7,588
Gross Mass	**60,746**	**27,554**	**29,474**	**13,369**

Lunar Lander Preparatory Study Phase 2

A blue-ribbon Review Board of Apollo astronauts, managers, and engineers evaluated NASA's in-house Lunar Lander Preparatory Study (LLPS) Phase 1 concepts. The concepts selected for Phase 2 had to meet the following criteria: the ability to satisfy the "fixed" requirements; the potential for performance, cost, or risk improvement; the potential to incorporate "desirements" (e.g., deployment of surface systems); and be innovative, original, and use out-of-the-box thinking.

The Review Board noted a number of recurring themes that were judged worthy of additional investigation. These themes included drop stages and two-stage descent, minimal ascent stages, zero/minimum cryo boil-off, mobility, ease of cargo loading, and reuse of propellant tanks (wet hab), as well as horizontal landers and assembly of an outpost from modular lander elements. The Board chose seven concepts that contained combinations of all the desired features and which represent potential Constellation Lunar Lander Designs. From that point, each of the design teams was assigned one of the seven concepts to investigate further. In certain instances, design teams were asked to explore concepts that combined features from various designs.

The Board also came up with a Phase 2 lander concept study philosophy. They sought to define the likely envelope of human lunar lander design solutions by choosing concepts that probed different corners of the lander design space. None of the seven concepts chosen for Phase 2 were optimized; however, each combined a number of features that were complementary. At the conclusion of Phase 2, NASA possessed seven in-house lander designs (and multiple other designs received via Request for Information) to prepare for the Constellation Program.

Each team was given a specific design direction in which they were to mature. Johnson Space Center (JSC) and Ames Research Center (ARC) were to further investigate the "suit lock" concept; Langley Research Center (LaRC) led common cost and risk analyses for all Phase 2 options to ensure common, relative measures. The Glenn

Research Center (GRC) team was to further research split descent with drop stage and cryo ascent with long-duration (180-day) lunar surface storage of cryo ascent propellants, explore surface storage of cryo propellants and keep-alive requirements for the lander, and assess risk, functionality criticality, modes and affects, etc. of the staged descent approach. The Goddard Space Flight Center (GSFC) team was to determine how payloads could be offloaded to the lunar surface from a tall descent stage platform and further investigate the minimum airlock ascent stage. The Jet Propulsion Laboratory (JPL) and ARC teams were combined and were to further investigate a drop stage and mobility, determine risk, functional criticality, modes and affects, etc. of the staged descent approach, and also investigate landing gear-mobility system synergies. The JSC team was to further develop the "habitank" concept using descent prop tanks for surface habitation, depict changeover from prop tank to hab outfitting and ops, further refine the minimum ascent stage concept, and investigate descent stage assets from lunar ascent. The LaRC team was to continue work on the Descent Assisted Split Habitat (DASH) concept, improve analysis of trajectory and aborts, further develop concepts for astronauts to don suits for Extravehicular Activity (EVA) (alternatives to suit ports), and develop a horizontal lander option using the combined horizontal lander expertise from all the design teams (Kennedy Space Center [KSC], Marshall Space Flight Center [MSFC], etc.) The MSFC team was to further refine a minimum airlock ascent stage concept, further investigate the removal of cargo, and further develop the minimum airlock ascent stage concept. The LLPS Phase 2 study direction is shown in the following matrix.

As the teams developed their Phase 2 products, they were asked to document their design process. Teams were encouraged to capture their design experiences both in technical detail as well as in a less technical "story." These sometimes colorful stories describing the LLPS Phase 2 lunar lander concepts have been interwoven among the technical descriptions in the following section.

Lunar Lander Preparatory Study Phase 2 Study Guidelines / Team Assignment	Phase 2 Lander Feature	Drop Stage/2-stage Descent	Minimal Ascent Stage	Airlock Ascent Stage	Suitlock	Zero/minimum Cryo Boiloff	Mobility	Ease of Cargo unloading	Underslung Cargo	Re-use of Propellant Tanks (wet hab)	Horizontal Landing	Modular Landing
GRC team		Further development descent concept investigate launch around packaging				Further develop arc boiloff story for 180 day cryo ascent		Investigate cargo lander option and cargo unloading techniques				
GSFC team				Develop airlock-based ascent stage more fully				Develop cargo unloading options				
JPL team (+ ARC mobility team)		Drop stage	Further develop small ascent stage				Integrate mobility work of ARC and URL; investigate ATHLETE + other mobility concepts					Investigate outpost deployment via docking of mobile elements
JSC team			Further develop small ascent stage		Investigate ops required to config cryo tank as habitable volume					Fully develop concept to config wet hab from descent prop tanks		
LaRC team		Continue DASH refinement, emphasis on drop stage issues	Further develop small ascent transport hab stage				Investigate cargo unloading from horizontal landers		Investigate options for underslung cargo		Fully develop horizontal lander concepts, including launch, landing and cargo issues	
MSFC team			Fully develop minimum ascent stage concept				Develop landed stage mobility, including outpost deployment concepts					Investigate outpost deployment via docking of mobile elements

■ primary task/lead assignment   ■ work collaboratively

Skycrane

Notes

Notional Concept Diagram(s)

Examine all issues associated with split descent stage (trajectories, att/velocity at staging, disposal, contingency ops); use cryo ascent propulsion and examine storage issues for 180 day surface stay; investigate mods required for cargo lander option.

Airlock ascent stage; develop payload unloading concepts more thoroughly (e.g., swing unloading).

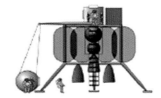

Build upon concept 1B; drop stage; integrate ARC team into mobility system refinement; further investigate mobility system landing dynamics.

Further refine concept 6 - re-use of descent stage cryo tanks as a surface habitat. Further refine wet hab outfitting.

Integrate all horizontal lander concepts, using all team members who contributed horizontal concepts; investigate payload unloading options. Additionally, continue refinement of DASH concept; further refine drop stage operations, trajectories, altitude/velocity at staging, disposal ops, contingency ops.

Further refine concept 6 (minimum ascent stage); investigate mobility options and outpost buildup scenarios; Further refine cargo deployment concepts.

Langley Research Center Lunar Lander Preparatory Study Phase II Horizontal Lander: 0609-LLPS-LaRC-A

The horizontal configuration of the Phase 2 Horizontal Lander facilitated large cargo deployment and simplified crew egress/ingress. The sortie lander was reconfigurable and directly extensible to outpost deployment and logistics resupply missions, with a split habitat and a minimum volume ascent stage to both improve vehicle performance and enhance payload-to-the-surface capability. A four-engine descent stage main propulsion system provided engine-out capability during descent.

Descent Stage	
Power	Three Proton Exchange Membrane (PEM) fuel cells, 3-hr lifetime with 5 kW capacity; 198 kg (436.5 lbm) fuel cell
Propulsion	Four RL10 derivative (Common Extensible Cryogenic Engine) throttleable descent engines. 57,826.9 N (13,000 lbf) thrust/engine, 13% minimum throttle, 459.7 sec Isp, 1,250 m/s (4,101 ft/s) LOI delta-v, 1,911 m/s (6,269.7 ft/s) descent delta-v
Telecommunications	Two Ultra High Frequency (UHF) transceivers, two UHF antennas
Thermal	2.25 m² (24.2 ft²) of MLI-50. Active thermal control systems: 10 mil Ag-Teflon Flexible Fabric Reflector and a fluid loop heat rejection system with 60% Prop Glycol/40% H_2O
Structures	Vertical cylindrical configuration, 1.75 m (5.7 ft) in diameter, volume approximately 6.0 m³ (212 ft³). Good structural support from existing truss underneath. More efficient design for airlock in smaller volume 6 to 10 m³ (212 to 353 ft³) range. Not as efficient if scaled up to around 20 m³ (706 ft³). Dust guard room in rigid central habitat may be necessary to support suit donning/doffing.
Guidance, Navigation & Control	Two radar altimeters
Ascent Stage	
Power	Four Li-ion batteries: 125 Wh/kg specific power and 200 Wh/L specific density. 3-hr lifetime, 4.5 kW capacity, 50 kg (110.2 lbm)/battery
Propulsion	MMH/NTO pressure-fed engine; 316 Isp and 1,911 m/s (6,269.7 ft/s) delta-v capability. Sixteen 445.2 N (100 lbf) thrusters for attitude control, two Main Propulsion System (MPS) engines
Telecommunications	Two S-Band transponders, one S-Band dual-beam antenna, one K-Band radar signal processor, two K-Band transponders. Phased Array Ka/Ku-Band antenna type, two UHF transceivers, two UHF antennas
Thermal	2.25 m² (24.2 ft²) of MLI-50. 10 mil Ag-Teflon Flexible Fabric Reflector; H_2O Fluid Evaporator system (60% Prop Glycol/40% H_2O). 1,764.2 W, 40.577 kg (89.5 lbm)
Structures	Aluminum Lithium, iso grid, semimonocoque; 65.5 kPa (9.5 psi) internal pressure
Guidance Navigation & Control	Two Gyros, two accelerometers, two cameras, four Global Positioning Systems (GPS)/inertial navigation systems

Mass Breakdown						
Subsystem	Payload Module		Lander Module		Retro Module	
	lbm	kg	lbm	kg	lbm	kg
1.0 Structure	2,709	1,229	996	452	1,184	537
2.0 Protection	132	60	172	78	0	0
3.0 Propulsion	0	0	1,611	731	4,396	1,994
4.0 Power	1,580	717	1,041	472	284	129
5.0 Control	0	0	0	0	0	0
6.0 Avionics	176	80	976	442	501	227
7.0 Environment	2,122	963	319	145	0	0
8.0 Other	1,679	761	1,056	479	677	307
9.0 Growth	1,680	762	1,234	560	1,104	501
Dry Mass w/Growth	10,078	4,571	7,404	3,358	8,146	3,695
10.0 Non-cargo	1,460	662	750	340	3258	1478
11.0 Cargo	1,967	892	220	100	0	0
Inert Mass	13,504	6,125	8,375	3,799	11,403	5,172
12.0 Non-propellant	1,604	727	15	7	0	0
13.0 Propellant	0	0	9,742	4,419	54,787	24,851
Gross Mass	15,108	6,853	18,132	8,224	66,190	30,023
Lander Wet Mass	14,977 kg (33,020 lbm)					
Total DASH Mass	45,000 kg (99,210 lbm)					

On the Shoulders of the Giants Next Door

Dave North

I grew up a few miles from NASA Langley Research Center in Hampton, Virginia, during the heyday of the Apollo Program. Many of my friend's fathers worked at Langley Research Center. I can remember listening intently to their backyard barbeque conversations as they described their work on the vehicles that took the first men to the Moon. Since space travel was a new thing, these men drew their experience from a diverse background. Some had crossed over from the aeronautics groups at Langley, some were military test pilots, whereas others had come from the shipbuilding industry. One characteristic that these engineers had in common was practical mechanical experience. They fixed their own cars, built their own airplanes, built their own houses in their spare time after work, and could fix any mechanical thing under the sun. I sensed at the time that their work on Apollo was special and important but I did not, until recently, have a full appreciation for their profound achievement.

During the past year I have had the privilege of working on a team at Langley that has developed one of the lunar lander concepts that will be considered for the next missions to the Moon. The goal, this time, is to establish a long-duration human outpost on the Moon and to develop the capabilities to go to Mars. Unlike the Apollo Lunar Module (LM), which was designed to get two men down to the surface of the Moon with small science cargos, the next lander will be a workhorse.

Building an outpost will require a lander that can carry four crew to the surface and back, and can also carry considerable cargo including large Habitation Modules, solar power units, and pressurized surface rovers. Some of my colleagues have compared our task to designing a heavy duty "dually" pickup truck. The lander mass will be 45,000 kg (99,200 lb), three times that of the Apollo LM.

Since cargo carrying and unloading will be the primary task, our lander is designed with this as the top priority. The payloads will be massive and, in most cases, bulky; therefore, the lander is designed with a large cargo bay that is low to the surface. The cargo can be easily unloaded from the cargo bay via two ramps that are dropped from either side of the lander (one of our team members commented that the ramps look like moat bridges on a medieval castle). The resulting configuration is a lander that is wider than it is tall, thus the categorization as a horizontal lander. We have named our concept Cargo Star (or in shorthand C*, for you rocket folks) to emphasize the superior cargo carrying and unloading capability, similar to the Air Force's designation for cargo aircraft.

The ascent stage is designed to be as small as possible to minimize mass. A very small ascent stage can be used because the crew will not live exclusively in the ascent stage as was done in Apollo. The ascent stage will only be occupied during the short 3-hour transit to and from the lunar surface. The crew will have a separate habitat module available for outpost and sortie missions. For egress to the lunar surface, the crew will pass through an airlock in the surface habitat and walk down the lander ramp.

An uncrewed cargo version of the lander uses the same descent stage as the crewed lander, but has no ascent stage. In this configuration, the real advantage of the Cargo Star lander becomes apparent. The cargo bay volume is more than 100 m^3 (3531 ft^3). This is equivalent to the volume of two standard 6 m (20 ft) sea shipping containers. The uncrewed cargo lander can carry more than 20 mt (22 t). That's about the mass of 10 average-sized sport utility vehicles.

During the conceptual design effort, our team poured over the details of the Apollo LM design. Studying the design, it became clear that the Apollo LM design was an extremely practical solution to the problem at hand. There is nothing aesthetically pleasing about the ungainly Apollo LM. It has un-aerodynamic shape and spindly legs. The beauty lies in the fact that every part on the vehicle was designed to fulfill a specific function with the utmost efficiency in mass. Each item put on the surface of the Moon is worth its weight in gold many times over.

We made the rookie mistake of showing four large panoramic windows in our ascent stage at the conceptual design review thinking that the astronauts would want this. The design review panel included several astronauts (John Young – Gemini/Apollo/Space Shuttle, Joe Engle – X15/Apollo/Space Shuttle, Andy Thomas – Space Shuttle, Carlos Noriega – Space Shuttle) and Owen Morris, manager of the Apollo lunar module program. These veterans instinctively knew that large windows are bad because of the mass penalty and they let us know it. John Young commented in his usual deadpan manner, "An astronaut couldn't even carry one of those windows in one-sixth G."

The Cargo Star Horizontal Lunar Lander

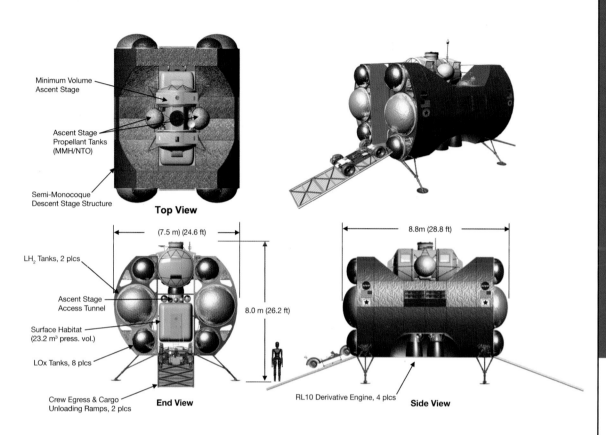

Minimum Volume Ascent Stage

Ascent Stage Propellant Tanks (MMH/NTO)

Semi-Monocoque Descent Stage Structure

Top View

LH₂ Tanks, 2 plcs

Ascent Stage Access Tunnel

Surface Habitat (23.2 m³ press. vol.)

LOx Tanks, 8 plcs

Crew Egress & Cargo Unloading Ramps, 2 plcs

End View

(7.5 m) (24.6 ft)

8.0 m (26.2 ft)

8.8m (28.8 ft)

RL10 Derivative Engine, 4 plcs

Side View

Ascent Module and Surface Habitat for the Crewed Lander

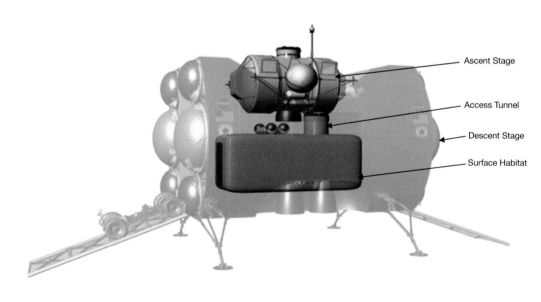

Ascent Stage

Access Tunnel

Descent Stage

Surface Habitat

The Uncrewed Cargo Star Lander

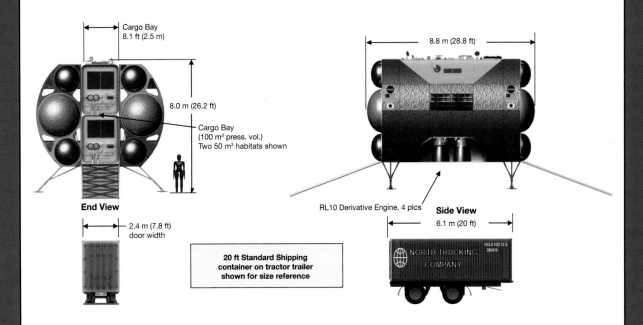

End View

Cargo Bay
8.1 ft (2.5 m)

8.0 m (26.2 ft)

Cargo Bay
(100 m³ press. vol.)
Two 50 m³ habitats shown

2.4 m (7.8 ft)
door width

**20 ft Standard Shipping
container on tractor trailer
shown for size reference**

8.8 m (28.8 ft)

RL10 Derivative Engine, 4 plcs

Side View

6.1 m (20 ft)

NORTH TRUCKING COMPANY

The Cargo Star design is also not pretty. Whereas the Apollo LM looked like a spider, the Cargo Star looks like a big tick with a fat body and little head. But it is designed to perform its crew carrying and cargo ferrying role in the new Moon missions with practical, no-nonsense solutions to each design requirement. The Apollo LM was successful because it was designed with a no-frills, "keep it simple" philosophy. We tried to stick to the same "KIS" principle on the Cargo Star lander concept.

Having been involved in the conceptual design of a lunar lander, I now have an even greater appreciation for the accomplishments of the people that worked on the Apollo program. They did it without high-powered computers, which I think may actually hinder the creative conceptual design process (commonly referred to in the engineering community as "paralysis by analysis"). I attribute much of their success to using engineering "horse sense" developed by hands-on experience with all things mechanical. Those dads in my neighborhood that were building houses and rebuilding their car engines were using this haptic knowledge to design spacecraft.

We are embarking on a new era of space exploration, one which will build a sustainable human presence, first on the Moon and then on Mars and beyond. In the next decade, this generation of engineers and scientists will design, test, and operate the new human lunar lander. The previous generation showed us that it is possible with a hearty dose of gumption and a lot of good old engineering common sense. They didn't let us down, and we cannot let them down or the generation that follows us.

Langley Research Center Phase II Descent Assisted Split Habitat Lander: 0609-LLPS-LaRC-B

The Descent Assisted Split Habitat (DASH) lander concept included a Retro Module that staged prior to landing, thus facilitating cargo deployment and crew egress/ingress. This sortie lander was reconfigurable and directly extensible to outpost missions. A split habitat, minimum-volume ascent stage improved vehicle performance to enhance payload-to-the-surface capability. Use of inflatables for expanded surface habitat volume provided excellent pilot visibility and the ability to tailor the pressurized volume for mission needs.

Descent Stage	
Power	Power (batteries) to support pressurized logistics in rigid core derived from the surface habitat.
Propulsion	Single non-throttling 110,049.2 N (24,740 lbf) RL10B-2 engine (LOX/LH$_2$); RM performs Lunar Orbit Insertion (LOI) and ~90% of the lunar descent.
Thermal	Reduced capability from sortie lander for the following: heat exchanger, fluid loop heat rejection, cold plates, 10 mil Ag-Teflon single-sided radiators, and Multi-Layer Insulation (MLI) blankets.
Structures	Vertical cylindrical configuration, 1.75 m (5.7 ft) in diameter, volume approximately 6.0 m^3 (212 ft^3). Good structural support from existing truss underneath. More efficient design for airlock in a smaller volume (6 to 10 m^3 [212 to 353 ft^3] range). Not as efficient if scaled up to around 20 m^3 (706 ft^3). Dust guard room in rigid central habitat may be necessary to support suit donning/doffing.
Ascent Stage	
Power	Four Li-ion batteries (125 Whr/kg specific power and 200 Whr/L specific density). 3-hr lifetime, 4.5 kW capacity, 55 kg (121.3 lbm)/battery
Propulsion	Two 26,689.8 N (6,000 lbf) Orbiter Main Engine (OME) derived MMH/NTO pressure-fed engines; 316 Isp and 1,911 m/s (6,269.7 ft/s) delta-v capability
Telecommunications	Two S-Band transponders, one S Band dual-beam antenna, one K-Band radar signal processor, two K-Band transponders. Phased array Ka/Ku-Band antenna type, two UHF Transceivers, two UHF antennas
Thermal	MLI-50 flexible blanket with 5.7-cm (2.25-in) thickness
Structures	Aluminum-Lithium (Al 2195) I Beams and grid-stiffened panels. 65.5 kPa (9.5 psi) internal pressure
Guidance Navigation & Control	Two star trackers, two Light Detection And Ranging (LIDAR)/LADAR, two cameras, two radar altimeter, four GPS/INS, two radar antennae, 445.2 N (100 lbf) NTO/MMH Reaction Control System (RCS) engines (16 total)

Mass Breakdown						
Subsystem	Descent Stage		Ascent Stage		Cargo Descent Stage	
	lbm	kg	lbm	kg	lbm	kg
1.0 Structure	2,709	1,229	996	452	1,180	535
2.0 Protection	132	60	171	78	0	0
3.0 Propulsion	0	0	1,608	729	4,345	1,971
4.0 Power	1,580	717	1,041	472	281	128
5.0 Control	0	0	0	0	0	0
6.0 Avionics	176	80	976	442	501	227
7.0 Environment	2,122	963	319	145	0	0
8.0 Other	1,656	751	1,056	479	658	298
9.0 Growth	1,675	760	1,233	559	1,090	494
Dry Mass w/Growth	10,050	4,560	7,400	3,356	8,055	3,653
10.0 Non-cargo	1,460	662	749	340	3,200	1,452
11.0 Cargo	1,102	500	220	100	0	0
Inert Mass	12,612	5,722	8,369	3,796	11,255	5,105
12.0 Non-propellant	1,604	727	15	7	0	0
13.0 Propellant	0	0	9,677	4,389	53,784	24,396
Gross Mass	14,216	6,449	18,061	8,192	65,039	29,501

Marathon Lunar Exploration Starts with a DASH

Dan Mazanek, Dave Cornelius, and Kandyce Goodliff

NASA's Descent Assisted Split Habitat lander may provide the key for future, routine access to the Moon's surface

" Houston, this is lander Hercules. All systems are ready for descent braking initiation."

– "Roger that Hercules, you are *go* for powered descent. "

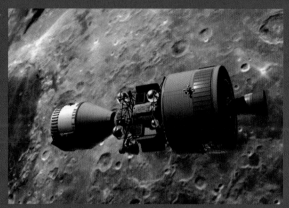

The DASH lander mated to the Orion Crew Exploration Vehicle in Low Lunar Orbit.

With that exchange between the commander of the lunar lander Hercules and NASA's Mission Control, the Lunar Expedition I crew began their historic descent to the lunar surface. On the afternoon of September 30, 2020, the four crew members climbed out of their Orion Crew Exploration Vehicle (CEV), entered the next-generation lunar lander, and safely landed at the Moon's Aristarchus Plateau. The lander will become NASA's workhorse for a series of missions designed to comprehensively explore the Moon and establish an outpost allowing for continuous human presence on the lunar surface. The Descent Assisted Split Habitat (DASH) lander was conceived by a team of engineers at the Langley Research Center located in Hampton, Virginia, during the summer of 2006. DASH is a versatile lander that uses a disposable braking stage, called a Retro Module, during most of the lunar descent along with a small crew module for the short trip to and from the surface. Human missions such as the proposed Apollo direct flight approaches included the use of a lunar braking module and the Russian LK lander included the use of a "crasher stage." These innovative approaches for landing humans on the Moon combined with the desire to get the crew and cargo extremely close to

The Retro Module performs the descent braking burn from an altitude of 15 km (9.3mi) to just over 5.3 km (3.3 mi).

The Retro Module separates from the Lander Module and Payload Module and impacts the surface over 3 km (1.9 mi) downrange of the landing site.

the lunar surface inspired the Langley engineers to conceive of the DASH lander. Fourteen years later, and more than 50 years after Neil Armstrong first set foot on the Moon, NASA's vision to return to the Moon has become a reality. Now 1 week later, with the crew safely aboard the CEV and about to begin their 3-day journey back to Earth, the Hercules lander is ready to perform its final operational maneuver – a short thruster burn to deorbit the vehicle. In the future, the lander will be modified to be refueled in lunar orbit and await the next outpost crew arrival. For now, Hercules' mission is complete. Provided here is a review of the DASH lander design and its role in NASA's successful return to the Moon.

The DASH lander is composed of three modules: the Lander Module, the Payload Module, and the Retro Module. Although the Lander Module, which carries the four crew members within the pressurized Transport Habitat, contains the primary vehicle flight controls and critical subsystems, the first phase of the lunar landing was dominated by the 9.3 m (30.5 ft) long Retro Module. The Retro Module is a high-performance in-space braking stage powered by a LOX/LH$_2$ propulsion system. The non-throttling engine is capable of producing 110 kN (24,740 lbf) of thrust. Having already successfully completed the lunar orbit insertion maneuver with the CEV attached, the Retro Module was activated again to perform two critical maneuvers. The first small burn kicked the DASH lander from its 100 km (54 nmi) altitude parking orbit into an elliptical orbit with a perilune altitude of 15 km (8 nmi). With the astronauts still weightless, it was time for the Retro Module to perform the second maneuver. The Retro Module operated flawlessly during its 5.4-minute braking burn that canceled the spacecraft's orbital velocity and effectively brought the lander to a relative standstill 5.3 km (2.9 nmi) above Aristarchus Plateau. With no direct viewing of the surface possible during this mission phase, Commander John Stevenson and Pilot Kathy Reynolds used heads-up displays and the lander instruments to guide themselves and Mission Specialists Scott Jones and Mike Ross to the Retro Module jettison altitude.

At this point, the Retro Module's job was complete. Moments after main engine cutoff, the expended stage separated and safely followed a predictable ballistic trajectory to its impact point 3.2 km (1.7 nmi) downrange of the landing site. This was a satisfying moment for the NASA engineers that proposed this alternative approach to traditional two-stage vertical landers. Dan Mazanek, the DASH concept team leader, recalls the initial resistance to the use of braking stages. "We use staging all the time in launch systems. If we didn't, we would still be stuck on Earth. I remember using the term 'separation anxiety' to describe some folks' early concern with braking stages. It's terrific to see how beautifully the DASH system performed. The lander's benefits far outweigh the relatively minor risks associated with staging." The biggest benefit is proximity to the surface. The large, empty propellant tanks on an equivalent two-stage lander force the crew or any large cargo to tower over three stories (~10 m [33 ft]) above the lunar surface. The tank height is primarily driven by the launch vehicle fairing diameter. Cranes, elevators, and other devices can overcome this, but add considerable complexity, cost, and risk to surface operations. The simplest approach is to be close to the surface and use ramps to deploy cargo and short ladders or ramps for crew access. The crew and cargo height from the surface for DASH is approximately 1.2 m (3.8 ft) and is limited only by the need to avoid rocks on the surface. Additionally, the DASH lander provides mass reductions compared to similar two-stage lander designs. Kandyce Goodliff, one of the DASH team co-leads, adds, "We found that the DASH lander was nearly a metric ton lighter than the two-stage lander. An Apollo-like approach with a single habitat was 3.5 mt (3.9 t) more massive than DASH – not to mention the surface access problems. The DASH lander has definite performance benefits."

Since the Moon has no atmosphere, the flight path of the vehicle is much easier to predict than for spacecraft going through the atmosphere, as with those returning to Earth or future missions to Mars. "This is aided by our much better understanding of the Moon's gravitational field than during the Apollo missions. The descent trajectory was designed to assure that the Retro Module impacts harmlessly downrange of the landing site," explains Mazanek. Although not critical on this 7-day sortie mission, this becomes an important consideration for outpost missions. Any design, even single-stage landers, must guarantee that surface assets are protected during nominal lander operations and abort situations. The DASH trajectory assures that if the Retro Module is jettisoned during a descent abort contingency, it will land no closer than 3 km (9,800 ft) from the outpost. "For much of the descent the impact point is tens to hundreds of kilometers downrange. Also, for outpost missions the surface assets will be placed out of plane from the lander descent path, and the lander will perform a 'dog-leg' type maneuver that curves toward the outpost location late in flight," adds Dave Cornelius, the other DASH team co-lead. On future missions the crew plans to visit the Retro Module's impact site to gain valuable engineering data on the vehicle's performance and survivability of components. It's even conceivable that someday the discarded stages could be used as a recyclable resource.

After jettison of the Retro Module, two highly reliable hypergolic engines ignited in unison and the Lander Module and attached Payload Module began the 90-degree pitch over maneuver to orient the lander for touchdown. The Lander Module engines perform the final portion of descent and the precision landing maneuvers, as well as provide abort to orbit at any point during the descent. Commander Stevenson commented that it was impressive to see the large Retro Module as it drifted away from the lander. The 30 mt (33 t) Retro Module represents two thirds of the entire DASH lander wet mass of just under 45 mt (49.6 t). "We had a terrific view of the Retro Module out the main windows as we pitched over. We were able to see it all the way to the surface," said Stevenson.

The 26.7 kN (6,000 lbf) Lander Module engines, derived from the Space Shuttle Orbital Maneuvering Engine (OME), provided a smooth, balanced thrusting for the last 2 minutes of the descent. The gem shape of the Transport Habitat allows for the efficient use of the limited volume, maximizing usable space at arm/chest height while simultaneously allowing for downward-facing windows for commander and pilot visibility during the landing phase. The mission specialists are seated at the rear of the Transport Habitat. The desire to provide efficient mass staging by splitting the habitable volume and allowing the Surface Habitat to remain on the surface required that multiple engines be used on the lander. The approach provided another huge benefit for the DASH design by greatly increasing the height of the engines above the surface to nearly 3.7 m (~12 ft). This effectively reduces surface plume debris and also permits a lower vertical touchdown velocity, which reduces landing gear mass. Unlike Apollo, which had to cut off the descent engine about a meter above the surface, DASH is able fire its engines until the landing pads actually touch down. Engine height also turned out to be critical to reduce dust interference with the hazard avoidance and landing system, which uses a laser imaging system to detect rocks and boulders on the lunar surface.

The Lander Module and Payload Module just prior to lunar touchdown.

As Reynolds carefully piloted the Hercules lander to the surface, she noted, "We had a great view of the lunar surface and the dust wasn't bad at all. The small, agile DASH lander was a pleasure to fly," said Reynolds. This agility will prove to be important on future missions where navigation over the mountainous polar terrain will be much more difficult. The compact lander also proved beneficial during its development on Earth. The complexity and cost of rigs to support the construction and testing of the DASH lander were significantly reduced, since the Retro Module was not connected during the crucial operations near the surface. The ability to build the modules separately and then integrate them with relative ease also helped in the lander development process.

Several engine configurations were considered for DASH; however, the two-engine configuration was chosen for multiple reasons. It was the simplest approach offering the best packaging and least mass solution, and eliminating coupled radiative heating and plume interaction issues encountered in four engine in-line and side-by-side designs. In addition, the demonstrated high reliability and extensive heritage of the N_2O_4/MMH engine systems have proven that the additional risk incurred by flying a two-engine design over a single-engine design is insignificant, since feed system redundancy was incorporated as was done for the Apollo Lunar Module descent stage. The OME was fired more than 2,000 times without failure during Space Shuttle flights, and was inspected for damage after each flight, so its characteristics were well understood. The only engine modification required for DASH was the ability to throttle the engine back to around half thrust during touchdown and ascent. The pintle throttle demonstrated on the Apollo descent stage provided confidence that the OME could be successfully and safely modified.

One of the design challenges for the DASH lander was controlling the exhaust plume from the Lander Module engines. When the concept team first proposed the dual use of plume shields as ramps for offloading of cargo, they knew that shield temperature control, pressure loading, vehicle plume heating, and contamination from

hypergolic propellants would need to be addressed. Careful design and testing resulted in plume shields that efficiently direct exhaust away from the vehicle. Stevenson confirmed that exhaust plume effects on the lander structure were virtually undetectable. "Houston, we've got a clean bird here at Aristarchus," was the message relayed by the commander after the crew inspected the lander during the initial surface Extravehicular Activity (EVA). Mission Specialists Jones and Ross were responsible for lowering the two shield ramps that protect the external cargo bays during the first EVA. Each bay can hold approximately 5 m³ (177 ft³) of unpressurized cargo, including the lunar rover and various scientific equipment. "The ramp mechanisms worked just like they did during training," complimented Ross after the 8-hour work shift on the surface.

Astronauts lower the Lander Module's plume shields, which double as deployment ramps, then activate the lunar rover.

The crew of the Hercules spent a total of 7 days exploring the Aristarchus Plateau region and performed a record 10 surface EVAs. They provided a comprehensive survey of the area and are returning over 100 kg (220 lbm) of rock and regolith samples. The DASH Payload Module, which is left on the surface, provides a versatile platform that can accommodate both pressurized and unpressurized payloads – specifically lunar surface habitats, outpost infrastructure and cargo, and other surface equipment. For this initial mission, the Payload Module contained a Surface Habitat, which consists of a 14 m³ (494 ft³) rigid central core module and a 12 m³ inflatable airlock located at the rear of the lander. When combined with the 6 m³ (212 ft³) Transport Habitat, which was used on the surface as separate sleeping quarters and for crew privacy, DASH had nearly five times the pressurized volume of the Apollo lander.

The initial DASH lander design included a smaller airlock on the front with a collapsible dust lock inside the central core and an alcove at the rear. Inflatables for expanded surface habitat volume allow for the ability to tailor the pressurized volume for mission needs while still providing excellent pilot visibility during descent. However, the initial design was modified to better control the electrostatically charged lunar dust. Lunar dust creates many surface suit design problems as well as respiratory health concerns for the crew if the dust were to enter the pressurized habitats. The final design combined the idea of externally mounted suit ports with a larger inflatable airlock. Two suit port connections were located on the rear face of the airlock, incorporated into the airlock door. The other two were located with one on each side of the airlock. This approach minimizes the amount of dust brought inside the lander and reduces atmospheric replenishment requirements, while allowing the astronauts to bring the suits inside the airlock when critical repairs are needed. The four suits plus spares are stowed in the rigid core during landing, transferred to the airlock after deployment, and then externally mounted to the suit port connections after the astronauts' initial lunar excursion. Jones commented on the dust mitigation, "Yeah, by the end of the mission the suits were getting pretty dirty, but the combination of approaches kept them functioning well and kept that nasty dust out of the lander."

After the crew had completed their surface activities, they re-donned their EVA-capable in-space suits used during descent and climbed back into the Transport Habitat for the ascent phase of the mission. A Low Impact Docking System (LIDS) hatch interface is located on top of the Transport Habitat for docking with the CEV after ascent from the lunar surface, as well as the earlier mission phases. Emergency surface ingress/egress is also available through the LIDS hatch on top of the vehicle via a ladder on the back of the DASH lander, but was never needed during the mission. After the Lander Module separated from the Payload Module, the crew was subjected to a nearly constant acceleration of about 0.7 Earth-g's. "The ascent was very smooth and comfortable," said Reynolds after rendezvousing with the waiting Orion CEV.

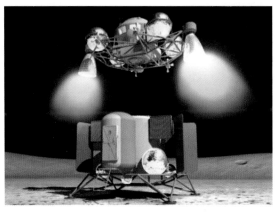

After 7 days on the lunar surface, the Lander Module fires its engines and ascends to the waiting Orion CEV.

Now safely aboard the CEV, the four astronauts have a little time to relax during the journey home, but NASA engineers and technicians are busy preparing for the next lunar mission. After a short series of sortie missions, NASA will begin the outpost buildup. The DASH lander will be up to the task. It is also an extremely capable outpost lander with multiple options for crew, cargo, and long-duration habitat accommodations. The crewed outpost lander configurations used for crew transport do not need to support extended surface activities. Therefore, the lander will only provide minimal crew accommodations and will remain on the surface in a quiescent mode for up to 210 days until used for crew ascent back to lunar orbit.

For a crewed outpost mission, the lander can be flown with just the rigid central core as a pressurized logistics module and deliver nearly 4 mt (4.4 t) of net payload. The crew will be ferried with the cargo from the landing zone to the outpost via a pressurized logistics rover, delivered previously by a DASH lander configured to carry the large surface vehicle. For unpressurized cargo, the Surface Habitat is replaced with a cage structure plus a deployment ramp and the payload capability increases to over 7 metric tons (7.7 t) when delivered with the crew. Uncrewed cargo and infrastructure delivery configurations can land even heavier payloads, 17 mt (18.7 t) of pressurized or 21 mt (23 t) of unpressurized cargo, since the Lander Module can use its entire propellant load for descent. In addition, two extended surface habitat options are being developed for deployment by the DASH lander. They consist of two-level habitat designs providing a total of 52-100 m^3 (1,836-3531 ft^3) of pressurized volume, depending on the configuration. This larger volume is roughly the equivalent of a room 5.4 m by 6 m (18 ft by 20 ft) with 3-m (10-ft) ceilings. Finally, development of surface mobility options may replace the traditional landing gear system and turn the lander into a pressurized mobile vehicle capable of extending human exploration across even greater regions of the lunar surface.

So now, as the Hercules lander makes one final descent to the lunar surface, the Lunar Expedition Crew I bid it a fond farewell, knowing that the DASH lander design provided the key component for the first safe and successful mission to the Moon in over 5 decades. It was the first of many human missions for a long-distance lunar marathon that NASA hopes will pave the way for an eventual mission to Mars – a journey that is taken one step at a time.

Marshall Space Flight Center Lunar Lander Preparatory Study Phase II Concept: 0609-LLPS-MSFC

The Phase II concept had a crew EVA hatch close to the surface (~3 m [10 ft]). The minimized mass/volume ascent stage allowed for increased payload capability. Potential radiation protection was provided by the propellant tanks surrounding the surface habitat. Combining the ascent stage and surface airlock provided increased payload capability and allowed easier cargo stowage and unloading (only for a sortie mission). Use of storable propellants in the ascent stage allowed for long-term storage on the lunar surface and potential cost and production time savings, using high Technology Readiness Level technology. Incremental outpost build allowed for easier incorporation of upgrades and increasing levels of redundancy. Cargo deployment occurred from the middle bay. At completion of the study, dust mitigation in the ascent vehicle/airlock still needed refinement.

Descent Stage	
Power	Two H_2-O_2 5 kW fuel cell power plants (one primary, one backup). Fuel cells were shown to have lower system mass than batteries in Phase 1 trade. Included 90% Power Management and Distribution (PMAD) efficiency (4.5 kW average delivered). Two units provided redundancy and reduced mass without sacrificing crew safety.
Propulsion	Assumptions: Fuel: LH_2, Oxidizer: LOX, Mixture ratio (Oxidizer/Fuel [O/F]): 6.0, Nominal Isp = 450 sec, MPS Thrust Level, Four 44,482 N (10,000 lbf) per engine (one engine out, three operating, three 66,723.5 N (15,000 lbf) per engine (one engine out, two operating), Thrust levels dictated by allowable Thrust-to-Weight (T/W) (0.4 for crewed, 0.3 for cargo) at Powered Descent Initiation.
Telecommunications	Two S-Band transponders (descent stage for lunar communications to Earth and descent stage to EVA and other habitats) consisted of independent strings. The Ka-Band transceiver on the descent stage was to be used for wideband data back to Earth, with an S-Band 802 16n wireless network for lunar communications between EVA crew, internal intercom, outpost to lunar rover, and habitat-to-habitat.
Guidance, Navigation & Control	One radar altimeter, one terrain avoidance system

Ascent Stage	
Power	Two 3.5 kW fuel cell power plants (one primary, one backup). Included 90% PMAD efficiency (3.2 kW average delivered). Reactants sized for 3-hour ascent operation with 5% residuals. Reactants stored in gaseous state in dedicated reactant tanks.
Propulsion	MPS Engine Assumptions: Fuel: MMH Oxidizer: N_2O_4, Mixture ratio (O/F): 1.65 Nominal Isp= 315 sec Thrust = 15,569 N (3,500 lbf); chosen to produce Apollo-like initial ascent T/W. Non-gimballable Main Engine, 15,569 N (3,500 lbf) thrust, Propulsion system two-fault-tolerant as necessary, designed for minimum risk. Operating Pressures, Propellant Tanks – 1.7 MPa (250 psi) Design Pressure – 2.8 MPa (400 psi) Pressurant Tanks – 31 MPa (4,500 psi) down to 3.4 MPa (500 psi), Helium pressurant sized for isothermal (plus 10%) Propulsion hardware Technology Readiness Level 9, design margin on all dry mass 20%.
Telecommunications	Two S-Band transponders (ascent stage to CEV and ascent stage to Earth) consisted of independent strings.
Thermal	MLI, heat exchanger, evaporative cooling system with Coldplates
Structures	The internal equipment mass was applied evenly to the 1st and 2nd floors. Launch loads = 5.0 g axial, 2.0 g lateral Staging loads = 1.2 g axial, 0 g lateral 10 Hz minimum frequency. Isogrid cylindrical habitat walls and interior 2nd floor. The panel material was Al Li 2195; the beam material was Al 7075.

Mass Breakdown						
Subsystem	Descent Stage / Sortie		Descent Stage / Outpost		Ascent Stage	
	lbm	kg	lbm	kg	lbm	kg
1.0 Structure	7,176	3,255	7,176	3,255	1,464	664
2.0 Protection	280	127	280	127	410	186
3.0 Propulsion	11,991	5,439	11,991	5,439	1,863	845
4.0 Power	913	414	913	414	1,014	460
5.0 Control	679	308	679	308	0	0
6.0 Avionics	869	394	869	394	977	443
7.0 Environment	4,747	2,153	4,747	2,153	1,250	567
8.0 Other	1,726	783	1,726	783	661	300
9.0 Growth	4,936	2,239	4,936	2,239	1,098	498
Dry Mass w/Growth	**33,317**	**15,112**	**33,317**	**15,112**	**8,737**	**3,963**
10.0 Non-cargo	12,815	5,813	12,522	5,680	2,716	1,232
11.0 Cargo	45,331	20,562	60,019	27,224	511	232
Inert Mass	**91,463**	**41,487**	**105,858**	**48,016**	**11,964**	**5,427**
12.0 Non-propellant	2,529	1,147	2,529	1,147	143	65
13.0 Propellant	124,724	56,574	110,330	50,045	11,627	5,274
Gross Mass	**218,716**	**99,208**	**218,717**	**99,208**	**23,734**	**10,766**

MSFC/JSC/GRC/ARC Team Lander Concept

Tara Polsgrove, Dan Thomas, Larry Kos, Andy Gonzales

Introduction and Lander Configuration

The major objective of this lander design was to propose an ascent stage/airlock combination with the smallest possible vehicle mass that could still accomplish the required mission phases. This, along with minimizing the descent stage structure, allowed the largest possible payload to be delivered to the lunar surface for the given launch vehicle capability. Another design goal was to reduce the height of the surface access port (i.e., the airlock hatch). Finally, a common lander was designed to accomplish three separate missions: crewed sortie, crewed outpost, and unpiloted cargo delivery. These considerations led to the lander configuration in the figure below.

The Marshall Space Flight Center (MSFC) team, which consisted of members from Johnson Space Center (JSC), Glenn Research Center (GRC), and Ames Research Center (ARC), developed several lander configurations. The study review board chose one of these for further study. The selected concept is depicted below. For those who are familiar with the Apollo lander, the most distinguishing features of this design are the large propellant tanks that surround the vehicle and the side-mounted ascent stage. Interior to the six large propellant tanks is a cylindrical surface habitat.

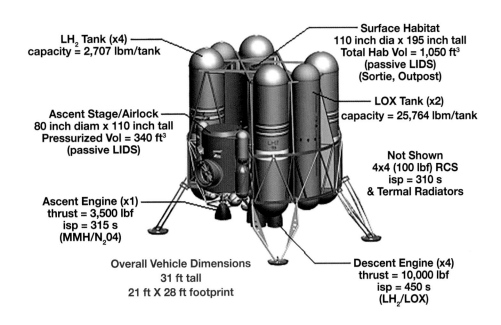

Lander configuration – selected concept.

Concept of Operations

This lander is launched on top of the Cargo Launch Vehicle (CaLV) into Low Earth Orbit (LEO) without its crew. The crew is launched separately on the Crew Launch Vehicle. The crew, in their Crew Exploration Vehicle (CEV) capsule, meet up with the lander in LEO. The CEV connects to the top of the lander, directly to the surface habitat (see figure). The crew then has access to the lander's habitable volumes during the remainder of the mission to the Moon. Once in Lunar orbit, the two ships undock, and the lander and her crew descend to the lunar surface while the CEV remains unpiloted in lunar orbit.

Minimized Ascent Stage

In the Apollo mission, the one habitat on the lunar lander functioned as living quarters, airlock, and ascent vehicle. A separate habitat became desirable with a larger crew of four and a longer surface stay of 7 days. The driving factor in the design of this vehicle was the mass of the ascent vehicle. Every kilogram/pound of ascent vehicle costs 0.8 kg (1.8 lb) of cargo that could have been carried down to the surface. Therefore, to

Lander/CEV configuration.

maximize the number of science instruments and equipment that could be carried, it was necessary to minimize the mass of the vehicle that brought the crew back up to lunar orbit after their surface mission was complete.

To do this, the physical size of the ascent vehicle was limited to the smallest diameter that could safely carry the four crew members and allow them to function during ascent. It will be a snug fit, but with a nominal ascent duration of only 3 hours, the small sacrifice in luxury is worth it. The ascent vehicle weight came in at just over 5 mt (11,000 lb), almost equivalent to that of the Apollo mission, but carries four crew members instead of two. Being similar in size to the Apollo ascent "cab" allows for an engine in the same thrust class as Apollo's engine. This heritage and experience base will be valuable when developing the rocket engines for the next-generation landers.

In another effort to minimize vehicle weight and maximize cargo carrying capability, the ascent vehicle is mounted on the side of the lander and doubles as the airlock – a notable feature of this concept. If there was not a separate airlock (as with the Apollo lander), the entire habitat volume would have to be depressurized every time an Extravehicular Activity (EVA) was needed, with precious air being lost to the vacuum of space. This would also require all four crew members to be suited up before depressurization. It is much less wasteful to have a small airlock for two crew members to leave and enter the vehicle without depressurizing the entire habitat. This airlock/ascent stage is shown in the figure and depicts possible locations of crew members in the surface habitat and the airlock/ascent stage. By mounting the ascent stage/airlock on the side of the vehicle, the structural loads are reduced (it is not in compression due to the load from the large CEV during the Trans-Lunar Injection and Lunar Orbit Insertion burns), and the surface access hatch is much closer to the surface. This configuration allows the hatch to be approximately 3 m (10 ft) off the surface, which is slightly lower than the Apollo lander.

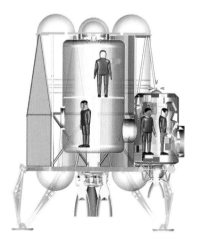

Crew in Habitat and airlock/ascent stage.

Subsystems

Although the Lunar Lander Preparatory Study (LLPS) lander is three times larger, the structure mass is only 60% heavier due to selection of this configuration, propellant choice, and numerous other innovations (including materials). This savings in structure mass contributes to larger LLPS lander payload delivery.

The six main propellant tanks provide LH$_2$ and LOX to the lander's main propulsion system. This is the same propellant that was used by the Space Shuttle's main engines. The LH$_2$/LOX combination is one of the most fuel-efficient rocket propellant mixes available (on a "miles-per-gallon" basis). This propellant combination is a cryogenic fluid, requiring refrigeration-like measures, compared to the Apollo storable hypergolic propellants, and therefore requires thermal management to maintain the LOX and LH$_2$. This thermal management involves the use of passive measures, namely Multi-Layer insulation (MLI) and spray-on foam insulation. Both Apollo's and this concept's higher technology use 5% of the lander's total mass for the propulsion subsystem.

The power, control, and avionics subsystems are both dramatically updated for the new lander. One example is the three orders of magnitude (or more) greater memory storage on the four flight computers (total on both stages) with three CPUs per computer. Proton Exchange Membrane (PEM) fuel cells are baselined as the power source for both the descent stage and ascent stage vehicles. These fuel cells are similar to the fuel cells that were used to power the Space Shuttle, but include many more advanced technologies. The fuel cells generate power by converting hydrogen and oxygen into water. The water produced during this process can then be used by the astronauts. The rest of the Power Management and Distribution (PMAD) equipment is based upon both off-the-shelf components and historical data for NASA spaceflight systems. The avionics design focused on the following four major areas: Communication & Tracking, Command & Data Handling (includes the flight computers), Displays and Controls, and Guidance, Navigation & Control. One notable feature of this concept is an S-Band wireless network for communication with the crew during Moon walks. The descent stage also has a wideband transceiver to send data such as video back to Earth. The Displays and Controls design includes controls that can be operated with gloved hands and operate in a vacuum in the event of depressurization. Each stage has two sets of displays and control panels. The ascent stage also has two sets of hand controllers for manual control of the spacecraft.

The ascent stage was investigated to determine if it had enough volume to accommodate four crew members (in modified ACES suits) during descent and ascent and two crew members in larger EVA suits during the lunar stay. The don/doff operation appeared feasible within the given cabin dimensions, but additional clearance between the knees and shoulders was needed to reduce the chance of crew and/or suit injury from bumping into wall-mounted avionics boxes. Therefore, a "keep-out zone" between the knees and shoulders was cleared of avionics boxes and other obstructions to provide clearance for the two crew members to doff and don the EVA suits. Environmental Control and Life Support System (ECLSS) atmosphere revitalization in the surface habitat includes a combined cabin and suit loop that provides CO$_2$ removal, atmosphere trace contaminant control, sensible heat rejection, and atmosphere humidity removal. An additional feature of this ECLSS design is its scarring such that eventually, if this lander becomes part of an outpost, CO$_2$ and water vapor could be recovered for closed-loop oxygen and water recovery rather than being vented overboard. Avionics and crew metabolic waste heat as well as environmental loads are thermally collected inside the descent and ascent stages and rejected through a fluid loop using radiators located on the descent stage.

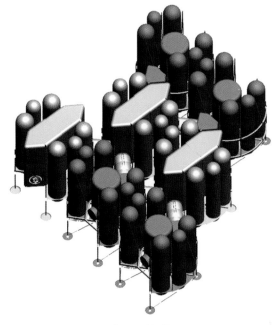

Home on the Moon.

Mobility
The next people to go to the Moon will eventually live and work for 6 months at a time from a central outpost. NASA's new lunar landing spaceships will bring people, supplies, and equipment to the lunar base. As with

MULE.

campers that drive their RVs across country then set them up in a campground as their home away from home, the lunar explorers will set the landers down on the surface then move them over land to the base. The figure on the previous page shows an example of a lunar base.

Due to navigation safety and the rocket nozzle exhaust ejecta damage problem, landers must set down at remote zones approximately 2 km (1.2 mi) from the outpost. The landers must then be moved to the outpost using a set of robotic transports. A set of four Mobility Utility for Lunar Exploration vehicles (MULEs) are used to accomplish this task (see next figure). MULEs, currently being studied by engineers at ARC, in California, are slightly smaller than golf carts and have a mass of 500 kg (1100 lb). Power is supplied by Li-Ion batteries that can be recharged from the outpost's central power station. MULE speeds range from 1 to 3 kph (0.6 to 1.9 mph). Even at these low speeds, lander transportation can be accomplished within half the time allocated for a standard 8-hour EVA.

Conclusions

This lander concept provides a minimum mass ascent stage, necessary for maximizing surface payload, and combines ascent stage and airlock functions. This design accomplishes the three separate missions with total lander masses of 45 mt (99,208 lbm) for the crewed sortie and outpost missions and 53.6 mt (118,168 lbm) for the cargo delivery version. The delivered additional payloads for the separate tasks are 1.7 mt (3,835 lbm) for the sortie case, 8.8 mt (19,498 lbm) for the crewed outpost mission, and 20.5 mt (45,215 lbm) for the uncrewed cargo lander. Also, the proposed MULE concept provides an efficient method of satisfying the lunar outpost mobility requirements and can be easily adapted to fit a variety of lander concepts.

Goddard Space Flight Center Lunar Lander Preparatory Study Phase II Concept: 0609-LLPS-GSFC

The GSFC LLPS Phase II concept included safe astronaut transport by EVA transfer or simple offloading of cargo via crane and Direct-to-Surface (D2S); a Minimum Ascent Vehicle (MAV) (the MAV concept was significantly increased per mission cargo capability compared to ESAS "Mass Wedge"); sortie: 3,220.5 kg (7,100 lbm) vs. 1,179.3 kg (2,600 lbm); and Crewed Outpost: 10,296.5 kg (22,700 lbm) vs.

4,218.4 kg (9,300 lbm). Efficiency of architecture can impact scope of approved lunar program via efficiency of Mass Wedge. Since the focus of this design cycle was the minimum MAV, the descent stage was not detailed, instead choosing to carry mass from earlier and other center's descent stage design efforts. The GSFC team offered its support to a continued architecture refinement effort.

Ascent Stage	
Power	Li-ion battery. EP SLC-16020 (129 Wh/kg, 303 Wh/L). Three batteries baseline; one extra battery for redundancy. 80% depth of discharge; 10% PMAD loss; 10% volume and weight growth at battery level.
Propulsion	The propulsion system had a single string, pressure-fed hypergolic MMH/NTO engine with an Isp of 318 sec. The baseline engine was a single, non-gimbaled, Space Transportation System-derived, AJ-10-190 engine with a thrust of 26,689.8 N (6,000 lbf). A zero-boil-off cryogenic (LOX/LH$_2$) option was also designed for a nearly 1,000 kg (2,205 lbm) mass savings for the ascent stage.
Telecommunications	S-band links for voice and telemetry. Nominal rates of 24 kbps, 200 kbps, and 1 Mbps. Ka-band links to Earth for high-rate telemetry and video. Nominally 150 Mbps to Earth, 25 Mbps from Earth.
Thermal	MLI (black surface, 0.6 kg/m^2 [0.1 lb/ft^2] / 0.001 psi) covered the entire external surface, absorbing 270 W during the worst case (lunar noon). This configuration could reject 100 W at polar region. Redundant pumped fluid loops remove heat. Nontoxic propylene glycol coolant. Cold plate for electronics and heat exchanger for atmosphere.

Mass Breakdown (MMH/NTO Option)		
Subsystem	lbm	kg
1.0 Structure	2,315	1,050
2.0 Protection	478	217
3.0 Propulsion (MMH/NTO MPS and RCS)	1,056	479
4.0 Power	538	244
5.0 Control	0	0
6.0 Avionics	602	273
7.0 Environment	712	323
8.0 Other	0	0
9.0 Growth	1,105	501
Dry Mass w/ Growth	**6,806**	**3,087**
10.0 Non-cargo	0	0
11.0 Crew + Cargo	1,058	480
Inert Mass	**7,864**	**3,567**
12.0 Non-propellant	0	0
13.0 Propellant	7,374	3,345
Gross Mass	**15,238**	**6,912**

Returning to the Moon: Goddard-Led Team Presents Lunar Lander Concepts to All-Star Panel

Tupper Hyde, Gabe Karpati, Ron Leung, Lloyd Purves, Jeff Stewart, Adam Matuszeski, Jason Budinoff, Molly Anderson, Shuvo Mustafi, and Tim Carnahan

For 4 months over the spring and summer of 2006, seven teams – including one led from Goddard Space Flight Center (i.e., Goddard) – examined the question of how NASA would land astronauts and cargo on the lunar surface when it returned late in the next decade. The 25-member Goddard-led team included some members from Glenn Research Center (GRC) and Johnson Space Center (JSC), and was tasked with looking at a minimum ascent vehicle and methods for offloading crew and cargo. The teams presented their ideas in September to an all-star panel of former and current NASA officials, including former astronauts John Young and Joe Engle, and Owen Morris, who headed the Apollo Lunar Lander Program in the 1960s. The Exploration Systems Mission Directorate is expected to use and refine some of the ideas in further studies. The images here – some created by summer and intern students who participated in Goddard's "skunkworks" effort – show a few of the ideas that the Goddard team presented.

Lander Concept

The GSFC-JSC-GRC Lander showed that a Minimum Ascent Vehicle (MAV) allows increased cargo to the surface compared to prior concepts where the ascent vehicle was also the habitat. Instead, a modular 7-day Sortie Habitat is used only on sortie missions, providing flexibility for even more cargo on crew rotation missions with no habitat. In fact, with minimal cargo, the crew rotation lander could be made light enough to enable a single Cargo Launch Vehicle launch mission (with the Crew Exploration Vehicle [CEV] on top as in Apollo). A vertical lander configuration with MAV, habitat, and cargo on top of an "all-mission-capable" generic descent stage is feasible; however, crew and cargo offload assistance from the 6-m (19-ft) high deck may be desired. An "EVAtor" system for crew and crane and direct-to-surface systems for cargo was shown to be effective, reliable, and safe.

Minimum Ascent Vehicle

The 3,000 kg (6,600 lbm) inert mass minimum ascent vehicle would contain 11.1 m³ (392 ft³) of pressurized volume and would taxi up to four astronauts wearing Mark III space suits to the lunar surface. It would include an external cargo area, inside storage space, windows, multiple exit points, including a full-size door, and a dust-collection system, among other features.

Crew deck.

The MAV crew cabin allows a pilot and co-pilot to stand beside one another to work the controls (on the right). The other two crew members can monitor vehicle systems. Cargo (samples to be returned to Earth), avionics, and life support equipment are stored beneath the floor. Access to the CEV, when mated, is through a Low Impact Docking System (LIDS) hatch in the roof. The main side door provides access to the habitat on sortie missions or to the outside on crew rotation missions.

Cryogenic Propulsion

The ascent stage is the most propellant expensive element in the entire Lunar Architecture; 1 kg (2.2 lbm) shaved off the ascent stage allows adding 1.5 kg (3.3 lbm) to 1.8 kg (3.9 lbm) to the Descent Stage. Having a high Isp propulsion system pays dividends like nowhere else. The problem is in storing cyrogenic propellants for more than 6 months on the lunar surface. In Phase 1, GSFC demonstrated that with some modification of existing technologies used for long-term storage of cryogens on scientific satellites, it might be possible to store cryogenic propellants in space and on the lunar surface for extended periods of time. In Phase 2, GSFC was tasked to design a MAV.

MAV crew cabin.

The option of a cryogenic propulsion system is extremely attractive for this goal since it would provide large mass advantages. Using a two-stage Dewar tank design, the mass advantage of cryo-propulsion over storable propellants was more than 900 kg (2,000 lbm) at a reasonable crycooler input power of just 180 watts.

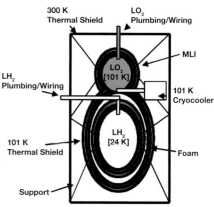

Cross-section of cryocooler.

This mass advantage has a multiplicative effect throughout the lunar architecture. In addition, LO_2/LH_2 are non-polluting green propellants; cross-enable fuel cells, water production, and life-support oxygen; have In-Situ Resource Utilization (ISRU) potential; and could provide a potential radiation safe haven. For these reasons, and since the mass advantage grows substantially for non-propulsion burnout masses that are higher than that for this minimum ascent stage, it is recommended that LH_2+LO_2 be seriously considered as the propellant of choice for the ascent stage.

For comparison, MAV designs with storable propulsion and cryo-propulsion were both done. The storable option used a single, pressure-fed engine (the Space Shuttle Orbital Manuevering Engine). The cryopropellant option for the MAV used a non-gimballed, two-engine arrangement with each engine pump feeding two bells. This allows two-for-one redundancy and for either pump to be shut down and still maintain centerline thrust.

EVAtor

To keep astronauts from descending directly into the lunar dust, which can be as sharp as razor blades, the Goddard team created an elevator, or EVAtor, system that would lower two astronauts and equipment from the top of the 6-m (19.7-ft) tall module to the surface. Equipped with a control panel, platform, fixed rails, cable supports, and

MAV design.

handrails, the EVAtor also would include a set of steps that would deploy directly to the surface. The team considered a range of options, including a scissors lift, a rappelling device, and even a Ferris wheel-like rotary lift, but settled on the elevator system after consulting with astronauts who preferred the elevator system.

Cargo Offload
The Goddard team examined a single crane and a direct-to-surface method to offload up to 21 mt (23 t) of cargo to the lunar surface, Although the team determined that both would meet NASA requirements, it found that the direct-to-surface system was more efficient and less risky under certain conditions. The system works simply by tilting the cargo and allowing the cushioned shipping containers to fall directly onto the surface. Due to the Moon's low gravitational pull, the impact would be no more severe than if someone pushed a padded container off a 1-m (3-ft) tall table.

EVAtor system.

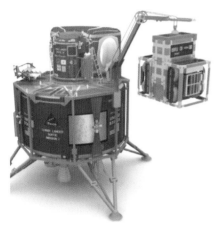

Single-crane method (left) vs. direct-to-surface method (right).

The Human Element of Lunar Lander Effort: Following in the Footsteps of Apollo
For many of the GSFC team members, the most rewarding part of this study effort was the deeper exposure it provided to the concepts, accomplishments, and – most importantly – some of the still-active veterans of the Apollo Program.

The significance of Apollo gets diminished when it is said that, if we can put a man on the Moon, then we can fix some vexing but seemingly less-difficult system – say, education. When the educational system fails to get fixed, it leaves the impression that putting humans on the Moon was more prosaic. However, in the opinion of numerous serious historians, the Apollo Project ranks as the greatest single technical undertaking in human history. It was also the definitive undertaking for NASA, which remains the working environment for all the team members.

What made the lunar lander particularly interesting is that, in some ways, it can be seen as the supreme engineering challenge on Apollo. While the Saturn V rocket was certainly the physically largest element of Apollo, it fundamentally looked and operated like a much larger version of earlier rockets. The Apollo command module is similarly related to the earlier Mercury and Gemini capsules. However, the Apollo Lunar Module had no precedent. Nothing before had taken humans to and from the lunar surface and nothing has since! Although the NASA Request for Proposal for the Lunar Module asked for a design concept, it also stated that not enough was known for NASA to select any concept. The winner would simply be the team that demonstrated the best understanding of the problem. The only purpose of the requested concept was to demonstrate this understanding. These and other pieces of interesting information about the lander were contained in a fascinating book by the Grumman project manager ("The Lunar Lander"), which was read with pleasure by various team members.

Another high point for the GSFC team was a visit to Smithsonian National Air and Space Museum to look at the display model of the Apollo lunar lander, which impressed many of the team by being larger than expected. An enjoyable comparison was the full-scale model of an artist's concept of the Victorian-era cabin of the lunar vehicle described in Jules Verne's book. Also of human interest was the display of an astronaut suit actually worn on the Moon, and which was still coated with dust. Another high point of this visit was the opportunity to see some of the lunar lander material in the museum library. The museum library is normally only open to approved researchers, but the Smithsonian staff was kind enough to extend that privilege to the GSFC team, which viewed some examples of original and well-preserved lunar lander documents from the Apollo era.

Meaningful as the above experiences were, it can be said that the human element of this study effort was most perfectly captured in an exchange during the final report presentation at JSC. The presentation was to a review board including three notable Apollo Program veterans: John Young, who actually walked on the Moon on the Apollo 15 mission and flew the Space Shuttle on its maiden flight; Joe Engle – also an Apollo astronaut and pilot of the X-15; and Owen Morris, the NASA manager of the Apollo Lunar Lander Program. More than one younger engineer from the various study teams would preface his or her comments by stating what a privilege it was to have the opportunity to address such notables. One presenter could not resist adding that Joe Engle had been one of his childhood heroes. Not missing a beat, Joe Engle turned to John Young and said that he had been one of Joe's childhood heroes. Amidst the ensuing laughter, John Young immediately said to Owen Morris that he had been one of John's childhood heroes. Owen responded with a quick, humorous "Thanks a lot!" knowing that there was no one present to whom he pass on that compliment. It should be noted that Owen had joined NACA, the NASA predecessor agency in 1947!

Concept Factory – VERY RAPID PROTOTYPING
Enthusiasm in the Goddard team was palpable. A meeting was held on a Thursday evening to kick off the Phase II design session, with the understanding that, after a few days of reflection, a second meeting would take place Monday to hash out concepts.

By the next Monday morning, to everyone's amazement, the Mechanical Team (Jeff Stewart, Drew Jones, Adam Matuzeski, Jason Budinoff, Luis Santos, et al.) delivered more than 10 mechanical concepts, most of them already fully built as animated three-dimensional (3-D) computer-aided design (CAD) models. Some of these are illustrated below:

Rapid prototyping, concept development, and 3-D CAD modeling.

We, as an intra-center team, had fun hashing out all the ins and outs of all the concepts and reviewing these with our astronaut team member, Andy Thomas, as well as JSC crew accommodations/human factors, Luis Trevino and Robert Howard. One concept had the lander literally hang upside down on tripod while the astronauts could "easily" emerge close to the lunar surface. We had a good laugh when someone pointed out that if an abort sequence was initiated, the ascent vehicle would shoot head first into the ground.

Lunar Lander Animation

The task of generating a lunar lander animation involved gathering model information of the vehicles involved and a lunar surface simulation. The early development of the animation involved an outline, or storyboard, of the activities desired to be prioritized, developed, and presented within the timeline. The lunar lander model involved a variety of different subsystems. Each of the subsystems was provided as a CAD model, using Pro/Engineer. These were then converted to Autodesk/Maya, the animation software used by the GSFC animation team in code 542. The subsystem models were further broken down into component mechanism parts, as needed. Thus, a model of the EVAtor included the ability to be animated as a deployable mechanism.

The astronauts were modeled in Maya with a previously unused feature: cloth simulation. This simulation technique allowed GSFC to model the astronaut suits and allow them to bend and flex as real cloth simulations.

The lunar surface model was taken from survey data provided by the GSFC Sciences Directorate, which provided a grid of x,y,z "realistic" data for the area around the Dawes crater and an image map for the region of interest. Using in-house developed code, the GSFC animation team converted the survey data to a solid representation of the lunar surface within the Maya tool.

Most of the mechanisms for the lunar lander were modeled as simple kinematic mechanisms. However, the fall bar device was modeled using a dynamic simulation system that took into account the action of the tip-off mechanism, the hinge release, and impact onto the lunar surface. This was a simulation that had not previously been done at GSFC.

Johnson Space Center Phase II Concept: 0609-LLPS-JSC

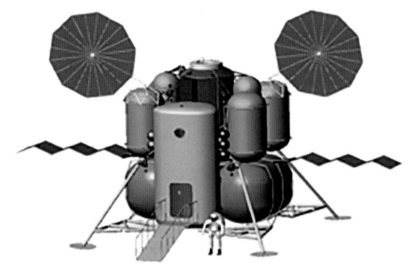

The "HabiTank" concept converts two of the descent propulsion hydrogen tanks into surface habitation units by pre-integrating an airlock between the two tanks. These tanks are fitted with access ports, located at each end of the tank, that are covered by sealing plates for tunnel attachment during the outpost assembly phase. The overall description of the HabiTank lander is a two-stage lander with an ascent stage and descent stage. The ascent stage is a cylindrical aluminum shell cylinder sized to fit four suited crew members – each donning a Mark III suit – during the descent landing and ascent to the CEV. It is sized for minimal occupancy duration, but is capable of a minimum of 3 hours as dictated by the Constellation Program Office. However, the study team indicated that the ascent stage should have a contingency operations timeline built into the design

for up to a range of 8 to 12 hours, pending further studies of abort and rendezvous scenarios. The figure depicts the habitable volumes of the lander concept. The Phase II concept included a single engine with dual pumps, providing adequate redundancy.

Offset Ascent Stage: Offset loads on the docking system drove the design to a canted arrangement and very high moments for an Earth Departure Stage (EDS) engine out case. Depending on packaging, CEV could require relocation after EDS or LOI burns.

Dual H_2 Tanks/Single Engine: Symmetric design provided for minimal center-of-gravity thrust vector offset, simpler flight control solution, adequate habitable volume, good engine packaging, and mitigated liquid feed issues via a sump tank.

Descent Stage	
Power	Solar arrays provided power to the Lander for Low Earth Orbit (LEO) operations performed on the lunar surface. During eclipse periods, Li-ion batteries were to be used to support these operations.
Propulsion	LO_2/LH_2 pump-fed engine, RL10 A-4 thrust = 101,419.4 N (22,800 lbf), based on Orbital Transfer Vehicle (OTV) engine from Pratt & Whitney Rocketdyne (PWR), but in RL-10 A4 configuration. Delta-v LOI = 1,250 m/s (4,101 ft/s) Descent = 1,911 m/s (6,269.7 ft/s) RCS = 272.2 kg (600 lbm) of propellant There was a 95-day loiter in LEO attached to EDS, single-fault tolerant for mission success. Provided LO_2 or LH_2 for fuel cells. LH_2 for boil-off was kept on EDS either in EDS MPS tank or separate tank mounted on EDS. This was the lowest mass option, since it did not carry a boil-off penalty to the Moon (i.e., larger lander descent tanks, cryo-coolers). Heat leak through MLI, supports/penetrations, target 50 W (~111.5 m^2 x 1135.6 joule/m^2/hr, or 1200 ft^2 x 0.1 btu/ft^2/hr); heat leak through airlock to tank connection, used S glass/epoxy thermal isolator (metal bellows on each end), ~ 20.3 cm (8 in) vestibule x 0.64 cm (0.25 in) thick, possibly some overwrap for pressure. Target 20 W heat leak (10 W each).

Descent Stage (Continued)

Thermal	Radiators could be partially/fully deployed and retracted. 62% of the Master Equipment List (MEL) line items were Commercial Off-the-Shelf (COTS) or scaled-COTS components. Used 60/40 propylene glycol/water solution as working fluid. Dissipated 6.4 kW during lunar operations, 4.9 kW during lunar descent, and 2.3 kW during lunar ascent.
Structures	Internal pressure (70.3 kPa/10.2 psi, Factor of Safety = 2.0), Al 2219 T87, 0.05 cm (0.020 in.) as minimum gauge pressure shell Window: Polycarbonate
Guidance, Navigation & Control	Thrust level estimate of 1,334.7 N (300 lbf); ~3 x size of Apollo LEM stack, engine envelope was 25.4 cm (10-in.) diameter by 61 cm (24 in.) length.

Ascent Stage

Power	Two 5 kW fuel cells provided descent power and initial 3 days for minimum lunar stay.
Propulsion	LO_2/LCH_4 pressure-fed engine, 33,361.2 N (7,500 lbf) thrust, ablative. Thrust picked to allow potential Service Module upgrade and lander ascent stage. Commonality included that the thrust is also similar to LOX/methane engine in development: Pc = 245, MR = 3.0 sec, Isp = 355 sec; RCS propellant stored in main tanks; sub-cooling of propellants allowed for zero boil-off; load at 173 R and allowed to warm to 224 R; common bulkhead tank (parent metal).
Thermal	Radiators could be partially/fully deployed and retracted. 62% of the Master Equipment List line items were COTS or scaled-COTS components. Used 60/40 propylene glycol/water solution as working fluid. Dissipated 6.4 kW during lunar operations, 4.9 kW during lunar descent, and 2.3 kW during lunar ascent.
Guidance Navigation & Control	16 thrusters, four quads at 90°, maximum moment arm, thrust level 445.2 N (100 lbf), Isp = 317 sec, engine envelope 17.8 cm (7 in.) diameter by 40.6 cm (16 in.) length. Capable of continuous burn of all main propellants as backup to main engine.

Mass Breakdown

Subsystem	Descent Stage / Sortie		Descent Stage / Outpost		Ascent Stage	
	lbm	kg	lbm	kg	lbm	kg
1.0 Structure	10,889	4,939	8,210	3,724	3,305	1,499
2.0 Protection	750	340	0	0	354	161
3.0 Propulsion	5,185	2,352	5,185	2,352	1,476	670
4.0 Power	3,446	1,563	3,722	1,688	782	355
5.0 Control	0	0	0	0	0	0
6.0 Avionics	580	263	580	263	489	222
7.0 Environment	1,543	700	0	0	110	50
8.0 Other	2,929	1,329	2,840	1,288	1,797	815
9.0 Growth	0	0	0	0	0	0
Dry Mass w/Growth	**25,322**	**11,486**	**20,537**	**9,315**	**8,313**	**3,772**
10.0 Non-cargo	0	0	0	0	0	0
11.0 Cargo	0	0	0	0	0	0
Inert Mass	**25,322**	**11,486**	**20,537**	**9,315**	**8,313**	**3,772**
12.0 Non-propellant	0	0	0	0	0	0
13.0 Propellant	57,721	26,182	57,721	26,182	6,423	2,913
Gross Mass	**83,043**	**37,668**	**78,258**	**35,497**	**14,736**	**6,685**

Lunar Lander "HabiTank" Concept

Johnson Space Center

Kriss Kennedy

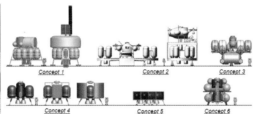

NASA Explores Alternative Concepts for Future Long-Term Lunar Missions

To support the Vision for Space Exploration, NASA sponsored a series of design studies of various lunar lander concepts with participation from most NASA centers. At Johnson Space Center (JSC), this Phase One design process was led by the Engineering Directorate for the Constellation Program Office. It explored numerous lander concepts, each of which had unique features. Some focused on unloading payloads, whereas others focused on reusability as a lunar taxi or reusing propellant tanks for habitation. Six lander concepts, shown above, emerged from analyzing program goals, desired outpost end-state, system capabilities, functional requirements, and operations concepts. The design philosophy was to have long-term needs for successful lunar surface exploration, while maximizing outpost capabilities, drive the lander design.

> The challenge of every team is to build a feeling of oneness, of dependence on one another because the question is usually not how well each person performs, but how well they work together.
>
> *– Vince Lombardi*

A multi-center Review Board was convened to evaluate these concepts as well as those from the studies of the other centers. In all, some 30 different lander concepts were evaluated, and the HabiTank concept from the JSC-led multi-center team was chosen to refine its design. Phase Two was to better understand the lander features, capabilities, derived requirements, and interface requirements that may affect the Crew Exploration Vehicle (CEV). As in Phase One, it was imperative in Phase Two that the expanded lander design team understand what they were tasked to do and that they were all on the same page.

A Challenge . . . A Vision . . . A Team

"The Challenge" given to the JSC team was to further explore and refine the concept of the "wet" habitat, namely using the spent propellant tanks as habitable volume after landing on the surface. The Lunar Lander Preparatory Study Team was formed to explore the HabiTank, as it came to be called, its design, its features, capabilities, derived requirements, and interface requirements, and how it might affect the design of the CEV.

"The Vision" was to develop a multifunctional and well-integrated lunar lander system that allowed sustainability and flexibility for landing crew and cargo to explore and establish a human presence on the Moon circa 2020.

The group, dubbed "The Habitank Team," was made up of individuals from multiple centers. Kriss Kennedy and Al Conde served as Study and Deputy Leads, respectively. The team was organized into functional disciplines represented by Pete Bethke and Ivan Cavenall for systems engineering and integration, John Zipay for vehicle engineering, Randy Rust for safety and mission assurance, Joe Cavallaro for mission operations, David Smitherman for surface operations, Robert Howard for human systems, and Andrew Thomas, representing the astronaut office. The design analysis was focused through these functional leads and the horizontal integration was conducted at the leads level.

In addition to the multi-center team, a group of veteran spacecraft engineers and managers known as the "wise owls" was used for peer reviews. Team members were: Warren Brasher, Jack Knight, Hal Lambert, Jim Jaax, Walt Guy, Joyce Carpenter, and Wil Ellis. This group reviewed the work at three separate reviews during Phase One and Phase Two. They held no punches in the review and evaluated the conceptual design from all aspects. They provided valuable design comments and suggestions, greatly aiding the design effort. This was a rewarding experience for all.

Creating a Design "WAR" Zone

The team was challenged to complete this study in approximately 8 to 10 weeks, a daunting task even in the best of conditions. It was first necessary to establish a design/meeting room, a space where the team would always have access, a place where everyone could come together and tackle the assignment. What the team needed was a "WAR" room. This room was pulled together quickly, and was up and running in less than 2 weeks, with several computers, Computer-Aided Design (CAD) stations, a smart board, teleconferencing, white boards, and workstations. It was also important that the team members from other NASA centers be able to participate from their home offices. Within this same 2-week time frame, a fully developed communication network was created that included an electronic file sharing system, WebEx and teleconferencing, and an events and calendar resource library – all accessible and workable from the WAR room.

Team meetings took place in the WAR room.

The team leads met in this room on a daily basis, and the full team of about 40 members met on a weekly basis. It became a room full of very serious engineers, space architects, and scientists, all with their distinct point of views but driven by the passion of visions of future space exploration. Amongst the serious design efforts and long hours were dashes of laughter, debates, comradery, and creative thinking that inspired all who entered the room. The donation doughnut-can became the focus of concern when it ran dry. (After all, there is nothing like a sugar buzz and caffeine to kick creativity into high gear.) The daily design sessions were of full of high energy, great expectations, and a can-do attitude. It was imperative the team work together face-to-face as much as possible to gain synergism among the systems and vehicle design.

Papers were scattered about, computers were operating at full capacity, drawings and sketches covered every inch of the walls. In addition, two full-scale mock-ups of the Ascent Module and HabiTank were built. Yet the atmosphere was like that of a symphony – all playing to the tune of one vision, one concept, and one challenge. As Aristotle once quoted, "Pleasure in the job puts perfection in the work."

The HabiTank Vehicle Concept

During the lunar Apollo missions, living spaces were small, there was no privacy, and the lunar surface stays were very brief.

The novel feature of the HabiTank Lander concept was the ability to dual-use the lander's two large hydrogen tanks as habitable volumes for a lunar outpost. The use of these tanks offered the capability for long-term human presence to be developed very quickly, and they also offered flexibility to build alternate outpost sites compared to deployment of an entirely new habitat and infrastructure. They also provided easy expansion of the habitable space of the outpost, and maximum utilization of all lander elements.

The team worked out many of the outfitting details of converting the tank components from cryogenic propellant tanks to fully outfitted living and working habitation spaces.

The team first decided that the HabiTanks should be designed and built with their end-state in mind. Rather than optimize the tanks for hydrogen storage, which represented only a small portion of their operational lifetime, they were optimized for their use as habitable elements. This was reflected first in their dimensions. Instead of an optimized cylindrical cross-section, the HabiTanks had a rounded rectangular cross-section, with a width of 2.6 m (8.5 ft) by a height of 2.9 m (9.5 ft) by 4.6 m (15 ft) long – each tank providing ~ 25 m³ (890 ft³) of volume. For the design to work, an airlock was required to be pre-connected and nestled in between the two large hydrogen tanks. Due to the time required to retrofit a tank into a habitable unit, it was deemed necessary to provide a "Sortie" Hab for missions of 3 to 7 surface days.

Each tank had a closed hatch on its aft face that was later used to interconnect the tanks together. They were also hard mated to an airlock with hatchways that were sealed while the tanks contained propellant. The Sortie Habitat that contained much of the equipment was later used to outfit the HabiTanks. The ascent stage of the vehicle was a minimalist design and provided crew access to the Sortie Habitat through a hatchway that had a pyrotechnic separation capability that was activated when the ascent stage departed at end of mission. Up to four crew members could be carried to the surface of the Moon in this lander. Power was provided by fuel cells and solar collection.

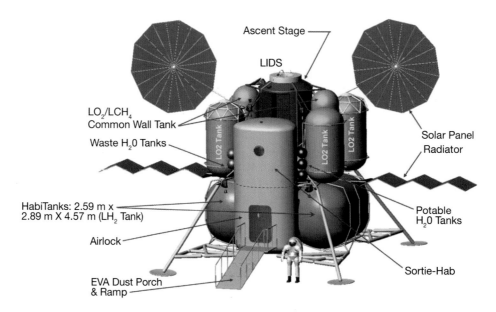

HabiTank vehicle construction.

Preparing the HabiTank for Human Entry

The design team studied the process required for the conversion of these vessels from cryogenic propellant tanks to fully outfitted living and working quarters. These steps included removing any residual propellant from the tanks, warming up the tanks, pressurizing the tanks with breathable atmosphere, verifying the pressure seal in the airlock/crew quarters vestibule, installing lighting, power and air circulation, disassembling the vertical baffles, installing the environmental monitoring system, alarm system, and communications systems, and activating airflow to the HabiTank.

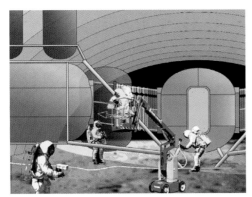
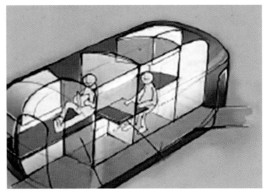

Tanks were converted to living quarters.

This process was repeated for each HabiTank with minor variations, driven by the specific items to be outfitted in each one. The concept was to convert each HabiTank into crew quarters, a galley and wardroom area, or other surface support areas such as extravehicular activity and mission operations.

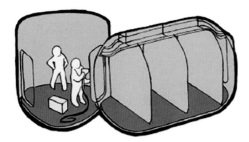
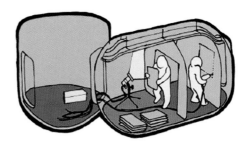

HabiTank cover plate removal. *Tank baffle disassembly.*

Once the lander had reached the lunar surface, crew or Mission Control personnel could begin to initiate the following steps to make the HabiTanks safe for human entry. First, the propellant tanks were closed off (dead-faced) and sealed from the propellant feed-lines, tank quantity sensors, repress lines, etc. Then the ground initiated pump-out of residual propellant. Next, the ground or crew was to initiate purge of residual propellant vapor. There was to be a time delay of ~13 hours for tanks to thermally condition, after which the internal atmosphere was sampled. Then, N_2 was bled into the HabiTanks to establish the correct PPN2. Once this step was complete, O_2 was to be introduced into the HabiTanks to establish the proper O_2/N_2 mix. Once the HabiTank was thermally stabilized and contained a breathable atmosphere, it was possible to begin the transformation from tank structure to outpost Habitation Module. The Pressurized Logistics Module (PLM) was mated to the HabiTanks with extendable inflatable tunnels.

The crew would perform several steps to prepare the HabiTank for habitation beginning with Crew Quarters Module 1. First, the crew would verify the pressure seal in airlock/crew quarters vestibule. Then they would open the equalization valve to equalize pressure between HabiTank and vestibule. When complete, they could open the hatch in the lander airlock, giving access to the airlock/crew quarters vestibule. The crew would then remove the thermal insulation from the vestibule, followed by the HabiTank cover plate. The passageway from lander airlock to HabiTank was then opened.

The crew members then were to install temporary lighting, power, and air circulation fans in the HabiTank so they could work intravehicular activity inside the tank to complete its transformation. The next step was to disassemble the removable sections of vertical baffle 1 and store the baffle plates temporarily in the airlock. They likewise disassembled removable sections of vertical baffles 2 and 3, and also temporarily stored those baffle plates in the airlock. Once the baffles had been removed, the crew needed to verify the pressure seal in the crew quarters to PLM vestibule, after which the crew could open the equalization valve to equalize pressure between the HabiTank and the vestibule. Next, the crew members were to remove the HabiTank cover plate and open the equalization valve to equalize pressure between the HabiTank and the PLM tunnel so that the hatch to the PLM could be opened.

Once the passageway tunnel from the HabiTank to PLM was open, the crew could begin to install the permanent utilities trunk (i.e., power, data, communications, air) in the HabiTank ceiling. Then, they could install the environmental monitoring, alarm, and communications systems, and the PLM airflow could be activated to the HabiTank. Any temporary air circulation fans could be removed. They would then configure the internal power and data cabling, and remove and stow any temporary power.

Next, the crew was to install Ortho-grid outfitting connectors and the wall liners (if applicable – some functional areas may have left the exposed aluminum skin). They could install and activate the permanent ambient light-emitting diode (LED) lighting. Any temporary lighting was removed and set up as task lighting. Next, the crew was to assemble the HabiTank furniture (chair, bed, desk, stowage, counter, table, etc., as appropriate) from the baffle plates temporarily stored in the airlock and fabric and padding stored in the PLM. The crew could position the furniture in designated locations in the HabiTank. Support cables and additional fabric partitions could be installed, and the remaining crew accommodations equipment (e.g., laptops, displays, crew personal items, etc.) were to be unpacked from the PLM and stowed in the HabiTank.

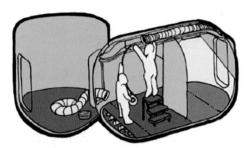

Utilities trunk installation.

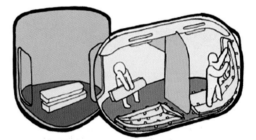

Wall liner installation.

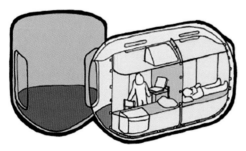

Completed HabiTank.

All the system utilities were then checked and verified operational prior to connection of electronic equipment. Upon a successful systems check, the HabiTank crew quarters were ready for occupation. This process was repeated for each HabiTank with minor variations driven by the specific items to be outfitted in each one. The Galley, EVA Maintenance, Geo Lab, Life Science, and Medical HabiTanks would have all also included a water line in their utilities trunks.

To refine the concepts and designs, and the outfitting process, the team built a full-scale mock-up of the HabiTank. By evaluating the mock-up, the team had a better understanding of the various issues that would impact the conversion process from a hydrogen tank to a habitable volume.

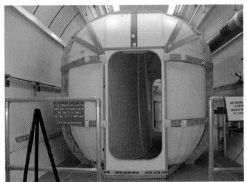

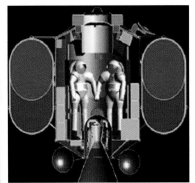

Exterior of HabiTank.

Working Through All the Mission Phases

The team also investigated the features of the ascent and descent stages. Using a full-scale mock-up of the ascent vehicle, the team was able to identify requirements and issues relating to crew accommodations, flight communications, ground communications, and mission operations.

The ascent stage avionics hardware and software provided Guidance, Navigation & Control (GN&C) information to enable the crew to land the combined ascent and descent stages on the Moon and support the later rendezvous of the ascent stage with the CEV. Displays and Controls provided the data necessary to control and manage the vehicle through all mission phases. Communications and Tracking equipment allowed the crew to talk to each other and to the ground mission control center.

Strategizing the Outpost Development and Lander Design

The HabiTanks from the spent lander descent stages formed Habitation Modules that could be connected together with the PLM to form a larger lunar outpost. The PLM was pre-integrated with inflatable tunnels and portals to allow connections to the opposite ends for the HabiTank/airlock system. The PLM or utility module served as a logistics module to transport the HabiTank outfitting and was also where the habitation subsystems were integrated and operated. This strategy allowed the outpost to be quickly assembled and become operational earlier. The HabiTanks and airlocks were planned to remain intact on the lander super structure to ensure structural integrity while transporting the entire lander stage to the final outpost location. Four descent stages and two PLMs were to be used to create the required functionality and volume for the outpost to support four crew members during their 180- to 210-day surface operations stay.

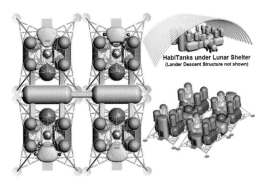
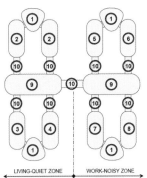

1. AIRLOCK & SORTIE HAB
2. CREW QUARTERS
3. GALLEY/WARDROOM
4. MISSION OPS
5. LIFE SCIENCE
6. MEDICAL OPS
7. GEO-SCIENCE LAB
8. EVA FACILITY
9. PLM/UTILITY MODULE
   (ENGINE ROOM)
10. INTERCONNECT TUNNEL

Lunar outpost functional layout.

The Lander HabiTank concept offered a number of advantages for lunar outpost development and lander design. These advantages included the following:

- Capability for long-term human presence developed very quickly.
- If the HabiTank failed on one flight (e.g., could not relocate, or could not be accessed), subsequent flights could provide it with little overall manifest impact.
- More useful volume (e.g., tanks, airlock, Sortie Habitat, etc.) came with every flight.
- The HabiTank was not locked into one outpost location – Sortie Landers with keep-alive capability could be deployed at different sites on the lunar surface to support an extended sortie strategy of exploration ("Cabin in the Woods").

Additional advantages of this lander configuration were:

- Single descent engine configuration met reliability and redundancy requirements.
- Spent descent stages did not create a field of impacted debris.
- Packaging brought the airlock porch close to surface.
- Good visibility for crew during landing.
- Propellant feed problems of large tanks mitigated by use of sump tank.
- Used a minimal ascent stage.
- Airlock was not thrown away with each flight.
- Only one common descent style was needed to perform a variety of missions:
  - Crew plus cargo (airlock, Sortie Habitat, HabiTanks)
  - Cargo only (but could carry airlock and HabiTanks, or not, as required)
  - Crew exchange (ascent stage only, no airlock or Sortie Habitat)

Jet Propulsion Laboratory Phase II Concept: 0609-LLPS-JPL

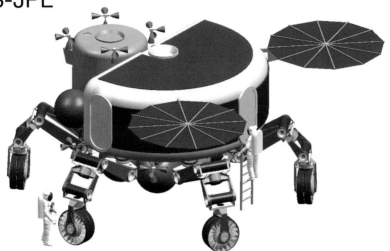

The Jet Propulsion Laboratory (JPL) Phase II concept horizontal configuration facilitated large cargo deployment and simplified crew egress/ingress. The sortie lander was reconfigurable and directly extensible to outpost deployment and logistics resupply missions.

The split habitat and minimum volume ascent stage improved vehicle performance to enhance payload-to-the-surface capability. The four engine descent stage main propulsion system provided engine-out capability during descent.

Descent Stage	
Power	9 kW photovoltaic array (30 m² [322.9 ft²] total in two Ultraflex solar arrays, 100 kg [220.5 lbm] mass). MobiLander Stage: regenerative H₂/O₂ fuel cell hybridized with large-format Li-ion batteries (5000 cycle lifetime, 27.8 kWh capacity, 216 kg [476.2 lbm] mass).
Propulsion	RL10A4-2 engine, Isp 451, thrust 99 kN (22,256.1 lbf), gimbal (±4°), throttleable (100% to 20%); also densified propellant, multiple tank configuration, increased in surface area/heat leak, multiple tank drain LH₂ systems sensitive to differential pressures.
Thermal	LOX/LH₂ active cryo cooling to support the 95-day LEO stay MobiLander: Passive cooling and boil-off for the trans-lunar flight and landing. Pre-cooling, passive cooling, and boil-off for the trans-lunar flight and landing. Sun/Earth shade to minimize cryo cooler power requirement in Low Earth Orbit (LEO). Thermal radiators for Environmental Control Life Support (ECLS) and fuel cell heat exchangers were mounted on the MobiLander habitat.
Guidance, Navigation & Control	Radar altimeter provided altitude and horizontal and vertical velocity relative to surface. LN-200S and Mars Exploration Rover (MER) heritage navigation cams and hazard cams were to be used for surface navigation and hazard avoidance.
Ascent Stage	
Power	Li-CFx, 8-hour lifetime, 12 kWh capacity, 25 kg (55.1 lbm) mass
Propulsion	Pump-fed MMH/NTO main engine, increase in Isp ~7.5%, XLR-132 engine Isp 340, thrust 22KN, fixed (no gimbal).
Thermal	Outer surface covered with foam insulation plus 60-layer MLI (consider foam core shield, provided both thermal insulation and micrometeoroid protection). Radiators were mounted to MobiLander stage. Evaporative cooling during ascent.
Guidance Navigation & Control	Storable (MMH/NTO) pressure-fed system, 16 at 490 N (110.2 lbf) thrusters, Isp 321 sec. Star trackers and gyros for stellar inertial attitude determination. Accelerometers for position determination during descent and ascent. Scanning LIght Detection And Ranging (LIDAR) for rendezvous (couple of kilometers to tens of meters). Wide-angle camera used during terminal rendezvous (tens of meters).

Mass Breakdown - Side Mounted						
Subsystem	**Descent Stage**		**Ascent Stage**		**Cargo Descent Stage**	
	lbm	kg	lbm	kg	lbm	kg
1.0 Structure	4,877	2,212	1,162	527	4,546	2,062
2.0 Protection	639	290	85	187	252	114
3.0 Propulsion	1,423	646	808	366	1,572	713
4.0 Power	2,450	1,111	494	224	2,074	941
5.0 Control	150	68	0	0	150	68
6.0 Avionics	393	178	452	205	393	178
7.0 Environment	3,631	1,647	742	337	728	330
8.0 Other	3,873	1,757	991	450	3,985	1,807
9.0 Growth	3,130	1,420	944	428	2,740	1,243
Dry Mass w/Growth	**20,566**	**9,329**	**5,678**	**2,724**	**16,440**	**7,456**
10.0 Non-cargo	860	390	634	287	0	0
11.0 Cargo	2,205	1,000	1,041	472	36,376	16,500
Inert Mass	**23,631**	**10,719**	**7,353**	**3,483**	**52,816**	**23,956**
12.0 Non-propellant	903	410	90	41	210	463
13.0 Propellant	9,129	4,141	5,859	2,657	5,739	12,652
Gross Mass	**33,663**	**15,270**	**13,302**	**6,181**	**58,765**	**37,071**
Mass Breakdown – Top Mounted						
Subsystem	**Descent Stage**		**Ascent Stage**		**Cargo Descent Stage**	
	lbm	kg	lbm	kg	lbm	kg
1.0 Structure	4,616	2,094	2,362	1,071	4,546	2,062
2.0 Protection	606	275	207	94	252	114
3.0 Propulsion	1,371	622	817	370	1,572	713
4.0 Power	2,442	1,108	497	225	2,074	941
5.0 Control	150	68	0	0	150	68
6.0 Avionics	393	178	452	205	393	178
7.0 Environment	3,631	1,647	742	337	728	330
8.0 Other	3,280	1,488	1,011	459	3,985	1,807
9.0 Growth	2,941	1,334	1,194	542	2,740	1,243
Dry Mass w/Growth	**19,430**	**8,814**	**7,282**	**3,303**	**16,440**	**7,456**
10.0 Non-cargo	860	390	634	287	0	0
11.0 Cargo	1,102	500	1,041	472	36,376	16,500
Inert Mass	**21,392**	**9,704**	**8,957**	**4,062**	**52,816**	**23,956**
12.0 Non-propellant	903	410	90	41	210	463
13.0 Propellant	8,897	4,035	7,458	3,383	5,739	12,652
Gross Mass	**31,192**	**14,149**	**16,505**	**7,486**	**58,765**	**37,071**

The MobiLander

Bob Gershman, Tess McEnulty, and Brian Wilcox
Jet Propulsion Laboratory

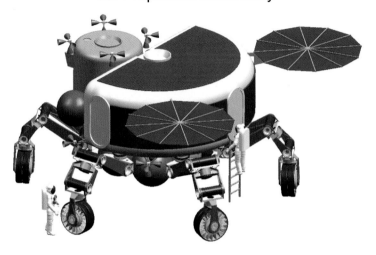

When Jet Propulsion Laboratory (JPL) was asked, along with the other NASA centers, to contribute innovative concepts for the next human lunar landing, we asked ourselves what could we bring to the table that others might not. After much internal discussion, we latched onto one of the principal goals of the study: to maximize reuse of hardware sent to the Moon, and particularly reuse of hardware from short-duration early crew visits (i.e., "sorties") in buildup of a permanent outpost. This goal implied a need to provide mobility for landed assets, and mobility on extraterrestrial surfaces is something we know a lot about – both from our Mars rover experience and from work we've been leading to develop the ATHLETE system described below. So, we set out to design a highly mobile habitat for the first lunar crews that could enhance exploration during the 4- to 7-day sortie mission and then could be moved, under telerobotic control from Earth, to become part of the lunar outpost.

We did most of the work in our "Team X" concurrent engineering environment, which facilitates rapid development of conceptual designs for a wide variety of space missions. At first we treated the crew members and their gear as just one more payload, to be delivered to the appropriate place in the Solar System, but we quickly realized that we had to deal with two major differences between crewed missions and the robotic solar system exploration missions that we are used to designing: (1) that crew safety is a critical overarching factor affecting every aspect of the design; and (2) that the crew is an integral part of the mission operations system. Fortunately, the sponsors of the study had established an environment to facilitate inter-center cooperation. We were able to make a highly experienced astronaut, Andy Thomas, a part of our team, and to call upon various other crew system experts to assure that our design was appropriate for a crewed mission.

The product of our effort was the MobiLander concept illustrated here. This concept comprises three elements: (1) the Lunar Orbit Insertion and Descent (LOID) stage, which provides all of the propulsive capability for lunar orbit insertion (LOI) and part of the capability for deorbit and descent before being discarded to impact the Moon many kilometers from the landing site; (2) the MobiLander element, which provides the remainder of the descent and landing propulsion, an integrated landing and mobility system, and a spacious habitat; and (3) a small ascent stage with minimum functionality needed to transport the crew from the lunar surface to the Orion Earth return vehicle waiting in lunar orbit. Once on the surface, the MobiLander has the capability to transport the crew in pressurized comfort tens of kilometers per day and, after a sortie crew returns home, to traverse hundreds or thousands of kilometers to perform scouting and be available as a backup at the next sortie landing site and/or to become part of a long-term outpost facility.

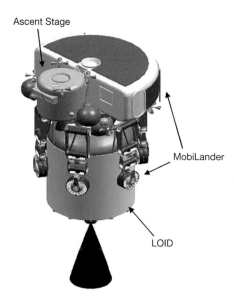

Ascent Stage

MobiLander

LOID

As launched from Earth, the MobiLander stack includes the LOID stage and the Ascent Stage as well as the MobiLander itself.

ATHLETE is the All-Terrain, Hex-Limbed, Extra-Terrestrial Explorer, which is a mobility, manipulation, and landing system being funded by the NASA Exploration Technology Development Program for lunar applications. It has six wheels on the ends of six limbs, each with six degrees-of-freedom so the limbs can place the wheels in any position and orientation within a substantial work volume. The wheels provide power-efficient rolling mobility on moderate terrain, while the limbs provide active suspension to reduce the "jouncing" effects of moderate-speed driving in low gravity, and also enable walking mobility on extreme terrain. Each wheel has a quick-disconnect tool adapter that allows tools to be extracted from a "tool belt," with a power take-off from the wheel supplying power to the tool. The prototype vehicles that have been built are half-scale at 2.75 m (9 ft) across, a mass of about 850 kg (1,874 lb), and a top speed of about 10 km/h (6.2 mph). The legs on a full-scale lunar system would have a combined mass of about 5% of the total vehicle mass of almost 20 mt (22 t). Landing is accomplished by using an air bag deployed under the launch adapter ring (that connects the MobiLander to the LOID from launch to the time the LOID stage is dropped) to dissipate the landing energy by venting gas through an orifice, while the ATHLETE limbs are used as outriggers to prevent tip-over.

MobiLanders link together to form the outpost core after erecting a dirt-covered tent for protection from solar radiation and cosmic rays.

Athlete climbing a hill.

Athlete using its tool adapter.

Athlete using its tool adapter to drill into the ground.

Having both mobility and manipulation in the MobiLander provides many benefits. The vehicle can squat while all six limbs perform manipulation for self-maintenance, science instrument placement, or sample gathering. A small glove box at the base of the vehicle will allow astronauts to handle and inspect samples without going through all the rigors of getting into their space suits. A small airlock for samples will allow them to bring samples of special interest into the habitat for study or archiving. The limbs will be able to perform construction operations such as building a tent that can be covered with dirt for protection from the radiation of occasional solar flares, or just from the long-term effects of galactic cosmic rays. A trenching tool will allow utility cables to be protected from micrometeorites. A larger "dozer blade" will allow substantial amounts of loose surface material to be collected for processing as a resource — e.g., to extract oxygen. Auger bits allow sampling of deeper materials to search for resources, as part of a science investigation, or to emplace anchors as needed to put up the radiation-protection tent or to support rappelling down steep slopes (such as into craters). Lunar outpost buildup requires mobility for large elements, since these cannot be landed in the middle of the outpost. Our study designed a long-range mobility system that can be incorporated into the crew habitats starting in the sortie phase at small incremental mass cost. This concept provides several advantages: maximum reuse of sortie hardware in outpost buildup, extensive robotic prospecting and detailed scouting of future landing sites, reduced number of cargo missions to achieve full outpost capability, long-range pressurized roving available in every mission with options for non-extravehicular activity (e.g., glove box) science, flexible manipulation capability, positioning of large cargo elements after landing, and safety and robustness for all lunar surface operations. Our study showed that these advantages of long-range mobility can be achieved consistent with program resources and constraints for mass, cost, risk, and technology development schedules.

Personal Views of the MobiLander Concept

Bob Gershman, Andy Thomas, and Tess McEnulty

Surface Mobility – Traditional human planetary surface exploration concepts derive largely from the Apollo model and center around a lander, from which surface Extravehicular Activity (EVA) excursions are made either on foot, or in an unpressurized rover. However, in either case, protection of the crew members from suit failures, rover failures, or solar radiation events does require that they not roam too far from the lander, or exceed the walk-back capability offered by the suit. Traverses with multiple unpressurized rovers can mitigate the rover failure issue. However, sleep, hygiene, and meal periods are not possible, so the range of exploration is therefore restricted. A pressurized rover can be used to perform more-distant traverses, with rest periods at remote sites. However, to protect for possible failures, most such scenarios require two rovers, with one being kept available for contingency rescue. Further, transfer to and from a pressurized rover from a lander requires either an EVA or sophisticated docking fixtures on both vehicles. An alternative strategy in which the lander itself has the surface mobility mitigates these problems. Such a concept allows the crew to traverse large distances without going EVA and maintain crew rest and sleep periods while being close to their ascent vehicle at all times. It also allows them to carry a larger suite of tools and science packages, thereby offering greater flexibility to the exploration and enhancing the return that the exploration offers.

The ATHLETE Lander Combination – Any surface mobility system must allow travel over uneven terrain, and be able to avoid obstacles such as boulders, craters, or embankments. The wheel/leg combination of the ATHLETE vehicle is unique in that it provides these and other operational benefits that improve crew safety, while enhancing capability. For example, the wheels of the vehicle provide mobility for travel over extended distances so that exploration to remote sites is feasible without being constrained by limitations of time in suit or crew sleep periods. The walking capability of the legs themselves enables the vehicle to negotiate very uneven surfaces, and with good obstacle avoidance. Further, this capability allows access to sites that a conventional rover or even a crew person on foot may not be safely able to access, such as up an embankment, down into a crater, or down into a rill. Finally, the articulation of the legs enables the vehicle to be used singly, or in combination, as manipulators, digging tools, drilling tools, etc. This means that surface operations and sample collections, and even repairs, can be performed without having to incur the risks of EVA. Thus, if properly implemented, the ATHLETE concept greatly enhances the capability and crew safety of human planetary surface exploration.

Bob Gershman, JPL Study Lead – As a veteran of nearly 40 years on NASA projects, I've been involved in dozens of conceptual design studies and thought I'd seen everything, but this study provided two pleasant surprises. The first was the ease with which we were able to mesh the conceptual design methodologies of the robotic and human mission elements of NASA to produce a strong concept. With timely inputs from folks at Houston, the JPL concurrent engineering process, developed over the course of literally hundreds of conceptual design studies, proved to be effective in piecing together a design that satisfied all key requirements for crew safety and performance. The second revelation was the synergistic cooperation among all of the participating NASA centers. Each of the participating teams, while led by one particular NASA center, drew on the strengths of other centers. That the result was an outstanding set of innovative concepts bodes well for the future of the Exploration enterprise of human planetary surface exploration.

Andy Thomas, Astronaut – Over the course of the study, I was impressed how well the different centers worked together and exchanged information freely. There was a great sense of cooperation, with no competition, and it allowed creativity to flourish and ideas to be exchanged. It spoke very highly of the personnel involved. In addition, the teams I witnessed, including the one at JPL, kept their size small, and they had creative thinkers involved. Most importantly, these individuals also had the right technical skills and experience. There was good leadership and the leaders were able to clearly communicate the objectives and status of the effort, as well as keep track of all the activities of the individuals. The process was not burdened by management overhead, or too much government bureaucracy or paperwork. Finally, it was refreshing to see that the centers that have not traditionally built human spacecraft were actively engaged in the process. It is apparent that there is a considerable skill level in spacecraft design at these centers, probably because there are more robotic spacecraft being built than human spacecraft. Those skills and capabilities are something that the human spaceflight centers could do well to embrace.

Tess McEnulty, New JPL Systems Engineer –

A giant six-legged robot watches as a small vehicle blasts toward the stars. The vehicle is carrying four astronauts back to the Orion spacecraft that is waiting in orbit around the Moon to bring them back to Earth. The robots that had served as the human's home during their stay are left behind to venture out on their own and prepare for the next set of human explorers to arrive. Controlled from the Earth, they travel across the surface together, driving around craters and large rocks that are impeding the path to the next landing site.

– One of the many scenes that I imagined while working on the MobiLander

It was the first week at my first full-time job. I had just graduated from the University of Michigan with a degree in Aerospace Engineering, and I was ecstatic to be starting a job that I had dreamt about since elementary school. I was still busy trying to set up my computer and all of the other basic items I would need for work when Bob Gershman, the study team lead, came in and asked me if I would want to work on a lunar lander study. My mouth dropped to the floor when he began to tell me about the concept, and I knew that my job was going to turn out to be everything that I had hoped for. I ended up working on surface scenarios for the MobiLanders, and on building up an outpost by connecting them to form a large habitat. In addition, I got to take part in Team X sessions and give input into the design of the MobiLander. Throughout the process I began to really appreciate Team X. It was incredible to work through design problems in real time with a group of subsystem experts from JPL. I also found interaction with other centers very helpful, since they have more experience with human space systems. I look forward to further concept studies, and to seeing some of them turn into reality over the years ahead.

Glenn Research Center Lunar Lander Preparatory Study Phase II Concept: 0609-LLPS-GRC

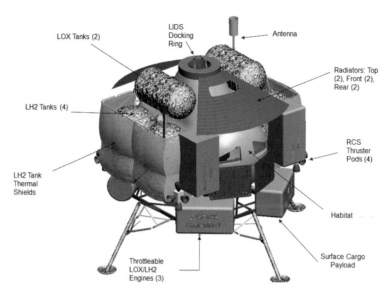

The GRC Lunar Lander Preparatory Study (LLPS) Phase II concept was a split descent lander with a drop stage and cryogenic ascent that enabled long-duration (180-day) lunar surface storage of cryogenic propellants.

Split Descent Issues and Risks: Risks and issues associated with the split descent stage included trajectories, altitude/velocity at staging, disposal and contingency operations. Details of surface storage of cryogenic propellants and keep-alive requirements for the lander (for 180-day surface stay) were also open issues.

Descent Stage	
Power	Power generation via H_2/O_2 PEM fuel cell; triple redundancy with each stack sized to provide full 5 kW at 28 Vdc; reactants stored with propellants. Additionally, the water produced from the fuel cell reaction was provided to the ECLSS. Photovoltaics via state-of-the-art 28% multi-junction solar cells. Two-axis tracking for deployed array (ATK Ultraflex). Power storage via PEM electrolyzer; triple redundancy; Li-ion batteries (Lunar Capture and Descent Stage [LCADS] only); battery load provided by set of two batteries with one included for redundancy. Two-axis solar array tracking (assembled by crew) provided power and charged regenerative fuel cells during 14-day illumination.
Propulsion	Main propulsion via three Main LOX/LH_2 engines; Reaction Control System (RCS) propulsion via four pods of four Gaseous Oxygen (GOX)/Ethanol thrusters distributed around vehicle, dual Ethanol tanks, dual GOX tanks, propellant tanks, two LOX tanks, four LH_2 tanks; pressurization system via two Helium tanks.
Telecommunications	High-rate communication trunks between Earth and Moon, direct communication when in view of Earth. Orbital satellite relay for majority of communications, CEV communication primarily through orbital relay; limited direct communication to lander or rover; direct link to Earth available (when in view). Ka-band for trunk line services.
Thermal	Radiators were fixed and external to the pressurized module. External fluid lines were not shown. All other active thermal components were internal to the module (e.g., pumps, cold plates, heat exchangers). Fan radiators on roof were ~11 m² (118.4 ft²) each. Window radiators were ~1.7 m² (18.3 ft²) each. Door radiators were ~ 2.1 m² (22.6 ft²) each. Total radiator area was ~29.5 m² (317.5 ft²).

Mass Breakdown		
Descent/Ascent Stage		
Subsystem	lbm	kg
1.0 Structure	3,448	1,564
2.0 Protection	0	0
3.0 Propulsion	2,615	1,186
4.0 Power	756	343
5.0 Control	950	431
6.0 Avionics	3,203	1,453
7.0 Environment	1,043	473
8.0 Other	2,321	1,053
9.0 Growth	1,041	472
Dry Mass w/Growth	**15,377**	**6,975**
10.0 Non-cargo	505	229
11.0 Cargo	0	0
Inert Mass	**15,882**	**7,204**
12.0 Non-propellant	0	0
13.0 Propellant	9,806	4,448
Gross Mass	**25,688**	**11,652**

NASA Glenn Research Center Team Lunar Lander Design

Brian F. Quigley and Steven R. Oleson

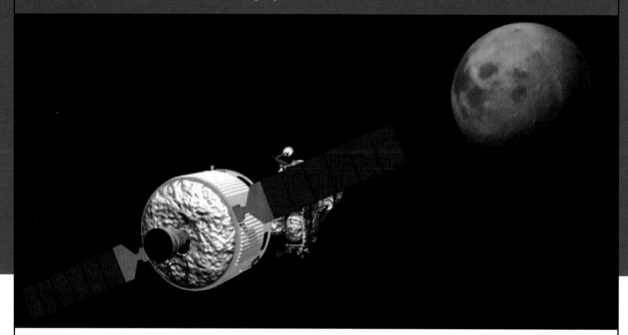

Imagine that you're on your way to the Moon, sitting inside NASA's Orion crew module. You and your fellow astronauts need to stop in Low Lunar Orbit (LLO) – that is, in a circular orbit about 97 km (52 nmi) above the lunar surface – and then land on the Moon. What kind of spacecraft is best to do that? One option might be to use a two-stage spacecraft, part of it for capture into Moon orbit and descent to the surface and another (on top) for return to lunar orbit (similar to the NASA's Apollo Lunar Module that landed humans on the Moon in the 1960s and 1970s). A simpler and cheaper option would be to use a disposable drop stage to capture into LLO at the Moon and then perform all but the last bit of descent to the surface. A crewed lunar lander spacecraft could then complete the landing. This human spacecraft would then be used to return to orbit. This simpler option was explored by a team of engineers at NASA Glenn Research Center and called "staged descent." The disposable drop stage would be based on stages that normally carry spacecraft into orbit and would cost much less than piloted spacecraft such as the Space Shuttle. Only a single spacecraft would carry and support you and your fellow three astronauts. This lunar lander is lighter than a vehicle that performs all of the descent, so you can carry more payload (or "useful stuff") to the lunar surface and can also take off more easily from the lunar surface because of its lower weight. Let's take a ride in the stage descent vehicle and see what it is like.

Staged Descent Concept for Piloted Lunar Landing

You are piloting the Orion with three other astronauts when you command the disposable drop stage rocket to fire in LLO so you don't fly by the Moon. Next, you all move to the lunar lander vehicle, separate from the Orion (which will stay in orbit waiting for your return) and then command the disposable drop stage to burn one more time to bring the lunar lander to a height of a few miles above the Moon's surface. You then command the drop stage to drop off and it lands many miles from your landing site. Your drop stage is called LCADS, which stands for Lunar Capture and Descent Stage. Once the drop stage is gone, you command the lunar lander rockets to fire, and you hover and steer the lander to safely land on the Moon. Two significant advantages of your staged descent landing are more payload to the lunar surface and a shorter lunar lander due to smaller propellant tank

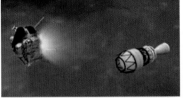

size, which means you have a shorter ladder to the Moon's surface. Another advantage is only one of the vehicles (the lunar lander in which you are riding) is made to support a crew, thus making the mission more than 30% cheaper than an Apollo-type mission. These advantages are a direct result of your use of the disposable LCADS to perform the majority of the descent burn and ejecting it prior to landing. The increase in payload capability is extremely important as it directly relates to the amount of expedition and science equipment you can use on the surface (things such as rovers and telescopes).

After you and your fellow astronauts have explored the lunar surface for a week, you command the lunar lander to drop its legs and use its rockets again to return to LLO to dock with the Orion. Three rocket engines are used for the landing and takeoff burns to ensure that, even in the event of the loss of a rocket engine, at least one will be available to get you back to the Orion. The Orion then provides you a triumphant return to Earth.

Lunar Capture and Descent Stage (LCADS) Description
The LCADS design was based on a Boeing Delta IV upper stage that uses very cold LOX/LH_2 propellants – the same propellants that were stored in the large external tank of the Space Shuttle. The propulsion system is a single LOX/LH_2 engine with a deployable nozzle, meaning the nozzle can be unfolded after launch to provide more thrust. When the nozzle is fully open (or deployed), the engine can provide a thrust level of 111,205.5 N (25,000 lbf). (An astronaut throwing a baseball in space only generates 4.4 to 8.9 N [1 to 2 lbf] of thrust.) The propellants are stored in a single LOX and a single LH_2 tank. Lithium-ion batteries are utilized to provide power. The LCADS can deliver a lander fully loaded with propellants that weighs about 17,690 kg (39,000 lb). This is about the same weight as ten mini-vans – with you, your family, and the dog included!

The LCADS weighs approximately 27,215 kg (60,000 lb) when fully loaded with propellants. After completing its 300-second burn (performing 70% of the lander's descent burn), the LCADS is discarded at an altitude of approximately 3,353 m (11,000 ft) where it free falls to the lunar surface while the lander completes the remaining 30% of the powered descent. The LCADS impacts the lunar surface approximately 1 minute after separation, 18 km (11.5 mi) from the landing site. The lander completes the descent approximately 4 minutes after separating from the LCADS.

Lunar Lander Description
A key way to judge a design's performance is to see just how much payload can be delivered to the lunar surface, and how much payload can be returned. In other words, we want to take equipment to the Moon and we also want to bring samples of lunar rocks and/or soil back to Earth. The lander can deliver 1,588 kg (3,500 lb) of payload (that is one loaded mini-van) in addition to the crew to the lunar surface and can return 100 kg (220 lb) of payload from the lunar surface.

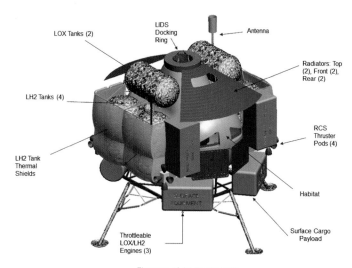

LOX Tanks (2)

LIDS Docking Ring

Antenna

Radiators: Top (2), Front (2), Rear (2)

LH2 Tanks (4)

RCS Thruster Pods (4)

LH2 Tank Thermal Shields

Habitat

Throttleable LOX/LH2 Engines (3)

Surface Cargo Payload

Elements of the lunar lander.

The main propulsion system consists of three LOX/LH$_2$ rocket engines, with each engine capable of providing 33,361.7 N (7,500 lbf) of thrust. The system has backups in case of rocket engine problems, since two of the rockets could shut down and the lunar lander would still be able to take-off safely back to the Orion. The Reaction Control System (RCS) propulsion consists of four sets of four gaseous oxygen/ethanol 444.8 N (100 lbf) thrusters distributed around the vehicle. An RCS is needed for attitude control and for small-scale maneuvers such as those required for rendezvous and docking with the Orion.

The lander has four LH$_2$ tanks and two LOX tanks fabricated from aluminum. The LH$_2$ tanks are placed on each side of the crew habitat; however, the heavier LOX tanks are placed near the top of the crew habitat to raise the vehicle center of mass. This high center of mass allows single engine thrusting for each of the three canted engines through the vehicle's center of mass.

Cryogenic propellant boil-off becomes a significant issue due to the requirement for the lunar lander to sustain a 95-day waiting period in Low Earth Orbit (LEO) before the Orion is launched and mated with the lander in LEO. If the cryogenic propellants are not kept cold enough, some of the propellants may warm up and evaporate, forming a high-pressure gas bubble in the tank that must be released into space before bursting the tank. This process, called propellant boil-off, reduces the amount of propellants in the tanks available for propulsion. Accordingly, the NASA Glenn Research Center investigated a Cryogenic Boil-off Reduction System to eliminate oxygen boil-off and reduce hydrogen boil-off of the propellants.

The Thermal Control System (TCS) is designed to maintain proper temperatures for electrical equipment, power sources, and crew living spaces. Excess heat is collected by the TCS and then radiated into space. Many components of the TCS (such as pumps, cold plates, and heat exchangers) are located inside the crew module. The heat rejection system, which consists of radiator panels, is, however, located external to the crew Habitation Module. There are two wedge-shaped radiators on the top of the crew Habitation Module, two radiators beneath the windows at one end of the module, and two radiators next to the door at the other end.

For a weeklong stay on the lunar surface, a lunar shade is utilized around the LH$_2$ tanks to protect them from the heat of the lunar surface. Without the shade, too much of the rocket fuel would boil away. The lunar shade reduces the temperature of the hydrogen tanks and also provides these tanks with protection from the heat of the lunar lander radiators.

Fuel cells are utilized to provide power during landing, surface operations, and for an 8-hour ascent back to the Orion. The power is produced by the reaction of hydrogen and oxygen to form water. The reactants (oxygen and hydrogen) for the fuel cells are stored within the propellant tanks. The average power requirement for the lunar lander is 3,500 kW (your house, on average, uses about 1,500 watts of power). The water that is generated by the fuel cells is used by the crew for life support.

The lander has a special docking system for mating with the Orion crew module, and a pressurized crew habitat and an airlock. A window is located in the top of the crew habitat to allow pilot viewing of the Orion during docking and undocking maneuvers. The crew habitat has a volume of 32 m³ (1,130 ft³) and is made from aluminum-lithium (your house is at least five times this size).

Nitrogen, oxygen, and water are required for crew life support. Nitrogen is stored and taken from three spherical tanks placed on the lander platform portion of the vehicle. Oxygen is stored and extracted from either of the propulsion system's two LOX tanks. Water is supplied by the water generated by the fuel cells for the power system.

Conclusions

The team at NASA Glenn Research Center found that the staged descent approach to landing on the Moon is both safe and delivers quite a bit of equipment to the surface for crew exploration. The team also found that this way to land on the Moon was much cheaper than the Apollo method, since an inexpensive disposable drop stage is used. The concept requires only two vehicles to be designed – the drop stage (which can be a modified design of an existing stage) and the lunar lander. So perhaps when you or your kids are astronauts traveling to the Moon in the Orion vehicle, you will use the staged descent lunar lander to begin your exploration of the Moon.

Once discarded, the LCADS free falls to the lunar surface.

Lunar Architecture Team Phase I and Phase II

The Lunar Architecture Study began in 2006 with the objective of defining a series of lunar missions to fulfill the lunar exploration elements of the Vision for Space Exploration and develop a process for future architecture updates, including plans for multiple human and robotic missions. To meet these objectives, a study team was formed to develop a baseline architecture concept and establish a periodic architecture refinement by December 6, 2006. This team's goals included baseline of an architecture traced to objectives, as well as documentation of a Concept of Operations, a Level 1 Exploration Architecture Requirements Document, and functional needs/technology analysis.

Phase I, or what became known as Lunar Architecture Team LAT-1, was to provide sufficient definition and supporting rationale to enable commitment to near-term missions, to define a campaign to 2025 with future awareness to 2030, with a concentration on early robotics. This study was to become a basis for discussions with international partners.

During LAT-2, or Phase II, completed in July 2007, the goals were to discuss, collaborate, and negotiate with international partners to optimize responses and seek the best resource leveraging, and to continue to refine architecture requirements, with trades for key variables. The LAT-2 study benefits from the creation of NASA's Altair Lunar Lander Project in early 2007, and the two efforts ultimately converged with common personnel and lander designs. This becomes evident when comparing the later LAT and Lunar Surface Access Module (LSAM) lander concepts, and the early Lunar Design and Analysis Cycle (LDAC) concepts in the following sections.

Revised 0610-LAT-1: 0610-LAT-2

This configuration was a revised 0610-LAT-1 with a Low-Impact Docking System (LIDS) on the Ascent Module, a hatch to the Habitation Module, Descent Module communications, 4 x Reaction Control System (RCS) quads on the Ascent Module, and surface access from the airlock. The crewed habitat lander held a crew up to four, with a minimal Ascent Module, and minimal surface stay before transfer to the habitat. The Habitation Module mass was 6 mt (6.6 t), and its volume was 35 m³ (1,236 ft³).

Descent Stage	
Power	Multiphase power profiling tool used to size fuel cells and batteries. 30% power margin and 2-fault tolerance used on Descent Module sizing. Provided 3 kW of power to Ascent Module from time of Trans-Lunar Injection (TLI) through 24 hours after landing. Fuel cell reactants provided by the boil-off from the Earth Departure Stage (EDS) and lander Main Propulsion System (MPS) tanks. Fuel cell reactant tanks launched empty. Fuel cells provided 34 kg (77.2 lbm) of water to Ascent Module.
Propulsion	Assumed LOX/LH$_2$ main propulsion system and LOX/LCH$_4$ RCS. Included Reaction Control System (RCS) for outbound transit through landing. Assumed three RL-10 derived engines at a nominal specific impulse of 450 sec.
Thermal	Passive cryogenic fluid management for MPS propellant tanks. 3.0 kW heat rejection load from Ascent Module. Used flash evaporator system for all heat rejection during descent (2 hr, 8.4 kW), partial heat rejection during lunar orbit (24 hr, 2.6 kW) and for peak heat rejection loads during other mission phases. Maximum radiator heat rejection capability: 7.5 kW.
Structures	Use of composites where applicable. Used finite element analysis/optimization to size structures.
Guidance, Navigation & Control	Descent Module provided high-gain communication system. Descent instrumentation data collected and sent to Ascent Module via data bus cables. Assumed Ascent Module provided GN&C to Descent Module's MPS and RCS for all phases of the mission.

Ascent Stage	
Power	8.3-hr duration for ascent. Using Li ion batteries at 3 kW average/5 kW peak.
Propulsion	Assume LOX/methane main propulsion and RCS. Includes RCS for Ascent Module only.
Thermal	Included Extravehicular Activity (EVA) suit cooling (liquid cooling loop). Assumed 6 hr on Fluid Evaporator System (FES) during ascent, docking, and disposal. Heat load assumptions (batteries only), assumed FES handled average 3 kW (5 kW peak).
Structures	LIDS docking adapter (active) and hatch included. Surface access pressurized hatch.
Environmental Control and Life Support System	ECLSS consumables sized for 12-hr ascent, plus nominal descent. Consumables carried aboard Ascent Module (minimizes additional tanks on Descent Module). Assumed no potable water.

Mass Breakdown				
Subsystem	**Descent Stage**		**Ascent Stage**	
	lbm	**kg**	**lbm**	**kg**
1.0 Structure	999	453	1,446	656
2.0 Protection	0	0	124	56
3.0 Propulsion	6,546	2,969	1,318	598
4.0 Power	635	288	1,740	789
5.0 Control	309	140	0	0
6.0 Avionics	322	146	822	373
7.0 Environment	774	351	941	427
8.0 Other	1,162	527	670	304
9.0 Growth	2,147	974	1,411	640
Dry Mass w/Growth	**12,894**	**5,848**	**8,4722**	**3,843**
10.0 Non-cargo	4,105	1,862	558	253
11.0 Cargo	31,352	14,221*	0	0
Inert Mass	**48,351**	**21,931**	**9,030**	**4,096**
12.0 Non-propellant	262	119	46	21
13.0 Propellant	50,596	22,950	8,236	3,736
Gross Mass	**99,209**	**45,000**	**17,312**	**7,853**

* Includes 7,853 kg (17,310 lbm) for Ascent Module; 6,368 kg (14,039 lbm) for additional cargo.

Cargo Variant of 0610-LAT-2 with Avionics Package Added to Descent Module: 0610-LAT-3

This configuration was a cargo variant of 0610-LAT-2 with an avionics package added to the Descent Module. It consisted of a cargo-only lander with multiple cargo modules; there was no Ascent Module.

Each cargo module had a volume of 45 m³ (1,589.2 ft³) (as shown, could increase height) and a cargo capacity of 20.5 mt (22.6 t) across multiple modules. As a separate configuration, this lander was only capable of delivering cargo to the lunar surface. The configuration consisted of a single cargo lander, with several bays available for cargo stowage.

Descent Stage	
Power	Multiphase power profiling tool used to size fuel cells and batteries. 30% power margin and 2-fault tolerance used on Descent Module sizing. Provided 3 kW of power to Ascent Module from time of TLI through 24 hrs after landing. Fuel cell reactants provided by the boil-off from the EDS and Lander MPS tanks. Fuel cell reactant tanks launched empty. Fuel cells provided 34 kg (75 lbm) of water to Ascent Module.
Propulsion	Assumed LOX/LH₂ main propulsion system and LOX/LCH₄ RCS. Included RCS for outbound transit through landing. Assumed three RL-10 derived engines at a nominal specific impulse of 450 sec.
Thermal	Passive cryogenic fluid management for MPS propellant tanks. 3.0 kW heat rejection load from Ascent Module. Used flash evaporator system for all heat rejection during descent (2 hr, 8.4 kW), partial heat rejection during lunar orbit (24 hr, 2.6 kW) and for peak heat rejection loads during other mission phases. Maximum radiator heat rejection capability: 7.5 kW.
Structures	Used composites where applicable. Used finite element analysis/optimization to size structures.
Guidance, Navigation & Control	Descent Module provided high-gain communication system. Descent instrumentation data collected and sent to Ascent Module via data bus cables. Assumed Ascent Module provided GN&C to Descent Module's MPS and RCS for all phases of the mission.

Mass Breakdown		
Descent Stage		
Subsystem	lbm	kg
1.0 Structure	1,179	535
2.0 Protection	0	0
3.0 Propulsion	6,627	3,006
4.0 Power	2,004	909
5.0 Control	309	140
6.0 Avionics	1,612	731
7.0 Environment	1,834	832
8.0 Other	1,162	527
9.0 Growth	2,945	1,336
Dry Mass w/Growth	**17,672**	**8,016**
10.0 Non-cargo	1,411	640
11.0 Cargo	45,993	20,862
Inert Mass	**65,076**	**29,518**
12.0 Non-propellant	262	119
13.0 Propellant	52,829	23,963
Gross Mass	**118,167**	**53,600**

Crew Delivery Lander Assuming Minimal Surface Stay: 0610-LAT-4

A crewed cargo lander that held a crew of up to four, with a minimal Ascent Module and a minimal surface stay before transfer to the habitat. Volume, mass of the cargo element was 6 mt (6.6 t), 35 m³ (1,236 ft³).

Descent Stage	
Power	Multiphase power profiling tool used to size fuel cells and batteries. 30% power margin and 2-fault tolerance used on Descent Module sizing. Provided 3 kW of power to Ascent Module from time of TLI through 24 hrs after landing. Fuel cell reactants provided by the boil-off from the EDS and lander MPS tanks. Fuel cell reactant tanks launched empty. Fuel cells provided 34 kg (75 lbm) of water to Ascent Module.
Propulsion	Assumed LOX/LH$_2$ main propulsion system and LOX/LCH$_4$ RCS. Included RCS for outbound transit through landing. Assumed three RL-10 derived engines at a nominal specific impulse of 450 sec.
Thermal	Passive cryogenic fluid management for MPS propellant tanks. 3.0 kW heat rejection load from Ascent Module. Used FES for all heat rejection during descent (2 hrs, 8.4 kW), partial heat rejection during lunar orbit (24 hrs, 2.6 kW) and for peak heat rejection loads during other mission phases. Maximum radiator heat rejection capability: 7.5 kW.
Structures	Used composites where applicable. Used finite element analysis/optimization to size structures.
Guidance, Navigation & Control	Descent Module provided high-gain communication system. Descent instrumentation data collected and sent to Ascent Module via data bus cables. Assumed Ascent Module provided GN&C to Descent Module's MPS and RCS for all phases of the mission.

Ascent Stage					
Power	8.3-hr duration for ascent. Used Li-ion batteries at 3 kW average/5 kW peak.				
Propulsion	Assumed LOX/methane main propulsion and RCS. Included RCS for Ascent Module only.				
Thermal	Included EVA suit cooling (liquid cooling loop). Assumed 6 hrs on FES during ascent, docking, and disposal. Heat load assumptions (batteries only), assumed FES handled average 3 kW (5 kW peak).				
Environmental Control and Life Support System	ECLSS consumables sized for 12-hr ascent, plus nominal descent. Consumables carried aboard Ascent Module (minimized additional tanks on Descent Module). Assumed no potable water.				

Mass Breakdown					
	Descent Stage			Ascent Stage	
Subsystem	**lbm**	**kg**	**lbm**	**kg**	
1.0 Structure	999	453	1,446	656	
2.0 Protection	0	0	123	56	
3.0 Propulsion	6,546	2,969	1,318	598	
4.0 Power	635	288	1,739	789	
5.0 Control	309	140	0	0	
6.0 Avionics	322	146	822	373	
7.0 Environment	774	351	941	427	
8.0 Other	1,162	527	670	304	
9.0 Growth	2,147	974	1,411	640	
Dry Mass w/Growth	**12,894**	**5,848**	**8,470**	**3,843**	
10.0 Non-cargo	4,105	1,862	558	253	
11.0 Cargo	31,352	14,221	0	0	
Inert Mass	**48,351**	**21,931**	**9,028**	**4,096**	
12.0 Non-propellant	262	119	46	21	
13.0 Propellant	50,596	22,950	8,236	3,736	
Gross Mass	**99,209**	**45,000**	**17,310**	**7,853**	

Horizontal Lander Configuration Using 0610-LAT-2 as Benchmark: 0611-LAT-1

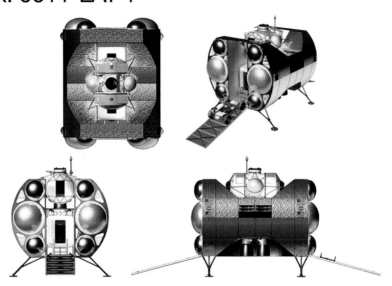

This horizontal lander configuration used 0610 LAT-2 as a benchmark. The LAT horizontal lander was composed of a minimum Ascent Module, a Descent Module, and remaining cargo mass that could be a habitat or other cargo. The Descent Module had the capability to deliver cargo as shown in the table below. This cargo could be a habitat, other cargo, or any combination of these. The Low Earth Orbit (LEO) loiter was assumed to be 14 days. Power during LEO loiters through TLI assumed to be provided by EDS. The assumption was that Crew Exploration Vehicle (CEV) provided power from EDS separation to CEV separation.

During Descent: Power for both the Ascent Module and habitat during descent was obtained from the Descent Module.

During Surface Operations: The crew transferred and lived out of a habitat; either one brought down with the lander or an external habitat already on the surface. The Descent Module provided power and cooling for both the Ascent Module and the Descent Module. Any cooling needs above and beyond the inherent capabilities of the Descent Module would be counted as part of the habitat/living module, but could be housed on the Descent Module.

Descent Stage	
Power	All power cases assumed an 8.3-hr duration. Used Li-ion batteries at 3 kW average/5 kW peak.
Propulsion	Assumed LOX/methane propulsion system. Included RCS system for Ascent Module only.
Thermal	Included EVA suit cooling (liquid cooling loop). Assumed 6 hrs on FES during ascent, docking, and disposal (additional time was achievable if power output reduced [similar to power assumptions]). Heat Load Assumptions: Batteries only, assumed FES handled average 3 kW (5 kW peak).
Structures	No pyros on Ascent Module. LIDS docking adapter (active) and hatch included; surface access via pressurized hatch.
Environmental Control and Life Support System	Consumables sized for 12-hr ascent plus nominal descent (Certification Acceptance Requirements Document requirement). Consumables carried aboard Ascent Module (minimized additional tanks on Descent Module). Assumed no potable water.

Mass Breakdown				
	Descent Stage		Ascent Stage	
Subsystem	lbm	kg	lbm	kg
1.0 Structure	6,021	2,731	1,140	517
2.0 Protection	170	77	128	58
3.0 Propulsion	5,913	2,682	1,144	519
4.0 Power	1,087	493	1,629	739
5.0 Control	203	92	0	0
6.0 Avionics	101	46	847	384
7.0 Environment	593	269	988	448
8.0 Other	1,462	663	996	452
9.0 Growth	3,111	1,411	1,373	623
Dry Mass w/Growth	**18,661**	**8,464**	**8,245**	**3,740**
10.0 Non-cargo	1,958	888	456	207
11.0 Cargo	27,190	12,333	0	0
Inert Mass	**47,809**	**21,685**	**8,701**	**3,947**
12.0 Non-propellant	79	36	46	21
13.0 Propellant	51,324	23,280	7,906	3,586
Gross Mass	**99,212**	**45,001**	**16,653**	**7,554**

Cargo Variant of 0611-LAT-1: 0611-LAT-2

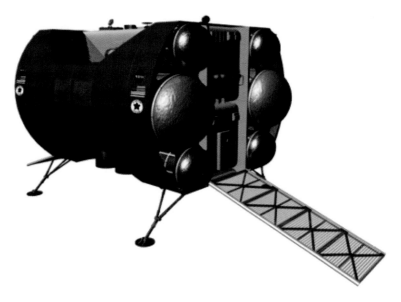

This configuration was a cargo variant of 0611-LAT-1. The LAT horizontal cargo lander used the same exact Descent Module as the human outpost lander, without an Ascent Module, keeping the 100 m³ (3,531.5 ft³) cargo bay. The Descent Module had the capability to deliver cargo to the poles, as shown in the table below. This cargo could be habitats, pressurized or unpressurized cargo, or any combination of these.

During Lunar Orbit Insertion: Provided power and cooling for itself with limited capability to support cargo, and pushed cargo (without CEV) through 845 m/s (2,772.3 ft/s) of delta-v.

During Surface Descent: Provided power and cooling for itself with limited capability to support cargo.

Descent Stage	
Power	All power cases assumed an 8.3-hr duration. Li-ion batteries at 3 kW average/5 kW peak.
Propulsion	Assume LOX/methane prop system. Includes RCS system for Ascent Module only.
Thermal	Included EVA suit cooling (liquid cooling loop). Assumed 6 hrs on FES during ascent, docking, and disposal (additional time was achievable if power output reduced [similar to power assumptions]). Heat load assumptions (batteries only), assumed FES handled average 3 kW (5 kW peak).
Structures	No pyros on Ascent Module. LIDS docking adapter (active) and hatch included; surface access via pressurized hatch.
Environmental Control and Life Support System	Consumables sized for 12 hrs ascent plus nominal descent (Certification Acceptance Requirements Document requirement). Consumables carried aboard Ascent Module (minimized additional tanks on Descent Module). Assumed no potable water.

Mass Breakdown		
Descent Stage		
Subsystem	lbm	kg
1.0 Structure	6,021	2,731
2.0 Protection	170	77
3.0 Propulsion	5,913	2,682
4.0 Power	1,087	493
5.0 Control	203	92
6.0 Avionics	101	46
7.0 Environment	589	267
8.0 Other	1,731	785
9.0 Growth	3,164	1,435
Dry Mass w/Growth	**18,979**	**8,608**
10.0 Non-cargo	1,437	652
11.0 Cargo	45,929	20,833
Inert Mass	**66,345**	**30,093**
12.0 Non-propellant	79	36
13.0 Propellant	51,747	23,472
Gross Mass	**118,171**	**53,601**

Global Access Lander: 0611-LSAM-A

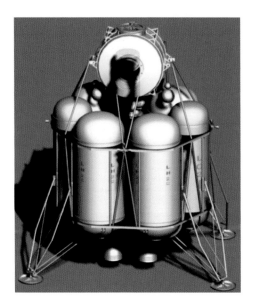

Developed for the Constellation Program Office Systems Requirements Review, the major design requirements of this concept included Global Access (1,250 m/s [4,101 ft/s]) using a 3-day loiter in LLO with the CEV supporting the crew, a 95-day loiter, a 7-day surface mission with a 210-day outpost mission, and 500 kg (1,102 lbm) of cargo delivered in crewed mode.

Major design features were LOX/LCH$_4$ main and RCS engines in the ascent stage, LOX/LH$_2$ main engines and LOX/LCH$_4$ RCS engines in the descent stage, open ECLSS, fuel cells on the descent stage and batteries on the ascent stage, metallic structures, with radiators on the descent stage and a fluid evaporation system on the ascent stage.

Mass Breakdown		
Subsystem	lbm	kg
Ascent Module	18,016	8,172
Lunar Hab Module	6,235	2,828
Descent Module	93,024	42,195
Total Launch Mass	**117,275**	**53,195**

Three-Module Lander (611-A Derivative): 0701-LSAM-A

NOTE: 611-A pictured above; no image of derivative available.

This concept was a derivative of the 0611-A lander with the following design requirements:

- Polar Access: 850 m/s (2,789 ft/s); other sites possible with reduced capability.
- 3-day CEV LLO loiter protected on LSAM (e.g., boil-off). This provided limited global access without trading additional on-orbit loiter and/or decreased crew size/cargo.
- A single crew lander that could deliver 6,000 kg (13, 228 lbm) cargo to the outpost versus a lander that delivered 500 kg (1,102 lbm) and 20,000 kg (44,092 lbm) in crewed and uncrewed modes, respectively.
- Cargo capability to non-polar sites (though required, this was not assessed during the study).

Its design features included the following:

- All technology choices remained consistent with 0611-A.
- Decreased LOI/increased cargo requirements, resulting in a net propellant savings of 5,483 kg (12,088 lbm). This decreased the height of descent stage by ~1 m (3.28 ft).
- Descent stage RCS was designed to use MMH/NTO (an error that was later corrected).

Mass Breakdown		
Subsystem	**lbm**	**kg**
Ascent Module	18,018	8,173
Available Cargo Mass	13,228	6,000
Descent Module	77,554	35,178
Total Launch Mass	**108,800**	**49,351**

Delta 701-A with Additional Propellant to Push Maximum Lunar Orbit Insertion Control Mass: 0701-LSAM-B

The Delta 701-A design requirements incorporated CA4140-PO, which allowed it to capture the CEV + 1,361 kg (3,000 lbm) Level 2 mass reserve into lunar orbit. Additionally, this version added 10 m/s (33 ft/s) for Trajectory Correction Maneuvers TCMs, and it corrected the descent stage RCS propellant mistake from the previous version, changing it from MMH/NTO to LOX/LCH$_4$.

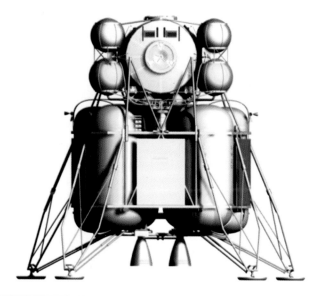

Mass Breakdown		
Subsystem	lbm	kg
Ascent Module	18,018	8,173
Available Cargo Mass	13,228	6,000
Descent Module	79,851	36,220
Total Launch Mass	**111,097**	**50,393**

Vertical, Crewed Lander Optimized for 45 mt Trans Lunar Injection: 0703-LAT-1

This was a vertical, crewed lander optimized for 45 mt (49.6 t) TLI. Its parametric design was based on the March 2007 Envision model.

Mass Breakdown				
	Descent Stage		Ascent Stage	
Subsystem	lbm	kg	lbm	kg
1.0 Structure	5,154	2,338	1,219	553
2.0 Protection	194	88	121	55
3.0 Propulsion	6,391	2,899	1,111	504
4.0 Power	1,526	692	1,437	652
5.0 Control	203	92	0	0
6.0 Avionics	123	56	822	373
7.0 Environment	1,098	498	1,003	455
8.0 Other	2,399	1,088	888	403
9.0 Growth	3,402	1,543	1,321	599
Dry Mass w/Growth	**20,490**	**9,294**	**7,922**	**3,594**
10.0 Non-cargo	3,446	1,563	201	91
11.0 Cargo	23,797	10,794	0	0
Inert Mass	**47,733**	**21,651**	**8,123**	**3,685**
12.0 Non-propellant	0	0	46	21
13.0 Propellant	51,476	23,349	7,055	3,200
Gross Mass	**99,209**	**45,000**	**15,224**	**6,906**

Vertical Uncrewed (Cargo) Landers Optimized for 53.6 mt Trans Lunar Injection: 0703-LAT-2, LAT-3

As with Option 1, Vertical Options 2 and 3 were slightly varied versions of an uncrewed (cargo) lander. Both were optimized for 53.6 mt (59.1 t) TLI, and their parametric design was based on the March 2007 Envision model.

Mass Breakdown		
Descent Stage		
Subsystem	lbm	kg
1.0 Structure	5,104	2,315
2.0 Protection	194	88
3.0 Propulsion	6,389	2,898
4.0 Power	1,625	737
5.0 Control	203	92
6.0 Avionics	454	206
7.0 Environment	280	127
8.0 Other	1,817	824
9.0 Growth	3,214	1,458
Dry Mass w/Growth	**19,280**	**8,745**
10.0 Non-cargo	3,508	1,591
11.0 Cargo	40,774	18,495
Inert Mass	**63,562**	**28,831**
12.0 Non-propellant	0	0
13.0 Propellant	54,606	24,769
Gross Mass	**118,168**	**53,600**

Vertical Crewed Lander Based on 0703-LAT-2 Cargo Lander: 0703-LAT-4

The Vertical Crewed lander was based on the 703-LAT-2 or -LAT-3 cargo lander with full descent propellant tanks to maximize landed payload mass. Resultant Trans-Lunar Injection (TLI) mass was > 45 mt (49.6 t). 24-hr (1-day) crew support on the lunar surface required the crew to transition to other surface habitation, which could have been lander cargo or already emplaced on the surface. It did not include an airlock: if one was required, its mass was bookkept as part of the cargo mass. The parametric design was based on the March 2007 Envision model.

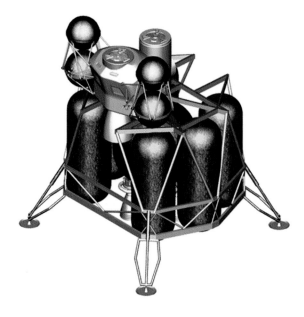

Lunar Lander
Project Office – Altair

In 2007, the Altair project office was formed at Johnson Space Center (JSC) as the lunar lander component of NASA's Constellation Program. As the Altair project was coming into existence, a Lunar Architecture Team (LAT, Constellation Architecture Team [CxAT]-Lunar) study (see previous section) was already underway as part of the larger Constellation Program effort. The LAT efforts and the design work that resulted from the Exploration System Architecture Study Lunar Surface Access Module design work were folded into the early phases of the Altair design work.

In support of the Constellation Lunar Architecture Team, Altair performed a large set of sensitivity studies to examine lander performance (initially using Initial Mass in Low Earth Orbit as the primary metric) as a function of changing single and multiple design variables. Lander design variables that were investigated included the following:

- Lunar Orbit Insertion (LOI) ΔV assignment – LOI burn performed by Altair, the Trans-Lunar Injection stage, or a dedicated LOI stage. The Constellation architecture also required that the LOI maneuver include a 23.1 mt (25.5 t) Crew Exploration Vehicle (CEV).
- LOI sequence – Polar (single burn), mid-latitude (single burn), or global access (3-burn)
- LOI ΔV magnitude – 891 m/s (2,923 ft/s) (minimum), 1,000 m/s (3,280 ft/s), 1,100 m/s (3,608 ft/s), 1,250 m/s (4,101 ft/s)
- Additional LLO loiter – Following LOI and 24 hrs in LLO prior descent, +1 to +6 days of additional LLO loiter
- Number of crew to surface – 2, 3, or 4
- Sortie "down" payload – 250 kg (551 lbm) or 500 kg (1,102 lbm)
- Offloaded Descent Module propellant – Given tanks sized for the LOI ΔV, offload various amounts (ΔV) of propellant
- Lander Margin Strategy – Full Mass Growth Allowance + 30% Program Manager's Reserve (PMR) (~50% total margin), Full Mass Growth Allowance + 20% PMR (~40% total margin)
- Lander Optimization – Crew optimized or cargo optimized

Configuration 1: 0707-LAT-1

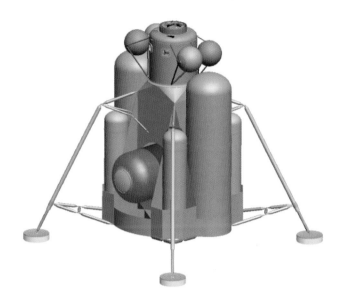

Descent Stage	
Power	Used removable MPU; mass was bookkept as Cargo – Mass estimate, margins and cost bookkept by Surface Power Flight Equipment (FE) – Prevented double dipping of mass growth and reserve. Parametric model refined based on LLPO design (included required redundancy for LAT).
Propulsion	Descent Module Main Propulsion System (MPS) changed to a single LOX/LH$_2$ engine (82,959.4 N (18,650 lbf), 448 sec Isp), Parametric estimate matched bottoms-up design very closely. The current estimate was within 5% of bottoms-up design. The LAT lander used parametric estimate for sizing.
Thermal	Ascent Module and Descent Module assumed Micrometeoroid Orbital Debris (MMOD) protection for non-tank areas; MMOD for tanks carried in propulsion; shielding mass provided by parametric model. Support structure mass = shielding mass per Apollo comparison; Descent Module system assumptions scrubbed, radiators sized for 8.4 kW heat rejection during transit, added mass for brackets and fasteners, mass increased from 134 kg (295.4 lbm) to 208 kg (458.6 lbm).
Structures	Point design based on lander configuration, NASA Engineering and Safety Center (NESC) used finite element models to size structure against loads. The Descent Module consisted of aluminum and titanium face sheets and a honeycomb core (preliminary analysis showed that metallics were more efficient in this application).
Guidance, Navigation & Control	MPS gimbal control system was designed for minimum risk for a single engine, using a Lunar Lander Project Office (LLPO) mass estimate for control system. This was not a significant change (LLPO = 34 kg [75 lbm], parametrics = 92 kg [202.8 lbm]).
Ascent Stage	
Propulsion	Ascent Module MPS was a single LOX/CH$_4$ engine (25,212.9 N [5,668 lbf])
Thermal	Ascent Module and Descent Module assumed MMOD protection for non-tank areas; MMOD for tanks carried in propulsion; shielding mass provided by parametric model. Support structure mass = shielding mass per Apollo comparison; Ascent Module Environmental Control and Life Support System (ECLSS) and Thermal Control System (TCS) parametric analysis lined up well with LLPO estimates.
Structures	NESC used finite element models to size structure against loads. The Ascent Module pressure vessel was made from composite face sheets and honeycomb core.

Configuration 2: 0707-LAT-2

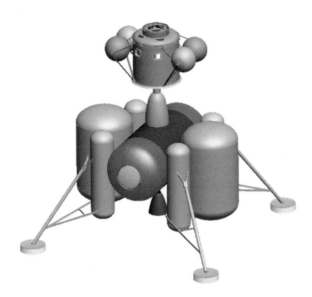

Descent Stage	
Power	Used removable MPU; its mass was bookkept as cargo. Mass estimate, margins, and cost bookkept by surface power FE, preventing double dipping of mass growth and reserve. Parametric model refined based on LLPO design.
Propulsion	Descent Module MPS changed to a single LOX/LH$_2$ engine (82,959.4 N [18,650 lbf], 448 sec Isp), a parametric estimate matched bottoms-up design very closely; the most recent estimate was within 5% of the bottoms-up design. LAT Lander sizing used the parametric estimate.
Thermal	Ascent Module and Descent Module assumed MMOD protection for non-tank areas. MMOD for tanks carried in propulsion; shielding mass was provided by the parametric model. Support structure mass = shielding mass per Apollo comparison; Descent Module system assumptions scrubbed, radiators sized for 8.4 kW heat rejection during transit, added mass for brackets and fasteners, mass increased from 134 kg (295.4 lbm) to 208 kg (458.6 lbm).
Structures	Point-design based on lander configuration, NESC used finite element models to size structure against most current loads. Descent Module consisted of aluminum and titanium face sheets and honeycomb core (preliminary analysis showed that metallics were more efficient in this application).
Guidance, Navigation & Control	MPS gimbal control system was designed for minimum risk for a single engine, used LLPO mass estimate for control system; not a significant change (LLPO = 34 kg [75 lbm], parametrics = 92 kg [202.8 lbm]).
Ascent Stage	
Propulsion	Ascent Module MPS was a single LOX/CH$_4$ engine: 25,212.9 N f (5,668 lbf).
Thermal	Ascent Module and Descent Module assumed MMOD protection for non-tank areas; MMOD for tanks carried in propulsion; shielding mass provided by parametric model. Support structure mass = shielding mass per Apollo comparison; Ascent Module ECLSS and TCS parametric analysis lined up well with LLPO estimates.
Structures	NESC used finite element models to size structure against most current loads. Ascent module pressure vessel made from composite face sheets and honeycomb core.

Mass Breakdown				
	Ascent Stage		Descent Stage	
Subsystem	lbm	kg	lbm	kg
1.0 Structure	5,864	2,660	1,975	896
2.0 Protection	450	204	262	119
3.0 Propulsion	5,362	2,432	1,539	698
4.0 Power	395	179	1,067	484
5.0 Control	75	34	0	0
6.0 Avionics	262	119	712	323
7.0 Environment	459	208	862	391
8.0 Other	1,579	716	0	0
9.0 Growth	2,888	1,310	1,283	582
Dry Mass w/Growth	**17,334**	**7,862**	**7,700**	**3,493**
10.0 Non-cargo	3,003	1,362	531	241
11.0 Cargo	8,521	3,865	0	0
Inert Mass	**28,858**	**13,089**	**8,231**	**3,734**
12.0 Non-propellant	0	0	55	25
13.0 Propellant	55,334	25,099	6,729	3,052
Gross Mass	**84,192**	**38,188**	**15,015**	**6,811**

Configuration 3: 0707-LAT-3

Descent Stage	
Power	Most-recent design used removable MPU. The mass for the removable MPU was bookkept as cargo – mass estimate, margins and cost bookkept by surface power FE – prevented double dipping of mass growth and reserve. Parametric model refined based on LLPO design and included required redundancy for LAT.
Propulsion	Descent Module MPS changed to a single LOX/LH$_2$ engine (82,959.4 N [18,650 lbf], 448 sec Isp). Parametric estimate matched bottoms-up design very closely.
Thermal	Ascent Module and Descent Module assumed MMOD protection for non-tank areas. MMOD for tanks carried in propulsion; shielding mass provided by parametric model. Support structure mass equaled shielding mass per Apollo comparison; Descent Module system assumptions scrubbed, radiators sized for 8.4 kW heat rejection during transit, added mass for brackets and fasteners, mass increased from 134 kg (295.4 lbm) to 208 kg (458.6 lbm).
Structures	Point-design based on lander configuration, NESC used finite element models to size structure against most-recent loads. Descent Module consisted of aluminum and titanium face sheets and honeycomb core (preliminary analysis showed that metallics are more efficient in this application).
Guidance, Navigation & Control	MPS gimbal control system was designed for minimum risk for a single engine, used LLPO mass estimate for control system. This was not a significant change (LLPO = 34 kg [75 lbm], parametrics = 92 kg [202.8 lbm]).
Ascent Stage	
Propulsion	Ascent module MPS was a single LOX/CH$_4$ engine: 25,212.9 N (5,668 lbf).
Thermal	Ascent Module and Descent Module assumed MMOD protection for non-tank areas; MMOD for tanks carried in propulsion; shielding mass provided by parametric model. Support structure mass equaled shielding mass per Apollo comparison; Ascent Module ECLSS and TCS parametric analysis lined up well with LLPO estimates.
Structures	NESC used finite element models to size structure against most recent loads. Ascent Module pressure vessel made from composite face sheets and honeycomb core.

Expanded Descent Stage with Restored Functionality and Redundancy: p0711-CxAT-1

As in previous LDAC versions, Envision was used to enhance the LDAC-1 configuration for the Constellation studies with additional functionality and redundancy. The descent stage was also expanded to fit within a 10 m (33 ft) shroud. Some basic design parameters included:

- Transportation for four crew to and from the surface
- 7 days on the surface
- Lunar outpost crew rotation
- Global access capability
- Anytime return to Earth
- Capability to land 20 mt (22 t) of dedicated cargo
- Airlock for surface activities
- Descent stage: LOX/LH$_2$ propulsion
- Ascent stage: Storable Propellant

Non-Lunar Orbit Insertion Parametric with LOX Descent and Hypergolic Ascent: p0801-CxAT-1

Three versions of the CxAT lander were designed using Envision: a Non-LOI parametric with LOX Descent and Hypergolic Ascent, a Non-LOI Parametric with All LOX Methane Ascent and Descent Stage Propulsion, and a Non-LOI Parametric with All Hypergolic Descent and Ascent. All three had the design characteristics shown in the following table.

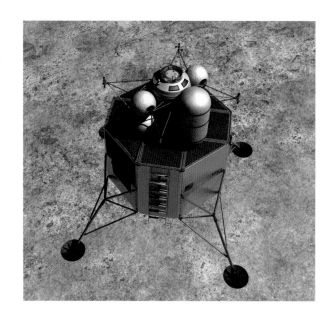

Descent Stage	
Crew Size (max)	4
Surface Duration (max)	7 days (sortie missions), up to 210 days (outpost missions)
Landing Site Capability	Global
Stages	2
Overall Height	9.9 m (32.5 ft)
Width at Tanks	8.8 m (28.9 ft)
Width at Footpads (diag.)	14.9 m (48.9 ft)
Crew Module Pressurized Volume	17.5 m³ (618 ft³) – crew module + airlock
Ascent Stage Mass	6,141 kg (13,510 lbm)
Ascent Stage Engines	1 – MMH/NTO
Ascent Stage Engine Thrust	24.5 Kn (5,500 lbf)
Descent Stage Mass	37,045 kg (81,500 lbm)
Descent Stage Engines	1 – pump-fed, throttling, LOX/LH₂
Descent Stage Thrust	83.0 Kn (18,650 lbf)

Altair Lander Design Analysis Cycle-1

The first in a series of Lander Design Analysis Cycles (LDACs), LDAC-1 began a risk-informed design process described in NASA's Engineering and Safety Center's Publication, "Design, Development, Test and Evaluation (DDT&E) Considerations for Safe and Reliable Human-rated Spacecraft Systems" (NESC PR-06-108).

In April 2007, with a group of experts chosen from across all NASA centers, this team of approximately 30 engineers spent 2 months co-located at NASA's Johnson Space Center, where they focused on the initial design of a stripped-down lander as a baseline for a risk-informed design process that was to follow. This design process was unique to NASA – it began with a vehicle that was capable of performing only the basic lander mission, and no more, and contained no redundancy or design margins. This initial design point was termed the "minimum functional" lander and would become the basis from which all further design enhancements would be measured.

Defining the minimum functional vehicle required the team to look at the requirements already imposed on the lander. These requirements were scrubbed back to a small number that described the essential functions that the lander must perform or the essential constraints that it must be designed within:

- Carry four crew to and from the lunar surface
- Perform a 7-day Polar Sortie Mission
- Perform a 210-day Outpost Mission
- Carry the functionality of an airlock (implemented on sortie mission only)
- Work within the Earth Orbit Rendezvous-Lunar Orbit Rendezvous Constellation Program transportation architecture
- Package within an 8.4 m (27.6 ft) shroud (this was changed to a 10 m [33 ft] shroud in later design cycles)
- Accommodate Trans-Lunar Injection (TLI) loads with 23.1 mt (25.5 t) Orion mass attached
- Perform the Low Orbit Insertion (LOI) burn with Orion attached

Two mass constraints were also levied on the minimum functional design:

- Total Lander mass at TLI for crewed missions does not exceed 45,000 kg (99,208 lbm)
- Total Lander mass at TLI for cargo missions does not exceed 53,600 kg (118,168 lbm)

The design process began from this minimum set of requirements. Minimum functional is a design philosophy that begins with a vehicle that will perform the minimum basic mission. It neither considers contingencies nor provides any added redundancy, and is approximately equal to a "single string" design approach. A minimum functional vehicle is not a design that would ever be contemplated as a "flyable" design. This design philosophy provided early, critical insight into the overall viability of the end-to-end Constellation transportation architecture. If a transportation architecture cannot "close" with a minimum functional lander, it will certainly not close when all the additional functionality is added back into the lander design. More importantly, the minimum functional lander design provides a starting point to make informed cost/risk trades and consciously buy down risk.

The minimum functional design approach was new to large-scale NASA human spaceflight projects; however, it built upon lessons learned from a number of NASA design exercises. The Orion Project conducted both "Smart Buyer" and functionality "buyback" exercises that informed the Altair design effort. Following that effort, Altair used a process detailed in a publication from the NASA Engineering Safety Center, "Design Development Test and Evaluation (DDT&E) Considerations for Safe and Reliable Human Rated Spacecraft Systems," as the outline for its early design process steps.

Design standards were also scrutinized in formulating the minimum functional design. Existing NASA standards on redundant systems were put aside for the initial design, and were used only as one possible risk mitigation option in later design cycles. Technical standards were individually scrutinized. For example, the initial design used the nominal design standard structural factors of safety of 1.5 (and 2.0 for pressure vessels), but left these open to trade during later design cycles.

The primary LDAC-1 design figure of merit was to maximize payload to the surface of the Moon with a crewed lander. Large payloads landed with crewed missions were being investigated as an option to incrementally building lunar surface capabilities, and Constellation studies sought to know the maximum payload that could be delivered with lunar crews. One of the LDAC-1 results was that a minimum functional vehicle (illustrating the extreme of maximizing delivered payload) could deliver less than 4 mt (4.4 t) to the lunar surface in addition to the crew – significantly less than the 6 mt (6.6 t) surface that system architects needed to contemplate an outpost architecture constructed from crew-lander-delivered cargo.

The Constellation Program concluded that small payloads could be delivered with crewed landers; however, a cargo variant of the lander would be needed to build up the lunar outpost.

The result of the initial design cycle was a bottoms-up design of a single-string vehicle that met all the fundamental design reference missions and requirements, but no more. Each subsystem provided detailed engineering analysis and bottoms-up design. Each then provided equipment lists, schematics, and computer-aided design (CAD) models to Altair's Integrated Vehicle Performance team, which assembled the products that described the overall lander's performance characteristics, which included:

• Master Equipment List (listing more than 2,000 components)
• Powered Equipment List
• Integrated vehicle schematic
• Integrated vehicle consumables and resource utilization analysis
• CAD model

Minimum Functional Configurations (1), (2) and (3): 0706-LDAC-1-1, -2 and 0709-LDAC-1-4

Three "minimum functional" configurations were developed: one for a polar sortie mission, one to transport crew to a polar outpost, and one to transport only cargo to the polar outpost. A fourth design configuration, which was eventually discarded, optimized the descent module structure of the minimal functional vehicle and provided enough descent module delta-v for a non-idealized trajectory. Abort and/or contingency operations were not investigated during this study cycle, assuming that future LDAC cycles would "buy back" the safety, reliability, and

additional functionality required. Design characteristics included polar access, 1 degree plane change, and a 14-day loiter in Low Earth Orbit (LEO).

Throughout Altair's design history, the team used the metric "unallocated differential" to describe the mass available to the team for design improvements and vehicle safety and reliability improvements. Unallocated differential was technically the difference between the vehicle's current design mass (inclusive of mass growth allowance) and the vehicle's control mass.

Mass Breakdown – Minimum Functional Designs						
	Polar Sortie Lander		Polar Outpost Crewed Lander		Polar Outpost Cargo Lander	
	lbm	kg	lbm	kg	lbm	kg
Ascent Module	11,757	5,333	11,795	5,350	N/A	N/A
Sortie Habitat	4,063	1,843	N/A	N/A	N/A	N/A
Descent Module	74,865	33,958	74,626	33,850	74,391	33,743
Unallocated Differential	8,525	3,867	12,787	5,800	36,244	16,440
Total Mass	**99,210**	**45,001**	**99,208**	**45,000**	**110,635**	**50,183**

Two Configurations, with and without Lunar Orbit Insertion: 0710-LDAC-1-1 and -2

As in Phase 1 of LDAC-1, interim configurations developed in Phase 2 were assumed to be minimal functional, without abort or contingency modes, used the same 45 mt (50 t), and mass estimates were developed using Envision. Launch configurations fit within an 8.4 m (27.6 ft) Ares V shroud. Two options were studied: one with LDAC-1 configuration including LOI, and the other with LDAC-2 configuration using hypergolic propellant and assuming no LOI.

Design Characteristics
Polar access only (890 m/s [2,920 ft/s])
1-degree plane change
Includes Descent Module delta-v for non-idealized trajectory
Mid-bay launch concept
14-day LEO loiter
Configuration 2: LOI not included; used hypergolic propellant

Minimum Functional Lander: 0711-LDAC-1-1

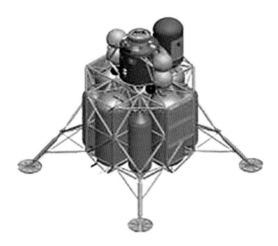

After defining the minimum functional vehicle in the first Lander Design Analysis Cycle (LDAC-1), a follow-on "delta" activity resulted in a bottoms-up design of a reconfigured single-string vehicle that met all the fundamental design reference missions and requirements. Each subsystem team provided detailed engineering analysis and bottoms-up design, resulting in a Master Equipment List that contained more than 2,000 individual components, a Powered Equipment List, an integrated vehicle schematic, an integrated vehicle consumable and resource utilization analysis, and a detailed CAD model.

LDAC-1 "delta" configurations assumed a flat-top concept with a leave-behind airlock. Specific vehicle characteristics for the three options – Sortie, Outpost, and Cargo – are shown in the table below.

LOI Lunar Lander Vehicle Concept Characteristics			
Lander Performance (14-day LEO loiter)			
Characteristic	**Sortie**	**Outpost**	**Cargo**
Crew Size	4	4	N/A
Surface Stay	7 days	180 + 30 days	N/A
Shroud Dia., O.D./I.D.	8.4/7.5 m (27.6/24.6 ft)	8.4/7.5 m (27.6/24.6 ft)	8.4/7.5 m (27.6/24.6 ft)
Launch Loads	5 g's axial, ±2 g's lateral	5 g's axial, ±2 g's lateral	5 g's axial, ±2 g's lateral
Lander Mass (launch)	45,000 kg (99,208 lbm)	45,000 kg (99,208 lbm)	53,600 (118,168 lbm)
Lander Mass (@TLI)	44,547 kg (98,269 lbm) (- LEO boil-off)	44,547 kg (98,269 lbm) (- LEO boil-off)	53,600 kg (118,168 lbm) (no boil-off)
Payload to Surface	3,401 kg (7,489 lbm)	4,269 kg (9,412 lbm)	17,378 kg (38,312 lbm)
Project Manager's Reserve	2,857 kg (6,299 lbm)	2,692 kg (5,935 lbm)	1,974 kg (4,352 lbm)
Lander Height	10.5 m (34.5 ft)	10.5 m (34.5 ft)	~9 m (30 ft)
Earth Departure Stage (EDS) Adapter Mass	662 kg (1,459 lbm)	662 kg (1,459 lbm)	662 kg (1,459 lbm)
TCM + Settling ΔV	22.55 m/s (73.98 ft/s)	22.55 m/s (73.98 ft/s)	22.55 m/s (73.98 ft/s)
LOI ΔV	891 m/s (2,923 ft/s)	891 m/s (2,923 ft/s)	889 m/s (2,917 ft/s) (Cap.)
Lunar Lander Plane Change ΔV Cap. (post Crew Exploration Vehicle [CEV] separation)	28.5 m/s (93.5 ft/s)	28.5 m/s (93.5 ft/s)	28.5 m/s (93.5 ft/s)

LOI Lunar Lander Vehicle Concept Characteristics (continued)			
Lander Performance (14-day LEO loiter – continued))			
Characteristic	**Sortie**	**Outpost**	**Cargo**
DOI + Settling ΔV	21.5 m/s (70.5 ft/s)	21.5 m/s (70.5 ft/s)	21.5 m/s (70.5 ft/s)
Descent Module Propulsion ΔV	2,030 m/s (6,660 ft/s)	2,030 m/s (6,660 ft/s)	2,030 m/s (6,660 ft/s)
Descent Dispersions ΔV	5,353 m/s (17,562 ft/s)	5,353 m/s (17,562 ft/s)	5,353 m/s (17,562 ft/s)
Ascent ΔV Capability	11,881 m/s (38,980 ft/s)	11,881 m/s (38,980 ft/s)	N/A
Ascent RCS ΔV Capability	30 m/s (98 ft/s) (not incl. in Ascent ΔV Capability above)	30 m/s (98 ft/s) (not incl. in Ascent ΔV Capability above)	N/A
Descent Module			
Mass (at TLI)	32,700 kg (72,091 lbm)	32,700 kg (72,091 lbm)	34,250 kg (75,508 lbm)
Main Engine Propellants	LOX/LH$_2$	LOX/LH$_2$	LOX/LH$_2$
Usable Propellant	20,084/3,652 kg (44,278/8,051 lbm) LOX/H$_2$	20,084/3,652 kg (44,278/8,051 lbm) LOX/H$_2$	21,855/3,974 kg (48,182/8,761 lbm) LOX/H$_2$
# Main Engines/Type	1/RL-10 derived	1/RL-10 derived	1/RL-10 derived
Main Engine Isp (100%)	448.6 sec (nom. 450 sec)	448.6 sec (nom. 450 sec)	448.6 sec (nom. 450 sec)
Main Engine Thrust (100%)	18,627 lbf (82,857 N) (nom. 18,650 lbf [82,959 N])	18,627 lbf (82,857 N) (nom. 18,650 lbf [82,959 N])	18,627 lbf (82,857 N) (nom. 18,650 lbf [82,959 N])
RCS Propellants	N$_2$O$_4$/MMH	N$_2$O$_4$/MMH	N$_2$O$_4$/MMH
Usable Propellant	246 kg (542 lbm) N$_2$O$_4$/149 kg (328 lbm) MMH	246 kg (542 lbm) N$_2$O$_4$/149 kg (328 lbm) MMH	246 kg (542 lbm) N$_2$O$_4$/149 kg (328 lbm) MMH
# RCS Engines/Type	16/100 lbf (445 N) each	16/100 lbf (445 N) each	16/100 lbf (445 N) each
RCS Engine Isp (100%)	300 sec	300 sec	300 sec
Sortie Airlock			
Habitable Volume	~7 m^3 (247 ft^3) (1.75-m diameter [5.74 ft] x 3-m height [9.8 ft])	N/A	
Crew Size	2+		
Ascent Module			
Characteristic	**Sortie**	**Outpost**	**Cargo**
Diameter	2.35 m (7.71 ft)	2.35 m (7.71 ft)	
Mass (w/crew/Crew Support Equipment [CSE] rocks)(371/121/100)	55,667 kg (122,724 lbm)	55,947 kg (123,342 lbm)	
Main Engine Propellants	N$_2$O$_4$/MMH	N$_2$O$_4$/MMH	
Usable Propellant (N$_2$O$_4$/MMH)	11,606 kg (25,587 lbm) /868 kg (1,914 lbm)	11,688 kg (25,587 lbm) /912 kg (2,011 lbm)	N/A
# Main Engines/Type	1/derived OME/RS18	1/derived OME/RS18	
Main Engine Isp (100%)	320 sec (min. 318 sec)	320 sec (min. 318 sec)	
Main Engine Thrust (100%)	5,500 lbf (24,465 N) (min. 5,400 lbf [24,020 lbf])	5,500 lbf (24,465 N) (min. 5,400 lbf [24,020 lbf])	
RCS Propellants	N$_2$O$_4$/MMH	N$_2$O$_4$/MMH	
Usable Propellant	Integrated w/MPS	Integrated w/MPS	
# RCS Engines/Type	16/100 lbf (445 N) each	16/100 lbf (445 N) each	N/A
RCS Engine Isp (100%)	300 sec	300 sec	

0711-LDAC-1 with Functionality, Redundancy Added Back Parametrically: 0711-LDAC-1-2

The second concept of the LDAC-1Δ study had upgraded performance from the first option, and included additional functions and redundancy. As in all the LDAC configurations, Envision was used in development of the parametric models, using its quick analysis capability to study descope options of lander, configuration, and performance, as well as transportation architecture trade parameters.

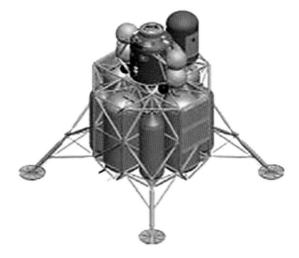

Transportation Architecture Trade Parameters			
LOI	**LOI Sequence**	**LOI ΔV Strategy**	**LLO Loiter**
• Lander • Dedicated • Earth Departure Stage (EDS) • LOI stage	• Polar (1 burn) • Mid-Latitude (1 burn) • Global access (3 burn)	• 891 m/s (2,923 ft/s) • 1,000 m/s (3,281 ft/s) • 1,100 m/s (3,609 ft/s) • 1,250 m/s (4,101 ft/s)	• 24 hrs • +1 to +6 days

Lander/Configuration/Performance Parameters					
Potential Descope Options					
Number of crew	**Sortie Down Payload**	**Offloaded Descent Module Propellant**	**Varying Orion mass at LOI**	**Lander Margin Strategy**	**Lander Optimization**
• 2 • 4	• 250 kg (551 lb) • 500 kg (1,102 lb)	• Various	• Various	• 1 mt (1.1 t) less of PMR	• Crew Cargo

LOI LL Vehicle Concept Characteristics			
Lander Performance (14-day LEO loiter)			
Characteristic	**Sortie**	**Outpost**	**Cargo**
Crew Size	4	4	N/A
Surface Stay	7 days	180 + 30 days	N/A
Shroud Dia., O.D./I.D.	8.4 m (27.6 ft)/7.5 m (24.6)	8.4 m (27.6 ft)/7.5 m (24.6)	8.4 m (27.6 ft)/7.5 m (24.6)
Launch Loads	5 g's axial, ±2 g's lateral	5 g's axial, ±2 g's lateral	5 g's axial, ±2 g's lateral
Lander Mass (launch)	45,586 kg (100,500 lbm)	45,586 kg (100,500 lbm)	53,600 kg (118,167 lbm)
Lander Mass (@TLI)	~45,000 kg (99,208 lbm) (- LEO boil-off)	~45,000 kg (99,208 lbm) (- LEO boil-off)	53,600 (118,167 lbm) (no boil-off)
Crew Payload to Surface	500 kg (1,102 lbm)	500 kg (1,102 lbm)	14,600 kg (32,187 lbm)
EDS Adapter Mass	662 kg (1,459 lbm)	662 kg (1,459 lbm)	662 kg (1,459 lbm)
TCM + Settling ΔV	2.5 m/s (8.2 ft/s)	2.5 m/s (8.2 ft/s)	2.5 m/s (8.2 ft/s)

LOI LL Vehicle Concept Characteristics			
Lander Performance (14-day LEO loiter)			
Characteristic	Sortie	Outpost	Cargo
LOI ΔV	891 m/s (2,923 ft/s)	891 m/s (2,923 ft/s)	889 m/s (Cap.) (2,917 ft/s)
LL Plane Change ΔV Cap. (post CEV sep.)	28.5 m/s (93.5 ft/s)	28.5 m/s (93.5 ft/s)	28.5 m/s (93.5 ft/s)
DOI + Settling ΔV	21.5 m/s (70.5 ft/s)	21.5 m/s (70.5 ft/s)	21.5 m/s (70.5 ft/s)
Descent Module Propulsion ΔV	2,030 m/s (6,660 ft/s)	2,030 m/s (6,660 ft/s)	2,030 m/s (6,660 ft/s)
Descent Dispersions ΔV	53 m/s (174 ft/s)	53 m/s (174 ft/s)	53 m/s (174 ft/s)
Ascent ΔV Capability	1,881 m/s (6,171 ft/s)	1,881 m/s (6,171 ft/s)	N/A
Ascent RCS ΔV Capability	30 m/s (98 ft/s) (not incl. in 1,881 [6,171])	30 m/s (98 ft/s) (not incl. in 1,881 [6,171])	N/A
Mass (at TLI)	~33,804 kg (74,525 lbm)	~33,804 kg (74,525 lbm)	~35,519 kg (78,306 lbm)
Main Engine Propellants	LOX/LH$_2$	LOX/LH$_2$	LOX/LH$_2$
# Main Engines/Type	1/RL-10 derived	1/RL-10 derived	1/RL-10 derived
Main Engine Isp (100%)	448.6 sec	448.6 sec	448.6 sec
Main Engine Thrust (100%)	18,627 lbf (82,857 N)	18,627 lbf (82,857 N)	18,627 lbf (82,857 N)
RCS Propellants	N$_2$O$_4$/MMH	N$_2$O$_4$/MMH	N$_2$O$_4$/MMH
# RCS Engines/Type	16/100 lbf (445 N) each	16/100 lbf (445 N) each	16/100 lbf (445 N) each
RCS Engine Isp (100%)	300 sec	300 sec	300 sec
Sortie Airlock			
Crew Size	2+	N/A	N/A
Ascent Module			
Diameter	2.35 m (7.7 ft)	2.35 m (7.7 ft)	
Mass (w/crew/CSE/rocks) (371/121/100)	7,084 kg (15, 617 lbm)	7,084 kg (15,617 lbm)	
Main Engine Propellants	N$_2$O$_4$/MMH	N$_2$O$_4$/MMH	
# Main Engines/Type	1/derived OME/RS18	1/derived OME/RS18	
Main Engine Isp (100%)	320 sec	320 sec	N/A
Main Engine Thrust (100%)	5,500 lbf (24,465 N)	5,500 lbf (24,465 N)	
RCS Propellants	N$_2$O$_4$/MMH	N$_2$O$_4$/MMH	
Usable Propellant	Integrated w/MPS	Integrated w/MPS	
# RCS Engines/Type	16/100 lbf (445 N) each	16/100 lbf (445 N) each	
RCS Engine Isp (100%)	300 sec	300 sec	

Constellation Architecture Team Crew Optimized Lander: p0804-LDAC-1-1

This configuration was an Envision parametrically sized lander concept informed by Altair's LDAC-1 Delta activity, with selected additional redundancy and delta-v's that were representative of realistic trajectories, but not optimized for Thrust to Weight. This concept illustrates how the work of the Altair design team and the work of the Constellation Architecture Team was merging at this point in time.

Vehicle Concept Characteristics	
Lander Performance (Sized by Crew Mission)	
Characteristic	**Crewed Lander**
Crew Size	4
Max. LEO Loiter Duration	4 days
Max. LLO Loiter Duration	11 + 4 days (mass delta for +4 day loiter: ~220 kg)
Surface Stay Time	7 days (sortie)
Shroud Diameter	10 m (33 ft)
Lander Design Diameter	8.8 m (28.9 ft)
Launch Loads	5 g axial, 2 g lateral
Lander Mass (launch)	44,142 kg (97,316 lbm)
Lander Mass (@TLI)	44,142 kg (97,316 lbm)
Lander Payload to Surface	500 kg (1,102 lbm)
Project Manager's Reserve	1,964 kg (4,330 lbm)
Lander Deck Height	6.93 m (22.74 ft)
EDS Adapter Mass (not included in numbers above, includes growth and Manager's Reserve)	860 kg (1,896 lbm)
LOI ΔV Capability	950 m/s (3,117 ft/s) (Tanks sized to 1,000 m/s [3,281 ft/s])
Plane Change and Loiter (Post CEV sep., 1 degree) ΔV	28.4 m/s (93.2 ft/s)
Descent Propulsion ΔV Capability	2,030 m/s (6,660 ft/s)
TCM ΔV Capability (performed by RCS)	2 m/s (7 ft/s)
Low Lunar Orbit Stack Attitude Control	~5.5 m/s (18 ft/s)
Descent Orbit Insertion Capability (performed by RCS)	19.4 m/s (63.6 ft/s)
Settling Burn Requirement (performed by RCS)	2.7 m/s (8.8 ft/s)
Descent and Landing Reaction Control Capability	11 m/s (36 ft/s)
Ascent ΔV Capability	1,881 m/s (6,171 ft/s)
Ascent RCS ΔV Capability	30 m/s (98 ft/s)

Vehicle Concept Characteristics (continued)	
Lander Performance (Sized by Crew Mission)	
Characteristic	**Crewed Lander**
Descent Module	
Mass (at TLI)	37,045 kg (81,670 lbm)
Main Engine Propellants	LOX/LH$_2$
Usable Propellant	24,903 kg (54,902 lbm) LOX/H$_2$
# Main Engines/Type	1/RL-10 derived (Pump Fed)
Main Engine Isp (100%)	448.6 sec
Main Engine Thrust (100%)	82,959 N (18,650 lbf)
RCS Propellants	N$_2$O$_4$/MMH
# RCS Engines/Type	16/445 N (100 lbf) each
RCS Engine Isp (100%)	300 sec
Airlock	
Pressurized Volume	7.5 m^3 (264.9 ft^3)
Diameter	1.75 m (5.74 ft)
Height	3.58 m (11.74 ft)
Crew Size	2+
Lander Performance (Sized by Crew Mission)	
Characteristic	**Crewed Lander**
Ascent Module	
Diameter	2.35 m (7.71 ft)
Pressurized Volume	10 m^3 (353 ft^3)
Mass (at TLI)	6,141 kg (15,539 lbm)
Main Engine Propellants	N$_2$O$_4$/MMH
Usable Propellant (N$_2$O$_4$/MMH)	3,013 kg (6,643 lbm)
# Main Engines/Type	1/derived OME/RS18 (pressure fed)
Main Engine Isp (100%)	320 sec
Main Engine Thrust (100%)	24,465 N (5,500 lbf)
RCS Propellants	N$_2$O$_4$/MMH
Usable Propellant	Integrated w/main
# RCS Engines/Type	445 N (16/100 lbf) each
RCS Engine Isp (100%)	300 sec

Optimized Cargo Variant of p804-A: p0804-LDAC-1-2

In the place of an Ascent Module, the cargo variant carried cargo on the upper deck. Characteristics of this configuration are listed in the table below.

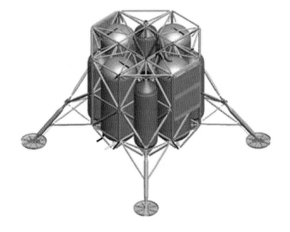

LOI Lunar Lander Vehicle Concept Characteristics	
Lander Performance (Sized by Crew Mission)	
Characteristic	**Cargo Lander**
Max. LEO Loiter Duration	4 days
Max. LLO Loiter Duration	1 + 4 days (mass delta for +4 day loiter: ~220 kg [485 lbm])
Shroud Diameter	10 m (33 ft)
Lander Design Diameter	8.8 m (28.9 ft)
Launch Loads	5 g axial, 2 g lateral
Lander Mass (launch)	53,449 kg (117,834 lbm)
Lander Payload to Surface	14,775 kg (32,574 lbm) (Note: Landing Gear must be upsized in cargo lander)
Project Manager's Reserve	2,220 kg (4,894 lbm)
Lander Height	6.93 m (22.73 ft)
EDS Adapter Mass (not included in numbers above, includes growth and Manager's Reserve)	860 kg (1,896 lbm)
LOI ΔV Capability	889 m/s (2,917 ft/s)
Plane Change and Loiter (Post CEV sep., 1 degree) ΔV	28.4 m/s (93.2 ft/s)
Descent Propulsion ΔV Capability	2,030 m/s (6,660 ft/s)
TCM ΔV Capability (performed by RCS)	2 m/s (7 ft/s)
Low Lunar Orbit Stack Attitude Control	~5.5 m/s (18 ft/s)
Descent Orbit Insertion Capability (performed by RCS)	19.4 m/s (63.6 ft/s)
Settling Burn Requirement (performed by RCS)	2.7 m/s (8.8 ft/s)
Descent and Landing Reaction Control Capability	11 m/s (36 ft/s)

Descent Module	
Mass (at TLI)	38,764 kg (85,460 lbm)
Main Engine Propellants	LOX/LH$_2$
Usable Propellant	26,723 kg (58,914 lbm)
# Main Engines/Type	1/RL-10 derived (Pump Fed)
Main Engine Isp (100%)	448.6 sec
Main Engine Thrust (100%)	82,959 N (18,650 lbf)
RCS Propellants	N$_2$O$_4$/MMH
# RCS Engines/Type	445 N (16/100 lbf) each
RCS Engine Isp (100%)	300 sec

Crew Optimized Variant of Constellation Architecture Team-Lunar Point of Departure: p0804-LDAC-1-3

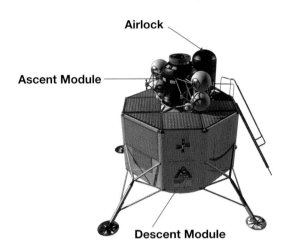

Airlock

Ascent Module

Descent Module

As with all Altair lunar lander designs from this point forward, this variant consisted of four major components: an Ascent Module, a Descent Module, an airlock, and the Ares V Earth Departure Stage/Altair Adapter (EDSA). All four components were to be used in the sortie missions; just the Ascent Module, Descent Module, and EDSA were to be used in the outpost missions, and only the Descent Module and EDSA were to be used for un-crewed cargo missions.

The Altair Ascent Module was designed around a crew cabin that served as the primary habitable volume for the crew during at least the descent and ascent phases of the crewed sortie mission. The Ascent Module provided pressurized access to the airlock and to the Orion after ascent from the lunar surface. The Ascent Module supported contingency Extravehicular Activity (EVA) capability in the event a mated, pressurized transfer path could not be established between the Orion and Altair after ascent.

The Ascent Module provided the capability to perform an in-plane ascent to rendezvous with the Orion. It also had the capability to perform descent aborts through the majority of the descent maneuver.

The Ascent Module provided its own internal power during lunar ascent. In certain off-nominal situations (e.g., an under-speed ascent), the module operated in a degraded mode, which used less power to extend Ascent Module lifetime. Power generation/storage on the module for post-ascent ops was one of the key drivers in the Altair design's mass. During all other phases of the mission, the Ascent Module obtained power from an external source (its Descent Module, Orion, or the Ares V EDS stage).

The main function of the Descent Module was to deliver hardware (Ascent Module with crew, airlock, cargo) to the surface of the Moon. It was built around the descent propulsion system, landing gear, and structure necessary to carry loads through all flight phases. Structural support to be provided for payloads and other support services (i.e., communications, power, thermal conditioning) was not included in this design; it was left to be considered in future vehicle-level trade studies. The Descent Module was "kit-able" to accommodate crewed or uncrewed missions.

The Descent Module propulsion system provided the capability to perform trajectory correction maneuvers and to capture Altair and Orion into lunar orbit, including some plane change capability. Following LOI and the transfer of crew/cargo from Orion to Altair, the Descent Module performed an in-plane descent to the lunar surface that included hazard avoidance and crew piloting capabilities. On the lunar surface, the Descent Module provided a translation path for the crew from the airlock to the lunar surface, and crew access to external cargo.

The airlock provided ingress/egress access to the Ascent Module in the sortie mission mode. The airlock allowed the crew to perform split operations (e.g., two crew members perform EVA while two crew members remain in the lander) and served as one of the primary mechanisms used to control the transport of lunar dust into the Ascent Module. The airlock was sized for a two-crew-member operation. The airlock was also to be used for stowage of crew equipment during descent, and as stowage volume during crewed sortie Ascent Module operations.

Lander Performance (Sized by Crew Mission)	
Characteristic	**Cargo Lander**
Crew Size	4
Maximum LEO Loiter Duration	4 days
Maximum LLO Loiter Duration	1 + 4 days Mass Delta for +4 day loiter: ~220 kg (485 lbm)
Surface Stay Time	7 days (sortie)
Launch Shroud Diameter	10 m (32.8 ft)
Lander Design Diameter	8.8 m (28.9 ft)
Launch Loads	5 g axial, 2 g lateral
Crew Lander Deck Height/Cargo Lander Height	6.93 m (22.74 ft)
LOI ΔV Capability	Crew Lander: 950 m/s (3,117 ft/s); Tanks sized to 1,000 m/s (2,181 ft/s) Cargo Lander: 889 m/s (2,917 ft/s)
Plane Change and Loiter (Post CEV Sep. 1 degree)	Crew/Cargo: 28.4 m/s (93.2 ft/s)
Descent Propulsion Delta-v Capability	Crew/Cargo: 2,030 m/s (6,660 ft/s)
TCM ΔV Capability	2 m/s (6.6 ft/s); performed by RCS
Low Lunar Orbit Stack Attitude Control	~5.5 m/s (~18.0 ft/s)
Descent Orbit Insertion Capability	19.4 m/s (63.6 ft/s); performed by RCS
Settling Burn Requirement	2.7 m/s (8.9 ft/s); performed by RCS
Descent and Landing Reaction Control Capability	11 m/s (36.1 ft/s)
Ascent ΔV Capability	1,881 m/s (6,171 ft/s)
Ascent RCS ΔV Capability	30 m/s (98.4 ft/s)
Vehicle Concept Characteristics	
Descent Module (Crewed)	
Propellants	Main Engine: LOX/H_2 RCS: N_2O_4/MMH
Number of Engines/Type	Main Engines: 1/RL-10 Derived (Pump Fed) RCS: 16/445 N (100 lbf) each
Engine Isp (100%)	Main: 448.6 sec RCS: 300 sec
Main Engine Thrust (100%)	82,959 N (18,650 lbf)
Ascent Module	
Diameter	2.35 m (7.71 ft)
Pressurized Volume	10 m³ (353 ft³)
Propellants	Main Engine/RCS: N_2O_4/MMH
Number of Engines/Type	Main Engines: 1/Derived OME/RS18 (pressure fed) RCS: 16/445 N (100 lbf) each
Engine Isp (100%)	Main: 320 sec RCS: 300 sec
Main Engine Thrust (100%)	24,465 N (5,500 lbf)

Lander Performance (Sized by Crew Mission) (continued)						
Characteristic	**Cargo Lander**					
Airlock						
Pressurized Volume	7.5 m³ (264.9 ft³)					
Diameter	1.75 m (5.74 ft)					
Height	3.58 m (11.75 ft)					
Crew Size	2+					
Mass Breakdown						
	Descent Module (Crewed)		**Descent Module (Cargo)**		**Ascent Module**	
	lbm	**kg**	**lbm**	**kg**	**lbm**	**kg**
Mass (at TLI)	81,670	37,045	85,262	38,674	13,539	6,141
Project Manager's Reserve	4,330	1,964	4,894	2,220		
Payload to Surface	1,102	500	32,573	14,775*		
Usable Propellant	54,902	24,903	58,914	26,723	6,643	3,013

Landing Gear must be upsized in cargo lander

Note: EDS Adapter Mass of 860 kg (1,896 lbm) is not included in totals above; includes Growth and Manager's Reserve

Post LDAC-1 Delta: p0804-A

The p0804-A lander concept was developed for NASA's Constellation Program's June 2008 Lunar Capability Concept Review (LCCR). The review was a formal Program milestone in which NASA provided conceptual designs that were at a level of maturity to allow the program to proceed. The concept was based on the LDAC-1 Delta activity lander, with selected additional redundancy and delta-V's that are representative of realistic trajectories, but are not optimized for Thrust to Weight. It was parametrically sized using Envision, and incorporated lessons learned from the Altair focused studies in areas such as:

- Optimization of the descent module structure
- Descent module tanks and structure
- Ascent module hab/airlock/flight deck configurations
- Number of descent engines/thrust/throttle
- Propellant selection
- Structural loads
- Center of gravity/controllability
- Launch shroud sizing
- Global access/LOI delta-V/LLO loiter
- Landing delta-v

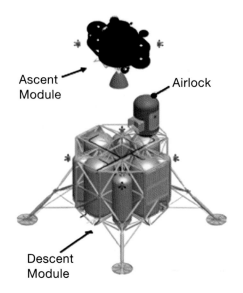

Ascent Module · Airlock · Descent Module

Later concepts incorporated more changes from these studies, which led to designs that were more technically mature and included a number of safety enhancements. This concept, developed while the Altair studies were ongoing, was a step up from the LDAC-1 Delta activity designs, but was not as refined as the final Altair configuration. Characteristics of this design are provided in the table below.

Lander Performance	
Crew Size	4
Max. LEO Loiter Duration	4 days
Max. LLO Loiter Duration	~4 days
Surface Stay Time	7 days (sortie); 180 days (outpost visit)
Launch Shroud Diameter	8.4 m (27.6 ft)
Lander Design Diameter	7.5 m (24.6 ft)
Launch Loads	5 g axial, 2 g lateral
Crewed Lander Mass at Launch	43,897 kg (96,776 lbm)
Crewed Lander Mass @ TLI	43,897 kg (96,776 lbm)
Crew Lander Payload to Surface	500 kg (1,102 lbm)
Project Manager's Reserve	1,955 kg (4,310 lbm)
Crew Lander Deck Height	6.91 m (22.7 ft)
Cargo Lander Mass at Launch	53,295 kg (117,495 lbm)
Cargo Lander Mass @ TLI	Not applicable
Cargo Lander Payload to Surface	14,723 kg (32,459 lbm)
Project Manager's Reserve	2,216 kg (4,885 lbm)
Cargo Lander Height	6.91 m (22.7 ft)

Lander Performance (continued)	
EDS Adapter Mass Not included in numbers above, includes growth and Manager's Reserves	860 kg (1,896 lbm)
Crew Lander LOI ΔV Capability Tanks sized to 1000 m/s (2,237 mph)	950 m/s (3,117 ft/s)
Cargo Lander LOI ΔV Capability	889 m/s (2,917 ft/s)
Crew/Cargo Plane change and Loiter (Post CEV separation, 1 degree)	28.4 m/s (93.2 ft/s)
PDI ΔV Capability	19.4 m/s (63.6 ft/s)
Crew Descent Propulsion ΔV Capability	2,030 m/s (6,660 ft/s)
Cargo Descent Propulsion ΔV Capability	2,030 m/s (6,660 ft/s)
TCM ΔV Capability (performed by RCS)	2 m/s (6.6 ft/s)
Descent Orbit Insertion Capability (performed by RCS)	19.4 m/s (63.6 ft/s)
Settling Burn Requirement (performed by RCS)	2.7 m/s (8.9 ft/s)
Descent and Landing Reaction Control Capability	11 m/s (36 ft/s)
Ascent ΔV Capability	1,881 m/s (6,171 ft/s)
Ascent RCS ΔV Capability	30 m/s (98 ft/s)
Vehicle Concept Characteristics	
Ascent Module	
Diameter	2.35 m (7.71 ft)
Mass at TLI	6,141 kg (13,539 lbm)
Main Engine Propellants	N_2O_4/MMH
Usable Propellant	3,013 kg (6,643 lbm)
Number of Main Engines/Type	1/Derived OME/RS18 (Pressure Fed)
Main Engine Isp (100%)	300 sec
Main Engine Thrust (100%)	24,465 N (5,500 lbf)
RCS Propellants	N_2O_4/MMH
Usable Propellant	Integrated w/main
Number of RCS Engines/Type	16/445 N (100 lbf) each
RCS Engine Isp (100%)	300 sec
Airlock	
Pressurized Volume	7.5 m³ (264.9 ft³)
Diameter	1.75 m (5.74 ft)
Height	3.58 m (11.75 ft)
Crew Size	2+

Descent Module (Crewed)	
Mass at TLI	36,800 kg (81,130 lbm)
Main Engine Propellants	LOX/LH$_2$
Usable Propellant	24,707 kg (54,470 lbm)
Number of Main Engines/Type	1/RL-10 Derived (Pump Fed)
Main Engine Isp (100%)	448 sec
Main Engine Thrust (100%)	82,959 N (18,650 lbf)
RCS Propellants	N$_2$O$_4$/MMH
Number of RCS Engines/Type	16/445 N (100 lbf) each
RCS Engine Isp (100%)	300 sec
Descent Module (Crewed)	
Mass at TLI	38,572 kg (85,037 lbm)
Usable Propellant	26,645 kg (58,742 lbm)

Lander Design Analysis Cycle-2

Altair's risk analysis team was key to the success of this cycle of risk-informed design, using the "minimum functional" design established in Lander Design Analysis Cycle (LDAC)-1 as the baseline from which to identify vehicle risks. Two lists of risks were developed to mature the design from one that was essentially "single string" to one that was "safety enhanced." One list used a top-down reliability model; the other used bottoms-up subsystems, vehicle fault trees, and hazard analyses. Using these tools, the team developed a Lander Reliability Model that numerically identified both vehicle-wide and subsystem top contributors to Loss of Crew (LOC). All risk inputs were then referred to a Risk Prioritization Team that took on the complex task of synthesizing the results from the Lander Hazard Analysis, Lander Reliability Tool, and Subsystems Single Point Failure Assessments, and created task sheets detailing 33 individual studies, five of which were deferred to later LDAC studies. The remaining 28 risk tasks were assigned to the Altair team in LDAC-2.

An example of the analyses supporting a "risk buyback" task and the data supporting the mitigation option decision provides an illustration of the process used to examine a known risk and then decide upon the course of action that would help reduce it. This example identifies the loss of the minimum functional vehicle's communication/state vector update as a risk that would result in the lander losing knowledge of its inertial position, ultimately leading to a situation where it would be unable to accurately return to LLO and rendezvous with Orion to return the lunar crew to Earth. Such a failure would result in LOC. Analysis identified several options to mitigate one or more of these single-point failures and increase communications reliability. Proposed options for recovering communications to update the vehicle state vector included full redundancy, selective redundancy, dissimilar redundancy, bypass switching, and in-flight maintenance patching. The figure below illustrates the X-Y plot of the mass and LOC probabilities for these options.

Option (E3) was selected for the best use of mass (+9 kg [+20 lbm]) for a combination of LOC "buy down" = 6.62 E-5 and Loss of Mission (LOM) buy down = 4.70 E-3. This option also provided full capability redundancy

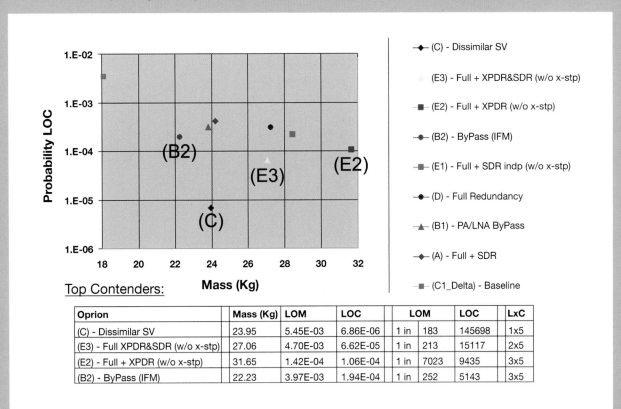

Probability (LOC) vs. mass for communications/loss of state vector risk.

Oprion	Mass (Kg)	LOM	LOC	LOM	LOC	LxC
(C) - Dissimilar SV	23.95	5.45E-03	6.86E-06	1 in 183	145698	1x5
(E3) - Full XPDR&SDR (w/o x-stp)	27.06	4.70E-03	6.62E-05	1 in 213	15117	2x5
(E2) - Full + XPDR (w/o x-stp)	31.65	1.42E-04	1.06E-04	1 in 7023	9435	3x5
(B2) - ByPass (IFM)	22.23	3.97E-03	1.94E-04	1 in 252	5143	3x5

without common mode failures due to the use of dissimilar radios. Option (E3) was implemented as one of 28 crew safety upgrades that were incorporated into the final LDAC-2 design.

The composite of all decisions made in LDAC-2 to reduce Altair's LOC probability resulted in the mass available for payload (unallocated differential) being reduced from 3,652 kg (8,051 lbm) (in the minimum functional, single-string LDAC-1 lander design) to 1,671 kg (3,684 lbm). This still exceeds the 500 kg (1,102 lbm) of payload required for the lander to deliver, but does not yet include the buyback of LOM risks or additional capabilities. LOC risk was improved from approximately 1 in 6 (LDAC-1) to 1 in 206, which began to approach the 1 in 250 requirement for Altair lander LOC.

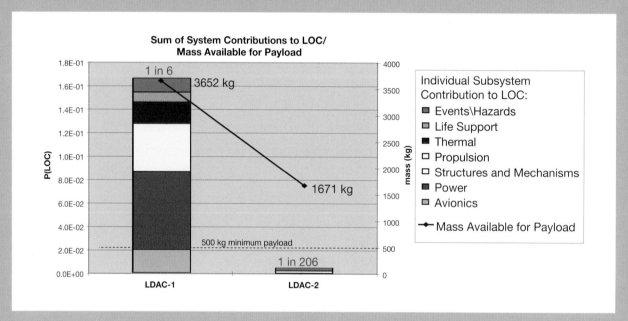

LDAC-2 summary metrics – probability of LOC, mass available for payload.

Bottoms-up, LDAC-2 Safety Enhanced Design: 0805-LDAC-2-1

LDAC-2 designs were "safety enhanced" versions of the LDAC-1Δ configurations, and launched using a 10 m (32.8 ft) shroud as opposed to the 8.4 m (27.6 ft) shroud assumed for the earlier configurations. As in the earlier studies, three options were considered – one intended for sortie missions, one to carry only cargo, and one to transport crew to an outpost. Envision was used in this design cycle, as in the previous studies, for parametric sizing and permutation of characteristics, and three versions were studied: a bottoms-up design, an Envision Parametric of 0805-A with 25% Program Manager's Reserve (PMR), and a single launch version, with a 17.5 mt (19.3 t) Crew Exploration Vehicle (CEV), without PMR.

Mass Breakdown				
Outpost Design Reference Mission				
Subsystem	Descent Stage		Ascent Stage	
	lbm	kg	lbm	kg
Avionics	245.4	111.3	317.2	143.9
Power	492.7	223.5	367.3	166.6
Struct. & Mech.	7,479.2	3,392.5	1,891.1	857.8
Propulsion	6,389.7	2,898.3	1,435.4	651.1
Thermal Control	2,133.2	967.6	545.6	247.5
Life Support	0.0	0.0	310.2	140.7
Dry Mass w/ Growth	**16,740.2**	**7,593.2**	**4,866.8**	**2,207.6**
Other	11.2	5.1	937.8	425.4
Non-propellant Fluids	2,763.1	1,253.3	242.1	109.8
Inert Mass	**19,514.5**	**8,851.6**	**6,046.7**	**2,742.8**
Propellant	54,804.9	24,859.1	6,133.7	2,782.2
Gross Mass	**74,319.4**	**33,710.7**	**12,180.4**	**5,525.0**

Sortie Design Reference Mission						
Subsystem	**Descent Stage**		**Ascent Stage**		**Airlock**	
	lbm	kg	lbm	kg	lbm	kg
Avionics	245.4	111.3	318.3	144.4	8.4	3.8
Power	562.8	255.3	356.0	161.5	36.4	16.5
Struct. & Mech.	7,479.2	3,392.5	1,912.5	867.5	898.8	407.7
Propulsion	6,389.7	2,898.3	1,435.4	651.1	0.0	0.0
Thermal Control	2,133.2	967.6	545.6	247.5	82.5	37.4
Life Support	0.0	0.0	368.2	167.0	231.9	105.2
Dry Mass w/ Growth	**16,810.3**	**7,625.0**	**4,936.0**	**2,239.0**	**1,258.0**	**570.6**
Other	11.2	5.1	341.1	154.7	1,032.4	468.3
Non-propellant Fluids	2,847.3	1,291.5	312.6	141.8	31.7	14.4
Inert Mass	**19,668.8**	**8,921.6**	**5,589.7**	**2,535.5**	**2,322.1**	**1,053.3**
Propellant	54,947.1	24,923.6	6,095.3	2,764.8	0.0	0.0
	74,615.9	**33,845.2**	**11,685.0**	**5,300.3**	**2,322.1**	**1,053.3**

2008 Contractor Broad Agency Announcement Studies

In 2008, NASA issued a Broad Agency Announcement (BAA) to seek input on the minimum functional design and innovative ways to buy down risk while minimizing mass impacts, paralleling the NASA LDAC-2 design activity. Five companies submitted design concepts for this study: Andrews Space, Boeing, Lockheed Martin, Northrop Grumman, and Odyssey Space Research. All five followed some common themes in their designs, including:

- Using some form of probabilistic analysis to prioritize safety buyback candidates
- Identifying propulsion, structures, and physical configuration trades as the largest performance drivers
- Analyzing ascent module-airlock functionality, size/split
- Reducing the number of descent module tanks
- Increasing lander structural stiffness
- Using a single, RL-10 derivative Descent Main Engine
- Analyzing LOX-methane as an Ascent Main Engine option
- Revisiting NASA delta-v's, trajectories, timelines
- Selecting upgraded components and systems for life support, thermal, avionics, power
- Adding abort options back in (separately from subsystem analyses) to decrease loss of crew (LOC)

Additionally, they were encouraged to pursue alternative design solutions, and each came up with unique design solutions:

- Northrop Grumman – Toroidal descent LOX and LH2 tanks, LOX/LH2 ascent propulsion, and Reaction Control System (RCS), horizontal cylinder ascent module w/ embedded engine.
- Odyssey Space Research – Three legs, Lunar Orbit Insertion (LOI) drop tanks, monoprop (Nitrous Oxide Fuel Blend) ascent propulsion, and aerospike engines.
- Andrews Space – Side-mounted inflatable shell ascent module, habitat module with suitlock, tank head idle for RCS burns, active propellant management, composite-wrapped cryo tanks, and components moved between Orion and Altair (i.e., emergency equipment, etc.).
- Boeing – Multi-engine ascent module, increased delta-v, single hydrogen tank descent module with stiff shell structure.
- Lockheed Martin – Single hydrogen descent module tank and toroid LOX tank, LOX/LH2 ascent propulsion, horizontal cylinder ascent module with six outboard engines.

Northrop Grumman: 0810-BAA-1

The Northrop Grumman team evaluated a large range of configuration and propulsion options, and their final design identified a mass savings of 3,600 kg (7,937 lbm), which allowed 2,300 kg (5,071 lbm) of enhanced safety options to be added to the baseline configuration as well as the ability to carry additional payload. The final proposal included:

- An 8.8 m (28.9 ft) shroud dynamic envelope
- A toroidal tank, allowing a lower deck height for crew surface access and easier cargo unloading
- A horizontal ascent module pressure vessel for good pilot visibility
- A dedicated equipment bay
- Pyrotechnic bolts within dedicated inter-stage mounts
- A ladder attached to the landing gear
- A side-mounted airlock with a canted separation plane
- Spherical ascent module LOX and LH_2 tanks mounted in quadrants with the LOX tanks and LH_2 tanks diagonally opposed to each other
- An embedded ascent module engine within the crew module
- Addition of an ascent module engine blast deflector on the descent module top face
- A descent module toroidal tank with a large nozzle descent module derivative engine

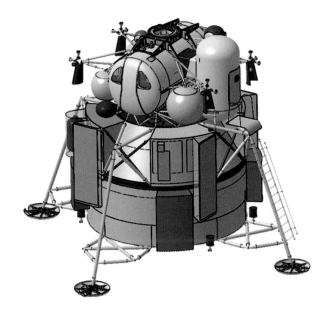

- Apollo Lunar Module (LM)-type landing gear
- The Earth Departure Stage (EDS) adapter truss affixed to the landing gear shoulders

The table below provides a list of safety enhancements as compared to the LDAC-1 design, as well as a subsystem mass breakdown.

Safety Enhancements		
Subsystem	**Descent Stage**	**Ascent Stage**
Propulsion	Redundant valves, regulators, and sensors	Redundant valves, regulators, and sensors; an increase from 12 to 16 RCS thrusters
Structures and Mechanisms	Gear actuation redundancy	Separation system redundancy
Power	Duplex power distribution units and fuel cells, resizing due to power increases	Duplex power distribution units, battery redundancy, resizing due to power increases
Avionics	Triplex redundancy	Triplex redundancy, duplex communications system
Thermal Control		Redundant pumps, accumulator, sensors and valves
Environmental Control and Life Support System		Redundant fans, amine beds, and sensors

Mass Breakdown					
Subsystem	Descent Stage		Ascent Stage		
	lbm	kg	lbm	kg	
Structures and Mechanisms	4,037	1,831	2,765	1,254	
Propulsion	4,081	1,851	1,967	892	
Power	357	162	331	150	
Avionics	194	88	247	112	
Environmental Control and Life Support System	238	108	229	104	
Thermal Control	1,728	784	452	205	
Other (ascent includes crew)	22	10	1,230	558	
Inert Mass	**10,657**	**4,834**	**7,221**	**3,275**	
Non-propellant	1,285	583	364	165	
Propellant	53,462	24,250	4,409	2,000	
Gross Mass	**65,404**	**29,667**	**11,994**	**5,440**	

Odyssey: 0810-BAA-2

The Odyssey Space Research design incorporated significant mass and safety/reliability improvements in the configuration, structure, propulsion, and Guidance, Navigation and Control (GNC). Their incremental approach to development yielded several improvement options, and identified significant areas to be considered for further work. They also identified some potential issues, most notably in landing, that did not appear to have been considered by the Altair team.

One of the most significant mass improvements was use of a tri-gear configuration. In addition to reducing mass when compared to the NASA LDAC-1 lander, the tri-gear allowed good options for staging spent LOI tanks while still providing clearance for the ascent module main engine, and delivered superior static stability while maintaining the necessary landing stability characteristics. Other configuration changes were then made to joint and truss configurations, including the use of hybrid and composite materials, modifications to the drop tanks for staging, and

lowering of the cargo deck and airlock by 60 cm (24 in.), thus improving load paths and structural efficiency while maintaining the absolute position of the ascent module.

The major changes to the propulsion system were to replace the LDAC-1 ascent and descent module engines with aerospike engines, and to use a high-performance, monopropellant that is at least as efficient as MMH/NTO bipropellant systems for the main and RCS engines in both modules. This modification decreased the number of required tanks from 12 to 7 and required only one single, centralized LOX tank, thus simplifying the drop tank approach and eliminating the need for LOX drop tanks.

GNC modifications included changes to the landing trajectory, staging and disposal strategies for the staging of spent LOI tanks, reconfiguration of the RCS on the ascent and descent modules, and resizing of the RCS on the ascent module.

Mass Breakdown						
	Descent Stage		Ascent Stage		Airlock	
Subsystem	lbm	kg	lbm	kg	lbm	kg
Structures and Mechanisms	3,817.00	1,731.36	1,283.71	582.28	687.22	311.72
Propulsion	5,188.07	2,353.27	1,066.55	483.78	0.00	0.00
Power	326.06	147.90	275.73	125.07	31.09	14.10
Avionics	159.61	72.40	304.74	138.23	7.45	3.38
Life Support	0.00	0.00	466.50	211.60	0.00	0.00
Thermal Control	2,147.08	973.90	374.15	169.71	71.74	32.54
Growth	2,235.05	1,013.80	718.05	325.70	184.97	83.9
Other	11.18	5.07	350.20	158.85	1,100.64	499.24
Dry Mass w/ Growth	13,884.05	6,297.70	4,839.63	2,195.22	2,083.11	944.88
Crew	0.00	0.00	817.92	371.00	0.00	0.00
Crew Support	0.00	0.00	266.76	121.00	0.00	0.00
Samples	0.00	0.00	220.46	100.00	0.00	0.00
Inert Mass	13,884.05	6,297.70	6,144.77	2,787.22	2,083.11	944.88
Non-propellant	3,841.22	1,742.35	280.63	127.29	9.24	4.19
Propellant	52,589.07	23,854.00	5,229.37	2,372.00	0.00	0.00
Gross Mass	70,314.34	31,894.05	11,654.77	5,286.51	2,092.35	949.07

Andrews Space: 0810-BAA-3

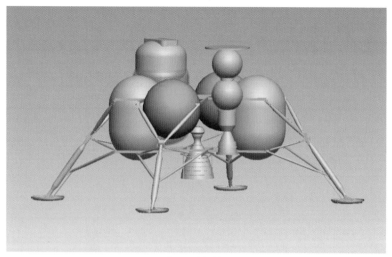

Descent Module.

Inflatable Ascent Module Crew "Cab".

Andrews Space, partnered with Ball Aerospace, Hamilton Sunstrand, Draper Lab, and Pratt & Whitney Rocketdyne, provided a novel approach by switching the descent module engine from LOX/LH_2 to Liquid Fluorine (LF)/LH_2, and propulsion for the ascent module from LOX/methane to LF/ammonia. Although the use of fluorine-type propellants offer the highest possible performance in liquid engines and optimize propellant tankage, thereby shortening the stack and minimizing the distance from the crew module to the lunar surface, corrosiveness is a fundamental engine design issue that requires increased reliance on analytic tools to reduce test times and limit exposure. Use of these toxic liquid propellants also calls for specific ground facility design and operational procedures for stringent environmental protection regulations.

In addition to the propellant change, the Andrews design minimized mass by using an inflatable ascent module crew cabin. This design optimized crew accommodations for a minimum dry mass – total mass for the 6.76 m³ (239 ft³) cab was only 19.2 kg (42.2 lb) – yet it still provided reasonable safety and required no reconfigurations for abort mode. It provided ECLSS for 2 hours descent and 5 hours ascent, with the baseline assumptions that crew would be wearing pressurized surface suits and that flight would be autonomous with high-level human override capability.

Further changes from the NASA LDAC-1 Altair design included:
- Moving the ascent module outboard for visibility and enhanced abort options
- Mounting the airlock/habitat (or pressurized rover) outboard for easy ground deployment
- Using the larger RL 10-B2 engine for a better thrust-to-weight ratio and an additional 13 sec Isp
- Putting a reinforced docking station for Orion on the Altair centerline
- Replacing aluminum tanks with tanks that are composite-wrapped
- Using the PLSS units as backups for critical ascent module subsystems
- Transferring Orion seats to the ascent module for descent and ascent
- Moving emergency equipment from Orion to Altair for the surface stay

Mass Breakdown		
	lbm	kg
Descent Module Inert Landed Mass	12,315	5,586
Ascent Module Landed Mass	7,000	3,175
Airlock/Habitat Inert Mass	3,386	1,536
Manager's Reserve	4,702	2,133
Usable Payload at Landing	24,370	11,054
Lunar Landed Mass	**51,773**	**23,484**

Boeing: 0810-BAA-4

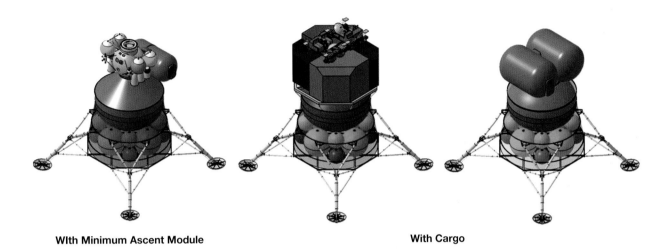

WIth Minimum Ascent Module **With Cargo**

Boeing's approach to redesign was to scrub each subsystem from NASA's LDAC-1 configuration to its minimum functional specification, then to add back safety and reliability capabilities to produce what they termed a "flyable" configuration. Using this method, they first performed an independent subsystem review of the NASA BAA design, providing assessments and suggestions to achieve minimum design and mass reductions. These typically minor changes included combining the camera and star tracker, adding antennas for enhanced coverage, replacing the aluminum used for the struts and shell with graphite, modifying the 16-point interface to an 8-point and from two planes to one, replacing LO_2 insulation with ground purge, and making a small increase in the radiator size for polar missions. Additionally, the GNC analysis recommended an update to the ΔV requirement using a short, shallow approach that resulted in a modification to propulsion sizing.

Level 2 of the redesign provided suggestions for improved clearance and access as well as modest mass reduction. Fuel migration, structural complexity, and substantial mass reductions were addressed in Level 3 analyses. Level 3 also produced two alternate ascent module designs to improve habitable volume and suggested replacing the single Orion engine with six Aerojet R-40B3 engines. Although slightly increasing mass, this engine modification resulted in better packaging and reduced thruster requirements, and provided engine out capability. The mass changes generated from the Levels 2 and 3 changes are listed below.

Mass Differences Between LDAC-1 and Minimum Redesign	
Subsystem	**Comments**
Avionics	Minor reductions in flight computers based on Orbital Express and International Space Station (ISS) designs. Increase in ascent module to account for Communications and Tracking cabling. Airlock increase due to formula errors in spread sheet
Power	Increases from wiring harness mass estimated in both ascent module and descent module.
Structure	Major decreases from use of composites in place of aluminum
Propulsion	Reductions in ascent module propulsion system mass. Mass increases in the descent module. Overall increased mass from the propulsion system.
Thermal Control	Reductions from Multi-Layer Insulation recalculations, use of Boeing satellite radiators and Space Shuttle component data.
Life Support	Minor increases from missing O_2 tank and underestimated mass for high-pressure O_2 system
Other	No changes identified
Non-propellant fluids	Lower boil-off, substantially smaller pressurant mass

Mass Differences Between LDAC-1 and Minimum Redesign (continued)	
Subsystem	**Comments**
Propellant	No significant changes in fuel and oxidizer masses based on propellant system analysis
Dry Mass	Decreased in modules for both basic and current best estimates
Inert Mass	Decreased for all cases except the cargo current best estimate
Total Module	Increased for basic configurations, decreased for current best estimate. Boeing guidelines do not apply a growth factor to propellant calculations.

Once the minimal functional design study was completed, each subsystem team was asked to look at their minimal design and consider the safety and reliability changes that would be required for a "flyable" design. These upgrades included:

- Margins (e.g., ΔV, propulsion loading, disposal burn, etc.) – these were compared to Apollo for credibility
- Operational design considerations and "fixes" such as hover/retargeting ΔV, habitable volume, structural frequency, etc.

- Mission- and configuration-specific risks, including ascent engine clearance, separation clearance, dust mitigation, cryogenic boil-off, and landing hazards
- Reliability upgrades based on risks common to all human spaceflight vehicles

The following table provides a mass breakdown for both the minimum functional and flyable configurations of the sortie/crewed and cargo-only designs.

Minimum Functional Mass Breakdown						
Sortie Design Reference Mission (DRM)						
Subsystem	**Descent Stage**		**Ascent Stage**		**Airlock**	
	lbm	**kg**	**lbm**	**kg**	**lbm**	**kg**
Structures and Mechanisms	3,858.3	1,750.1	1,355.2	614.7	606.3	275.0
Propulsion	5,753.2	2,609.6	1,099.0	498.5	0.0	0.0
Power	405.9	184.1	308.4	139.9	30.2	13.7
Avionics	133.4	60.5	265.2	120.3	60.0	27.2
Life Support	0.0	0.0	570.6	258.8	0.0	0.0
Thermal Control	1,359.4	616.6	310.2	140.7	36.4	16.5
Other	11.2	5.1	350.3	158.9	1,100.5	499.2
Dry Mass	**11,521.4**	**5,226.0**	**4,258.9**	**1,931.8**	**1,833.4**	**831.6**
Non-propellant Fluids	2,974.0	1,349.0	345.5	156.7	9.3	4.2
Inert Mass	**14,495.4**	**6,575.0**	**4,604.4**	**2,088.5**	**1,842.7**	**835.8**
Propellant	53,068.8	24,071.6	4,692.5	2,128.5	0.0	0.0
Gross Mass	**67,564.2**	**30,646.6**	**9,296.9**	**4,217.0**	**1,842.7**	**835.8**

Outpost (Down And Out) DRM						Uncrewed Cargo DRM	
Subsystem	Descent Stage		Ascent Stage			Descent Module	
	lbm	kg	lbm	kg		lbm	kg
Structures and Mechanisms	3,858.5	1,750.2	1,646.2	746.7		3,858.5	1,750.2
Propulsion	6,419.2	2,911.7	1,108.9	503.0		5,862.5	2,659.2
Power	403.0	182.8	308.4	139.9		388.9	176.4
Avionics	122.1	55.4	254.0	115.2		290.3	131.7
Life Support	0.0	0.0	224.2	101.7		2.4	1.1
Thermal Control	1,377.7	624.9	310.2	140.7		1,938.7	879.4
Dry Mass	**12,180.5**	**5,525.0**	**3,851.9**	**1,747.2**		**12,341.3**	**5,598.0**
Other	11.2	5.1	1,016.1	460.9		0.0	0.0
Non-propellant Fluids	2,859.4	1,297.0	287.9	130.6		3,100.6	1,406.4
Inert Mass	**15,051.1**	**6,827.1**	**5,155.9**	**2,338.7**		**15,441.9**	**7,004.4**
Propellant	53,068.8	24,071.6	5,849.1	2,653.1		57,791.5	26,213.8
Gross Mass	**68,119.9**	**30,898.7**	**11,005.0**	**4,991.8**		**73,233.4**	**33,218.2**

Flyable Mass Breakdown							
Sortie DRM							
Subsystem	Descent Stage		Ascent Stage			Airlock	
	lbm	kg	lbm	kg		lbm	kg
Structures and Mechanisms	5,718.8	2,594.0	1,646.9	747.0		641.1	290.8
Propulsion	6,139.2	2,784.7	1,444.5	655.2		0.0	0.0
Power	652.1	295.8	425.5	193.0		30.2	13.7
Avionics	145.3	65.9	283.3	128.5		60.0	27.2
Life Support	0.0	0.0	845.5	383.5		0.0	0.0
Thermal Control	2,065.1	936.7	495.4	224.7		71.7	32.5
Other	11.2	5.1	350.3	158.9		1,100.5	499.2
Dry Mass	**14,731.7**	**6,682.2**	**5,491.4**	**2,490.8**		**1,903.5**	**863.4**
Non-propellant Fluids	4,325.0	1,961.8	560.4	254.2		9.3	4.2
Inert Mass	**19,056.7**	**8,644.0**	**6,051.8**	**2,745.0**		**1,912.8**	**867.6**
Propellant	56,791.1	25,760.0	8,657.3	3,926.9		0.0	0.0
Gross Mass	**75,847.8**	**34,404.0**	**14,709.1**	**6,671.9**		**1,912.8**	**867.6**

| Subsystem | Outpost (Down And Out) DRM | | | | Uncrewed Cargo DRM | |
| | Descent Stage | | Ascent Stage | | Descent Module | |
	lbm	kg	lbm	kg	lbm	kg
Structures and Mechanisms	5,718.8	2,594.0	1,646.9	747.0	5,718.8	2,594.0
Propulsion	6,139.0	2,784.6	1,444.5	655.2	6,139.0	2,784.6
Power	673.7	305.6	368.8	167.3	645.5	292.8
Avionics	145.3	65.9	289.9	131.5	313.3	142.1
Life Support	0.0	0.0	220.5	100.0	2.4	1.1
Thermal Control	2,065.1	936.7	404.1	183.3	2,085.6	946.0
Dry Mass	**14,741.9**	**6,686.8**	**4,374.7**	**1,984.3**	**14,904.6**	**6,760.6**
Other	11.2	5.1	1,016.1	460.9	0.0	0.0
Non-propellant Fluids	4,210.4	1,909.8	560.4	254.2	4,250.1	1,927.8
Inert Mass	**18,963.5**	**8,601.7**	**5,951.2**	**2,699.4**	**19,154.7**	**8,688.4**
Propellant	56,403.1	25,584.0	8,657.3	3,926.9	60,422.1	27,407.0
Gross Mass	**75,366.6**	**34,185.7**	**14,608.5**	**66,26.3**	**79,576.8**	**36,095.4**

Lockheed Martin: 0810-BAA-5

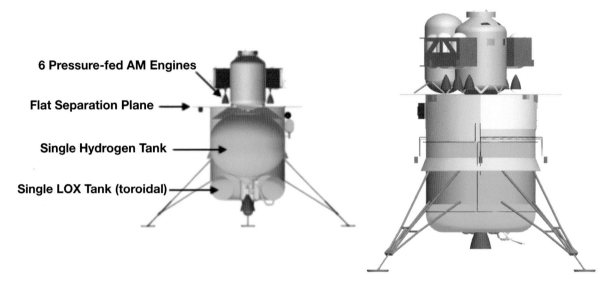

6 Pressure-fed AM Engines

Flat Separation Plane

Single Hydrogen Tank

Single LOX Tank (toroidal)

After careful study, the Lockheed Martin team determined that the Altair LDAC-1 design met the minimum functional requirements for the in-flight phases of its life cycle, and recommended only minor modifications, including simplification of the ascent module sensors and RCS by using Orion as the active vehicle for rendezvous, and by providing additional cargo accommodation. Therefore, the team focused on safety buyback modifications for their alternate configuration. These revisions, which focused on LOC instead of Loss of Mission improvements, included:

1) Using a flat descent module/ascent module separation plane that simplified lift-off by avoiding the "fire-in-the-hole" concept.

2) Minimizing the number of main propellant tanks in order to reduce propellant residuals, the complexity and mass of the propulsion system, and heat leak into cryogenic propulsion tanks.

3) Using load-bearing tanks and cylindrical shells rather than a space-frame with a suspended tank, thus reducing mass and complexity of the primary structure while simplifying the EDS interface.

Further buyback recommendations included the addition of both descent abort and anytime surface abort capability as well as separation of propulsion manifolds for ascent module propellant and descent module RCS (including additional RCS isolation valves).

Estimates of the mass deltas associated with these changes concluded that although there were changes in individual structures or subsystems, they tended to offset each other, thus the overall mass changes to NASA's LDAC-1 baseline were minimal.

Lander Design Analysis Cycle-3

Risk-informed design provides early, critical insight into the overall viability of the end-to-end architecture, and provides a starting point from which to make informed cost/risk trades so that risks can consciously be bought down. In 2008, the third Altair Lander Design Analysis Cycle (LDAC)-3, focused on Loss of Mission (LOM) risks in the same way that Loss of Crew (LOC) risks were addressed in the previous cycle. The NASA Engineering Safety Center Report NESC PR-06-108, "Design, Development, Test and Evaluation (DDT&E) Considerations for Safe and Reliable Human-rated Spacecraft Systems," stated that this design phase should "make the design reliable by considering additional elements or other 'legs', preferentially an additional primary leg of equivalent performance but not necessarily identical design for mission success."

The Altair team used the education afforded by risk-informed design to look at risk reduction in its many forms and not to blindly apply fault tolerance rules or preconceived risk-reduction solutions. This process inherently produced risk metrics for each added capability and cost analyses that could easily be added to facilitate evaluation of the true cost and risk changes that accompanied each added capability. Perhaps most importantly, risk-informed design created a true "Smart Buyer" team that inherently understood the balance of risk drivers and mass performance within the design.

Risk-informed design works best when the configuration of the spacecraft is held constant, so as not to introduce additional variables into the design. It is also a time-consuming process that may not work for projects with compressed schedules (the first three design analysis cycles took the Altair team approximately 24 months to complete). To optimize the risk-based design effort, the Altair team chose to hold the vehicle design constant throughout the design cycles, with a plan to revisit vehicle configuration once LOC and LOM "buyback" cycles were complete.

In the process of upgrading the Altair design from a LOC-focused design to a LOC + LOM-focused design, the team also began to incorporate other capabilities, such as the ability to land on any site on the lunar globe. This "Global Access" capability was "bought back" in the same way that safety and reliability were reintroduced into the minimum design – with known impact to risk and performance.

Reliability Enhanced Designs: 0903-LDAC-3-1, -2, -3, and -4

The LDAC-3 configurations addressed all the goals of the LDAC-3 study, resulting in a reliability enhanced design, including changes to most subsystems for LOM buyback. Four configurations were studied, including a bottoms-up design, a parametrically optimized version, one with slight modifications, and a fourth with mass to overcome threats and opportunities added in. As in the previous studies, three mission configurations were developed: one for sortie missions, one to transport cargo only, and one for transport of crew to an outpost.

A summary of the subsystem changes made to accomplish these goals is included following the mass summary.

Mass Summary						
	Sortie Mission		Cargo Mission		Crew to Outpost Mission	
	lbm	kg	lbm	kg	lbm	kg
Ascent Module	14,317	6,494		N/A	14,910	6,763
Habitation Module (airlock only)	2,586	1,173		N/A		N/A
Descent Module	73,817	33,483	81,961	37,177	72,971	33,099
Program Manager's Reserve	4,427	2,008	4,416	2,003	4,187	1,899
Unallocated	2,765	1,254	32,615	14,794	5,849	2,653
Gross Mass	**97,912**	**44,412**	**118,992**	**53,974**	**97,917**	**44,414**

LOM Reduction Buy Back Summary	
Subsystem	**Changes**
Power	• Updated cable mass assumptions • Improved reliability of the power bus by adding circuit bypass and change to latching relays • System resized to 3 kW average and 6 kW peak power
Propulsion	• Implemented series – parallel redundant bi-prop valves with vehicle supplied pneumatics for the Ascent Main Engine • Added three-string regulators with pyro ladder on Ascent Module Reaction Control System (RCS) to isolate NTO during surface stay • Incorporated autogeneous pressurization to Descent Module system (reduces helium need) • Adopted warm/cold helium strategy for oxidizer/fuel pressurization • Added redundant injector heaters and heat pipes for Descent Module RCS
Structures/Mechanisms	• Updated Descent Module, Earth Departure Stage/Altair Adapter (EDSA), and RCS struts to composite construction • Updated airlock pressure shell design to composite • Improved fidelity of Ascent Module pressure vessel and hatch (to Orion) design • Selected guillotine cutter concept for umbilical separation and matured EDSA separation system
Life Support	• Cabin air and suit loop O_2 LOM reliability improvement • Sized potable "fixed charge" and Environmental Control and Life Support System bellows water tanks for redundancy • Added handheld water mist extinguisher for local fire suppression • Added point of use filters at water supply valves
Thermal	• System resized to ~6.1 kW, increasing radiators to four • Implemented sublimator bypass and accumulator with bubble filter for LOM redundancy
Command & Data Handling	• Included capacitive discharge pyro firing circuit architecture • Implemented three flight computers (from two)
Communications and Tracking	• Improved fidelity of radio frequency cable mass estimates
Guidance, Navigation & Control	• Added optical navigation sensor suite, third Inertial Measurement Unit (IMU), and sixth descent radar antenna for LOM • Enhanced LIght Detection And Ranging (LIDAR) targets and added running lights to support Rendezvous, Proximity, Operations, Docking, and Undocking operations
Extravehicular Activity	• Updated battery charger to a three-channel Li-ion charger • Added additional contingency equipment • Added two suit donning stands in airlock
Vehicle System	• Added vehicle functional checkouts to timeline/ops con baseline • Incorporated basic hardware for lunar surface propellant scavenging

Lander Design Analysis Cycle-4

Early design cycles developed the vehicle concept to a coarse definition of the mission. This was enough to understand primary functionality, and evaluate risks and develop mitigations to the point the concept was considered safe. These hazard mitigations were bought into the vehicle concept in Lander Design Analysis Cycle (LDAC)-2 and LDAC-3. This process is referred to as a buyback as it costs vehicle mass margin in order to implement.

With an acceptable risk posture, the increase in mission fidelity uncovered new functionality that should be addressed by the concept. Examples are increased control by the pilot, increased data rates in the communication system to accommodate high-definition video, and the addition of hot water to the potable water dispenser. Although these capabilities were not required in a minimum functional design, they were valid requirements based on mission needs as defined by the concept of operations. Understanding the cost of both risk reduction and functionality increases is key to avoiding costly design changes later in the product life cycle.

With the completion of the risk and reliability design cycles, the next step of the Altair design process was to prioritize the configuration and maturation studies that would have the greatest impact on the vehicle design, but that were not necessarily associated with either the vehicle safety or the reliability. In many cases, these performance or functionality features were the subject of one or more requirements given to the Altair team by NASA's Constellation Program.

Altair considered a list of more than 200 potential configuration/maturation trades, and from that list chose the following studies as the basis for LDAC-4:
• Alternate Descent Module Configuration
• Alternate Ascent Module and Airlock Configuration
• Alternate Ascent Module/Descent Module Separation Concepts and Analyses
• Structural Stiffness Design
• Descent Module Tank Residuals
• Human Piloting Capability Maturation
• Ops Con/Ops Timeline Maturation
• Spacecraft "Safe" Configuration for Critical Faults

The Altair Project had established systematic methods for performing human spaceflight vehicle design that respond effectively to changing requirements, and which could be adapted to different vehicles and different destinations. Human space vehicle design is one of the ultimate systems engineering challenges, involving complex tradeoffs among design disciplines that each influence the vehicle's cost, performance, safety, and reliability. Each of these vehicles must further exist within a system of other spacecraft, launch vehicle, and operating systems, and within an even larger system of national and international policies. A strong systems engineering framework, as developed and practiced by the Altair Project, provided a robust set of lessons for any future human spacecraft.

p1006D-LDAC-4-Requirements Enhanced

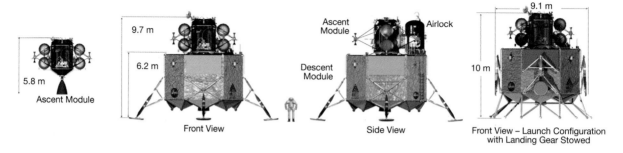

Ascent Module — 5.8 m

9.7 m / 6.2 m — Front View

Ascent Module / Airlock / Descent Module — Side View

9.1 m / 10 m — Front View – Launch Configuration with Landing Gear Stowed

This final Altair design retained the same three variants as earlier Altair designs – a sortie mission option that allowed crews of four to explore the surface for up to 7 days, a cargo variant where the Ascent Module was replaced by significant one-way cargo, and a "down-and-out" variant that took a crew of four to the surface and allowed them to access other surface assets without the need for a dedicated lander airlock.

The Ascent Module featured 14.0 m³ (494 ft³) of pressurized volume within its 2.35-m (7.71-ft) diameter, and utilized storable N_2O_4/MMH propulsion and an OME/RS-18-derived engine for lunar ascent. The surface airlock added 7.5 m³ (264.9 ft³) to the

usable landed crew volume and provided storage for Extravehicular Activity (EVA) suits and systems. The workhorse descent stage utilized approximately half of its fuel for Lunar Orbit Insertion (LOI), with Orion attached, in a sortie or outpost mode, and the remainder for lunar descent using LOX/LH$_2$ fuel and a throttleable, RL-10-derived main engine. In cargo mode, the descent stage could land 14.5 mt (16 t) of payload on the lunar surface.

At the time of the Constellation Program cancellation, configuration studies were underway to split the LOI and descent functions into separate stages and greatly reduce Altair's landed height.

Mass Summary						
	Sortie Mission		Cargo Mission		Crew to Outpost Mission	
	lbm	kg	lbm	kg	lbm	kg
Ascent Module	14,004	6,352		N/A	14,910	6,763
Habitation Module (airlock only)	3,003	1,362		N/A		N/A
Descent Module	81,035	36,757	86,254	39,124	72,971	33,099
Program Manager's Reserve	4,127	1,872	3,045	1,381	3,975	1,803
Unallocated	6,676	3,028	31,967	14,500	5,849	2,653
Gross Mass	**108,844**	**49,371**	**121,376**	**55,005**	**97,704**	**44,318**

LDAC-4 Buy Back Summary	
Subsystem	**Changes**
Propulsion	• Ascent Module disposal delta-v added
Structures/Mechanisms	• Landing loads assessment and resizing
Life Support	• Feed-the-leak capability added • Return to Orion in an unpressurized Ascent Module cabin
Command & Data Handling	• Improved vehicle data recording • Enhanced imagery and high-definition video
Communications and Tracking	• Enhanced antenna coverage
Guidance, Navigation & Control	• Distributed avionics replaced centralized avionics system
Extravehicular Activity	• EVA donning/doffing volume and operations study
Vehicle System	• Enhanced human system integration – EVA donning/doffing, Ascent Module and airlock reconfiguration, Net Habitable Volume assessment • Landing lighting system • Enhanced launch availability • Mass "threats and opportunities" added to reported vehicle mass at 90% confidence

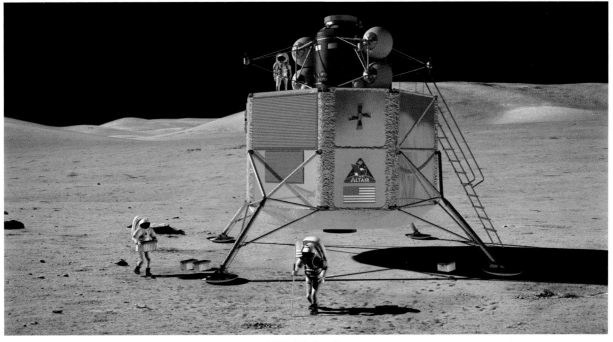

LDAC-4 Configuration.

Post-Landing Checklist

As this document was being compiled, NASA celebrated the 50th anniversary of the Apollo 11 lunar landing, and accolades for the crew, mission controllers and design engineers were abundant. "Those Apollo guys were really smart, given that they started with nothing as a reference" was often heard. One standout among the many engineering achievements of Apollo was the fragile Lunar Module, which would become both an icon of the Apollo program and the standard by which future human landers would be compared. Many of the lunar lander concepts cataloged in this book derive some part of their DNA from the LM.

The designs in this book illustrate how, when an engineering system is stripped down to its fundamental functions, the form of the design ultimately responds to fundamental physics, human factors, and just a bit of a nod to science fiction. But design is a living thing, and new crewed lander designs will continue to emerge up until the point that humans return to the moon in new machines. These designs may take new forms, but until some breakthrough technology or new physics principle is created, future lunar landers will continue to respond to the same design parameters as the concepts in these pages, and will continue to build upon the design of the vehicle that got us to the moon the first time.

When designing landers for the future, NASA looks to the Moon . . . and beyond.

Appendix A. Acronyms and Abbreviations

ACS	Attitude Control System	H$_2$	hydrogen
Al	Aluminum	H$_2$O	Water
ARC	Ames Research Center	IMU	Inertial Measurement Unit
ATK	Alliant Techsystems Incorporated	in.	inch
atm	atmosphere, standard	INS	Inertial Navigation System
CAD	computer-aided design	Isp	Specific Impulse
CaLV	Cargo Launch Vehicle	ISRU	In Situ Resource Utilization
CE&R	Concept Exploration and Refinement	ISS	International Space Station
CEV	Crew Exploration Vehicle	JIMO	Jupiter Icy Moons Orbiter
CIRA	Curtin Institute of Radio Astronomy	JPL	Jet Propulsion Laboratory
COTS	Commercial Off-the-Shelf	JSC	Johnson Space Center
CxAT	Constellation Architecture Team	kg	kilogram
CXV	Crew Transfer Vehicle	klbf	Thousand pounds force
DASH	Descent Assisted Split Habitat	km	kilometer
DRM	Design Reference Mission	kN	kilonewton
DSN	Deep Space Network	kPa	kilopascal
ECLS	Environmental Control and Life Support	kW	kilowatt
ECLSS	Environmental Control and Life Support System	LADAR	Laser Detection and Ranging System
EDS	Earth Departure Stage	LaRC	Langley Research Center
EDSA	Earth Departure Stage/Altair Adapter	LAT	Lunar Architecture Team
EIRA	Exploration System Architecture Study (ESAS) Initial Reference Architecture	LBSS	Lunar Base Systems Study
		lbf	pound-force
EM	Earth-Moon	lbm	pound (mass)
EMU	Extravehicular Mobility Unit	LCADS	Lunar Capture and Descent Stage
ESAS	Exploration System Architecture Study	LCCR	Lunar Configuration Concept Review
EVA	Extravehicular Activity	LDAC	Lander Design Analysis Cycle
FBC	Faster, Better, Cheaper	LEM	Lunar Excursion Module (Apollo)
FC	Fuel Cell	LEO	Low Earth Orbit
FE	Flight Equipment	LEV	Lunar Excursion Vehicle
FES	Fluid Evaporator System	LF	Liquid Fluorine
FLO	First Lunar Outpost	LH	Liquid Hydrogen
FPR	Flight Propellant Reserves	LH$_2$	Liquid Hydrogen
ft	foot	Li	Lithium
ft^2	square foot	Li-CFx	Lithium Carbon Monofluoride
ft^3	cubic foot	LIDAR	LIght Detection And Ranging
g	gravity (acceleration due to)	LIDS	Low-Impact Docking System
gal	gallon	Li-ion	Lithium Ion
GH$_2$	Gaseous Hydrogen	LiMnO$_2$	Lithium Manganese Dioxide
gm	gram	LL	Lunar Lander
GN&C	Guidance, Navigation & Control	LLO	Low Lunar Orbit
GOX	Gaseous Oxygen	LLPO	Lunar Lander Project Office
GPS	Global Positioning System	LLPS	Lunar Lander Preparatory Study
GRC	Glenn Research Center	LLV	Lunar Landing Vehicle
GSFC	Goddard Space Flight Center	LM	Lunar Module
HGL	Hybrid Global Lander	LOC	Loss of Crew
HLLV	Heavy Lift Launch Vehicle	LOI	Lunar Orbit Insertion
HLR	Human Lander Return	LOIDS	Lunar Orbit Insertion and Descent Stage

LOIS	Lunar Orbit Insertion Stage		PLSS	Portable Life Support System
LOM	Loss of Mission		PMAD	Power Management and Distribution
LOS	Lunar Orbit Stage		PMR	Program Manager's Reserve
LO_2	Liquid Oxygen		POD	Point of Departure
LOX	Liquid Oxygen		psi	Pounds per square inch
LRU	Line Replaceable Units		PV	Photo-Voltaic
LSAM	Lunar Surface Access Module		PWR	Pratt & Whitney Rocketdyne
LTV	Lunar Transfer Vehicle		RAC	Requirements Analysis Cycle
L2	LaGrange Point 2		RCS	Reaction Control System
m	meter		RFI	Request for Information
MAV	Mars Ascent Vehicle		RFP	Request for Proposal
	Minimum Ascent Vehicle		s, sec	seconds
MEL	Master Equipment List		S1	Spiral 1
MEMS	Micro Electro Mechanical Systems		S2	Spiral 2
MER	Mars Exploration Rover		S2C	Spiral 2 - Cargo
mi	mile		SAM	Surface Access Module
MLI	Multi-Layer Insulation		SEI	Space Exploration Initiative
mm	millimeter		ST	Star Tracker
MMH	Monomethyl hydrazine		std	Standard
MMOD	Micrometeoroid Orbital Debris		t	Ton (short, US)
mph	miles per hour		T/W	Thrust-to-Weight
MPS	Main Propulsion System		TCM	Trajectory Correction Maneuver
MPU	Main Power Unit		TCS	Thermal Control System
MR	Mixture Ratio		TEI	Trans-Earth Injection
MSL	Mars Science Lab		TLI	Trans-Lunar Injection
mt	Metric ton		TRL	Technology Readiness Level
m^2	square meter		UHF	Ultra-High Frequency
m^3	cubic meter		USAF	United States Air Force
MTO	Mars Telecommunications Orbiter		Vdc	volts direct current
N	Newton		VHF	Very High Frequency
NASA	National Aeronautics and Space Administration		Wh	Watt Hours
NESC	NASA Engineering and Safety Center			
nmi	nautical miles			
NTO	Nitrogen Tetroxide			
N_2	Nitrogen			
N_2O_4	Nitrogen Tetroxide			
O_2	Oxygen			
O_4	Tetraoxygen			
O/F	Oxidizer/Fuel			
OME	Orbiter Main Engine			
OMS	Orbital Maneuvering System			
OTV	Orbital Transfer Vehicle			
PC	Chamber Pressure			
PCM	Pulse Code Modulation			
PDR	Preliminary Design Review			
PEM	Proton Exchange Membrane			
PLM	Pressurized Logistics Module			

Appendix B. Human Lunar Lander Concept Timeline 2005-2008

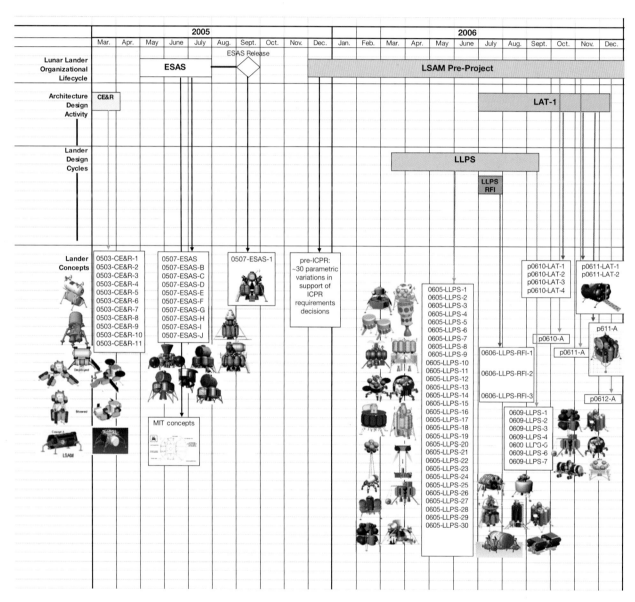

	2005										2006									
	Mar.	Apr.	May	June	July	Aug.	Sept.	Oct.	Nov.	Dec.	Jan.	Feb.	Mar.	Apr.	May	June	July	Aug.	Sept.	Oct.	Nov.	Dec.

Lunar Lander Organizational Lifecycle: ESAS — ESAS Release — LSAM Pre-Project

Architecture Design Activity: CE&R — LAT-1

Lander Design Cycles: LLPS — LLPS RFI

Lander Concepts:

0503-CE&R-1
0503-CE&R-2
0503-CE&R-3
0503-CE&R-4
0503-CE&R-5
0503-CE&R-6
0503-CE&R-7
0503-CE&R-8
0503-CE&R-9
0503-CE&R-10
0503-CE&R-11

0507-ESAS
0507-ESAS-B
0507-ESAS-C
0507-ESAS-D
0507-ESAS-E
0507-ESAS-F
0507-ESAS-G
0507-ESAS-H
0507-ESAS-I
0507-ESAS-J

MIT concepts

0507-ESAS-1

pre-ICPR: ~30 parametric variations in support of ICPR requirements decisions

0605-LLPS-1
0605-LLPS-2
0605-LLPS-3
0605-LLPS-4
0605-LLPS-5
0605-LLPS-6
0605-LLPS-7
0605-LLPS-8
0605-LLPS-9
0605-LLPS-10
0605-LLPS-11
0605-LLPS-12
0605-LLPS-13
0605-LLPS-14
0605-LLPS-15
0605-LLPS-16
0605-LLPS-17
0605-LLPS-18
0605-LLPS-19
0605-LLPS-20
0605-LLPS-21
0605-LLPS-22
0605-LLPS-23
0605-LLPS-24
0605-LLPS-25
0605-LLPS-26
0605-LLPS-27
0605-LLPS-28
0605-LLPS-29
0605-LLPS-30

0606-LLPS-RFI-1
0606-LLPS-RFI-2
0606-LLPS-RFI-3

p0610-LAT-1
p0610-LAT-2
p0610-LAT-3
p0610-LAT-4

p0610-A

0609-LLPS-1
0609-LLPS-2
0609-LLPS-3
0609-LLPS-4
0600-LLPS-5
0609-LLPS-6
0609-LLPS-7

p0611-LAT-1
p0611-LAT-2

p611-A

p0611-A

p0612-A

Note: Lunar Lander taxonomy above may differ from that used in concepts in this catalog.

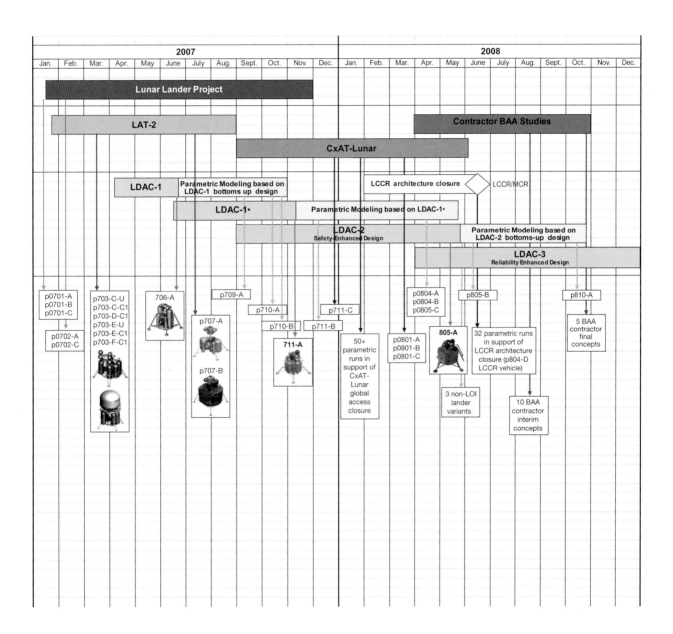

Appendix B. Human Lunar Lander Concept Timeline 2009-2010

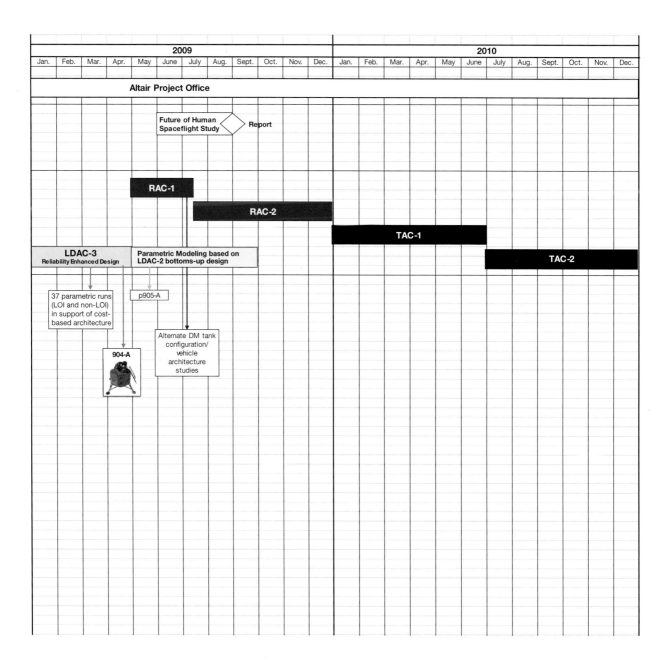

GPO U.S. GOVERNMENT PUBLISHING OFFICE 2019 – 746-641